of the

ASME/ARPEL INTERNATIONAL
PIPELINE GEOTECHNICAL CONFERENCE
– 2019 –

GEOHAZARD CONSIDERATIONS FOR DESIGN AND CONSTRUCTION
PIPELINE ROUTE SELECTION AND CHARACTERIZATION

GEOHAZARD RISK ASSESSMENT AND
PIPELINE INTEGRITY MANAGEMENT PLANNING

MONITORING, MITIGATION, AND EMERGENCY REPAIRS

presented at

ASME/ARPEL 2019 INTERNATIONAL PIPELINE GEOTECHNICAL CONFERENCE
JUNE 25-27, 2019
BUENOS AIRES, ARGENTINA

THE AMERICAN SOCIETY OF MECHANICAL ENGINEERS
Two Park Avenue * New York, N.Y. 10016

WELCOME FROM THE CONFERENCE CHAIRS

The American Society of Mechanical Engineers (ASME) together with the Regional Association of Oil, Gas and Biofuels Sector Companies in Latin America and the Caribbean (ARPEL) are pleased to present the third biennial International Pipeline Geotechnical (IPG) conference held in Buenos Aires June 25 – 27, 2019.

As in prior versions, all papers from the 2019 conference will be published by ASME.

The ASME International Pipeline Geotechnical Conference (IPG2019) is an international event to promote knowledge sharing, technological progress and international cooperation for advancing the management of natural forces impacting pipelines with the intent of protecting the public, environment, energy infrastructure assets and ensure safe and reliable operations.

The pipeline risk factors associated with natural forces include:
Landslides and mass movement
Tectonics/seismicity — including fault crossings and liquefaction
Hydrotechnical — including river scour and channel migration
Erosion and upheaval displacement
Geochemical — including karst and acid rock drainage
Unique soil structure — including residual and sensitive soils
Desert mechanisms — including dune migration
Volcanic mechanisms
Freezing of unfrozen ground
Thawing of permafrost terrain

These forces have become critical in the integrity management of pipelines due to the occurrence of failures causing loss of human life, damage to the environment and business impact. These risk factors are known as Geohazards resulting from natural processes of a geotechnical, geological, hydrological, or tectonic origin that represent potential threats usually induced during the pipeline construction and operations.

The suite of activities constituting geohazard management practice including special design and construction; monitoring and inspection; risk assessment and associated data management have seen considerable advancements in recent years as the topic has gained prominence within the pipeline community.

Please enjoy the conference and your time in Buenos Aires!

Best regards,
Arturo Heinke, YPF, Technical Program Co-Chair
Moness Rizkalla, Visitless Integrity Assessment Ltd., ASME PSD Senator, Technical Program Co-Chair

CIDs and ASME Conference Proceedings

Beginning with the 2013 conference proceedings, ASME transitioned to e-first publication of conference proceedings. As a result, instead of traditional page numbers, the online pagination has been by 11-digit citation identifiers (CIDs); For instance, using the CID V###T##A### as an example, the structure of the basic 11-digit citation is defined as follows:

- First four digits (V00#): indicate the **Volume Number**
- Middle three digits (T##): indicate the **Track Number**
- Last four digits (A###) indicate the **Article order** in which the paper is published within the Track.

In the print version, the CID appears on every page of the paper followed sequentially by the page number of each article starting with page one. For example, the pagination for a three page article would use the following sequence:

V###T##A###-1

V###T##A###-2

V###T##A###-3

In The ASME Digital Collection version, the CID appears on the Table of Contents where the paper is published. The CID also appear on the abstract page, followed by the total number of pages in the paper. For example: V###T##A###; 3 pages

CIDs and Citations

When citing an article that has been published with a CID, enter the CID where the page range would have gone previously; do not include the page numbers used on the PDF or print.

Errata

Errata submitted by authors after publication of this volume are published with the relevant paper on The ASME Digital Collection

http://asmedigitalcollection.asme.org/

CONTENTS

GEOHAZARD CONSIDERATIONS FOR DESIGN AND CONSTRUCTION PIPELINE ROUTE SELECTION AND CHARACTERIZATION

IPG2019-5336...**V001T01A001**
Utilisation of Sheet Piles in the OCENSA's Right of Way for Slope Stabilisation and
Bioengineering Works
  Hugo García

IPG2019-5343...**V001T01A002**
A New Approach for the Geotechnical Zoning of the Rights of Way
  *Julian Chaves Agudelo, Jaime Aristizabal Ceballos, Carlos Motta Tierradentro, and
    Juan Alvarado Franco*

GEOHAZARD RISK ASSESSMENT AND PIPELINE INTEGRITY MANAGEMENT PLANNING

IPG2019-5301...**V001T02A001**
Retroerosion in a TBG Gas Pipeline Crossing and its Rehabilitation
  Cesar Augusto Costa, Walter Schultz Neto, and Thiago Wichrestink Zozula

IPG2019-5314...**V001T02A002**
Watercourse Crossing Program: 10 Years Performance
  Gerald Ferris, Sarah Newton, and Minh Ho

IPG2019-5321...**V001T02A003**
Cost Optimisation in Risk Reduction Management Based on Gross Disproportionation Concept
  Alejandro Marín and Jon Hernández

IPG2019-5325...**V001T02A004**
An Analytical Approach for Pipeline Geohazard Management
  Otto Huisman, Moness Rizkalla, Matt Tindall, Alejandro Reyes, and Erika Santana

IPG2019-5327...**V001T02A005**
Risk Management of Pipeline Breakage at River Crossings Through Quantitative Analysis of the
Threat, Vulnerability and Consequences
  Carlos Debandi, Fernando Martearena, and Natalia Roth

IPG2019-5328...**V001T02A006**
Assessing and Managing Geologic Hazards in the Appalachian Region of the United States
  Martin P. Derby and Bailey Theriault

IPG2019-5339...**V001T02A007**
Finite Element Modelling of a Series of Ground Displacement Episodes and
Stress Relief Procedures
  Hamid Karimian, Pete Barlow, Chris Blackwell, and Chris Campbell

IPG2019-5342..**V001T02A008**
Natech Risk Management on Pipelines of Cenit
  Jaime Aristizabal Ceballos, Julian Fernando Chaves Agudelo,
   Carlos Eduardo Motta Tierradentro, and Maria Isabel Montoya Rodríguez

IPG2019-5346..**V001T02A009**
Enhancing Geohazard Management Practice for South American Pipelines
  Michael Porter, Elisa Scordo, Pete Barlow, Daniela Welkner, and Miguel Leach

MONITORING, MITIGATION, AND EMERGENCY REPAIRS

IPG2019-5303..**V001T03A001**
Oil Pipeline Geohazard Risk Mitigation via On-Line Optical Fiber Strain Monitoring
  Alexis Méndez and Andrés Salazar Ferro

IPG2019-5304..**V001T03A002**
Field Data Collection Using GIS Technology for the Management of Geohazards and
Third-Party Damage Threats in the Pipeline Transportation System of Natural Gas (NG) and
Natural Gas Liquids (NGL)
  Karin Oviedo and John Erick Malpartida Moya

IPG2019-5312..**V001T03A003**
Risk Control Through Evaluation of Catastrophic Scenarios
  José Vicente Amórtegui Gil

IPG2019-5313..**V001T03A004**
Interferences by Third Parties: The Challenge of the Construction of Highways on the
Right of Way of Oil Pipelines — Case of Autopistas Del Nordeste-Ocensa
  Julian Javier Corrales Cobos

IPG2019-5320..**V001T03A005**
River Crossings: Developing a Mobile GIS Approach to Monitoring Activities
  Martin Carnicero and Maureen Vázquez

IPG2019-5324..**V001T03A006**
Monitoring and Screening of Pipelines for Movement: A Fast and Cost-Effective Alternative for
Pipeline Operators to Measure Drift in Pipelines
  Michael Schorr, Klaas Kole, and Ferdinand Foessing

IPG2019-5332..**V001T03A007**
Simple Method for DTS/DSS Data Interpretation: An Application to Pipeline
Geotechnical Monitoring
  Fabien Ravet, Sanghoon Chin, Fabien Briffod, and Etienne Rochat

IPG2019-5333..**V001T03A008**
Ground Based Interferometric Synthetic Aperture Radar Combined With a Critical Slope
Monitoring Program Will Provide Early Detection of Slope Movement Along Pipeline Corridors
  Steven E. Borron and Martin P. Derby

IPG2019-5344..**V001T03A009**
Learnings About Geohazards in Cenit Pipeline Integrity Management
  Carlos Motta Tierradentro, Jaime Aristizabal Ceballos, Julian Chaves Agudelo, and
   Camilo Eliecer Torres Castro

Author Index .... **vii**

IPG2019-5336

UTILISATION OF SHEET PILES IN THE OCENSA'S RIGHT OF WAY FOR SLOPE STABILISATION AND BIOENGINEERING WORKS

Hugo García[1]
OCENSA - Oleoducto Central S.A.
Bogotá, Colombia.

ABSTRACT

On the maintenance carried out by OCENSA for slope stabilization in areas with geotechnical issues, protection of lateral streams´ banks, maintenance of the Right of Way (RoW) embankment or access roads, sheet piles have been successfully used. The paper describes the different alternatives and their uses. Among them are: terraces to facilitate drainage and plant recovery, PVC sheet piles for protection of stream banks, sheet piles made of carbon steel pipe and steel deck in which the piles can be driven by percussion or previously excavated with drilling machine.

Keywords: Sheet pile, slope stabilization, bioengineering.

INTRODUCTION

Ocensa pipeline transports crude from Los Llanos foothills to Coveñas marine terminal, eight hundred and thirty kilometres long; crossing the Colombian territory from east to west. Since the pipeline crosses the eastern Andes mountain range and the foothills of the Andes central mountain range, along its route there are varied geological formations and watercourse crossings, which make it necessary to make slope stabilizations and construction of protection at the crossing of streams, where the oil pipeline goes through buried (Figure 1).

FIGURE 1: OCENSA pipeline location

Usually, to guarantee the stability of these slopes and watercourse crossings, containment structures such as gabion walls, or reinforced concrete walls have been used. However, this option does not always turn out to be optimal from a technical, durability, logistical or environmental point of view. Sheet piling; metal or PVC, can be an alternative in many cases. The document presents the calculation methodologies used, and the types of cases in which this solution has been successful.

1. DEFINITION

The sheet pile is a straight and slender prefabricated piece with lateral edges whose shape allows its interlacing with other similar pieces; these parts are driven into the ground to form a continuous containment structure called sheet piling (4).

Sheet piling is used in different engineering works, its function is generally to contain a material and give stability to a geological formation. Its main uses are related to excavations, construction of low-level structures, seaports, fluvial structures,

[1] Contact author: hugo.garcia@ocensa.com.co

containment of pollutants, water treatments, river channels and stabilization of slopes.

International technical literature identifies sheet piles within steel profiles; robust structures driven into the ground by hammer or percussion hammers, vibratory hammers or hydraulic presses. These systems are expensive and impractical for the needs of the pipeline. Instead, solutions with polyvinyl chloride (PVC) sheet piles and piles with steel deck sheets on the upper part have been effective and suitable for Colombian needs and conditions.

2. CALCULATION METHODOLOGY

The design of a containment structure such as sheet piles is based on dynamic movements and static pressures. For a logical approach, tools for the estimation of the lateral earth pressure are presented, specifically by the Rankine theory. For this, it is necessary to know parameters such us shear strength, unit weight of soil and soil drainage condition, data that can be obtained in the laboratory and by on-site measurements.

Rankine assumes a static approach, not based on a discrete fracture plane, but rather on Mohr-Coulomb boundary condition; regarding major tensions across the soil wedge to be considered. Using Mohr-Coulomb failure criterion it follows that, according to Rankine, soil pressure, due to the weight of soil, increases linearly with depth. To achieve such pressure distribution, a planar fracture is assumed, obtained just for one rotation of the sheet pile on its base for the active case, and just for one translation in the passive case.

The equations derived from performing the balance of these forces and moments, allow to determine the depth of embedment for the sheet piling in the ground necessary to obtain its stability, or the tension force required in an anchoring when it is not possible to reach the required rebar depth.

In the case of soils whose behaviour can be approximated to that of sand, the pressure diagram takes the following form:

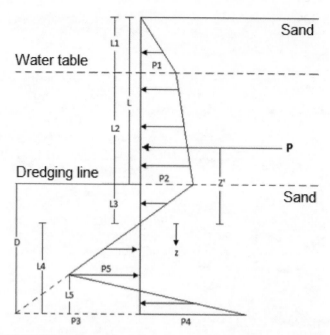

FIGURE 2: Sheet pile driven into sand – Pressures distribution

Similarly, if the sheet pile is anchored in a soil in which the behaviour resembles that of cohesive soil (clays or rocks), the pressure diagram is estimated as in Figure 3

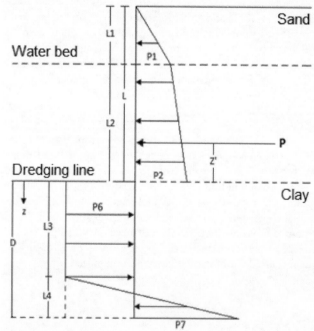

FIGURE 3: Sheet pile driven into clay - Pressures distribution

To carry out the sheet piling calculation, a process must be followed:

1. Determine depth of driving.
2. Determine earth pressure technique to use.
3. Raise the balance of horizontal forces and moments.

4. Solve the static problem and obtain the theoretical driving depth.
5. Calculate the stress laws and deformations.
6. Size profiles and anchors (if necessary).
7. Set the depth of driving depending on the method used.

Das B., 2001, exposes in detail the calculation methodology for different cases. In [2] a table is presented to estimate the driving initial value as an estimate according to the type of soil:

TYPE OF SOIL	INITIAL DRIVING LENGTH
Dense	0.75H
Firm	H
Loose	1.50H
Very loose	2.00H

TABLE 1: Estimated value of driving according to soil type

Flórez L., 2011, performed numerical verification of the results found by the analytical methodologies, and found that the sizing is satisfactory and safe for the analysed cases.

3. Sheet-piling types and construction methods

3.1 Metal and Timber Barriers.
They are smaller sheet piles, without a structural function of stabilization as defined as in the case of sheet piles. Their function is to make terraces on the slopes, to facilitate surface drainage and the growth of vegetation (Figures 4 and 5). They are traditionally constructed of wood but have a reduced lifespan. In OCENSA they are built with 3" carbon steel pipe, manually driven into the ground with a mallet, and the face shaped with a mesh and non-woven geotextile (Figure 6).

FIGURE 4: Timber barrier with channel on its back

FIGURE 5: Barriers with timber stakes and mesh on the body

FIGURE 6: Metallic barrier with steel piles and mesh

3.2 Sheet-pile with piles in steel pipe and metal sheet profiles
Its vertical elements are formed with SCH 40 carbon steel pipe, from 4" to 6" in diameter, driven by percussion or pressure with the bucket of the backhoe, hydraulic hammer connected to the arm of the backhoe, or hitting with tripod and weight that hits in free fall following a guide (Figures 7, 8 and 9). Generally, the spacing of the piles is from 0.8 m to 1.2 m, according to the request. This type of sheet pile can be used in soft soils of important thicknesses such as fillings, colluviums and deep profiles of residual soils. The body of the sheet pile (1 m or 2 m above), is made up of steel sheet metal profile, joined to the piles, usually with wire (Figure 10).

FIGURE 7: Steel piping piles pressed by the backhoe bucket

FIGURE 8: Steel pipe piles driven by percussion with hydraulic hammer attached to the backhoe arm

FIGURE 9: Piles of steel pipe driven by percussion with tripod and weight

FIGURE 10: Sheet piling with 4" steel pipe and steel sheet as body of the system

When there are soils with rock blocks (alluvial type) in the foundation, or where the rock itself is reached, the steel pipe can be placed in the ground, pre-excavating with a rotary drill the hole, which allows to embed it in a more competent stratum (Figure 11)

FIGURE 11: Steel pipe embedded in holes pre-excavated to reach competent stratum

3.3 PVC sheet pile

The profile of the sheet pile body is made of PVC, they have been typically used pre-excavating the trench with heavy equipment and placing them to protect stream banks from slow current and preventing scour.

They are prefabricated elements, of standard dimensions, that have accessories that fit in their ends, to be able to join them forming the body of the sheet piling (Figure 12).
Due to the material that makes up the sheet piles, they are not driven by percussion, but are placed pre-excavated, typically used in industry as light retaining structures, to retain liquids, as barriers for contaminants and to avoid scour.

FIGURE 12: PVC sheet pile detail

FIGURE 14: Digging trenches for tension relieve

FIGURE 15: PVC sheet piles retaining slopes in temporary excavations.

4. TYPES OF USE

4.1 As a barrier to facilitate drainage and growth of vegetation

It is done with barriers in slopes with superficial movements or erosion, they allow and facilitate the recovery of ground vegetation (Figure 13)

FIGURE 13: Slope stabilized by metal trenches

4.2 To temporarily contain ditch slopes

When digging in buried pipeline, in places with unstable soils, as is the case of stress relief, it is a viable solution to avoid the convergence of the slopes and ensure the safety of the excavation (Figure 14)

In excavations that need temporary containment by terraces, PVC sheet piles are also a viable and efficient solution (Figure 15).

4.3 In stabilization of slopes

When there are slow slides; creeping type, it is possible to realize the stabilization with sheet piles with steel pipe and sheet. Depending on the size of the movement, several sheet pile lines can be combined with metal trusses and different types of surface and subsurface water control. (Figure 16). To achieve control of the movement, it must be ensured that the steel pipe piles are embedded in the resistant layer, below the moving surface.

FIGURE 16: Slope stabilization using combined sheet piling with steel pipe and sheet and metal barriers

4.4 To maintain the right-of-way or access road banking

They become an optimal solution to recover or maintain the side of roads built on the hillside or on the back (Figure 17)

FIGURE 17: Sheet pile of pipe and sheet maintaining access road banking. Photograph courtesy of the JH Ingeniería company

4.5 At watercourse crossings

To avoid the scouring of rivers and streams, PVC sheet piles have been used, being a durable solution (given that it does not interact with water) and aesthetic solution (Figures 18 y 19).

FIGURE 18: PVC sheet pile protecting margin of stream

FIGURE 19: Aerial view of river margin protected with PVC sheet piles (left side)

CONCLUSIONS

The results obtained after the construction of the different types of sheet piling have been satisfactory, the objective foreseen in the design has been fulfilled. The technology has been a good option for the solution of problems of embankments, revegetation of banks, banking recovery, stabilization and margin protection, becoming a versatile and effective solution.

Sheet piles become an option to traditionally used solutions such as gabion walls and reinforced concrete. They are useful when there are drawbacks in achieving non-renewable materials, there is limited space or access problems.

The analytical calculation methods using simplified hypotheses have been safe and sufficient for the design of sheet piles.

REFERENCES

[1] Das B. Principio de Ingeniería de Cimentaciones. Cuarta edición. México: International Thomson Editores; 2001. 862 p.

[2] Sanmartin Carrillo A. Cálculo de tablestacas según normativa europea [Tesina de especialista]. Barcelona: Universidad Politécnica de Cataluña. Departamento de Ingeniería de la construcción; 2009. 204 p.

[3] Flórez García L. Diseño de muro de tablestaca como obra de protección para margen de río en el oleoducto OCENSA. Requisito parcial para optar el título de Ingeniería Civil de la Universidad Nacional de Colombia; 2011. 35 p.

IPG2019-5343

A NEW APPROACH FOR THE GEOTECHNICAL ZONING OF THE RIGHTS OF WAY

Julian Chaves Agudelo[1], Jaime Aristizabal Ceballos[2],
Carlos Motta Tierradentro[3]
Cenit Transporte y Logística de Hidrocarburos
Bogotá D.C. Colombia

Juan Alvarado Franco[4]
Universidad de los Andes
Bogotá D.C. Colombia

ABSTRACT

Usually, the definition of geotechnically homogeneous zones is established through the analysis of information on a regional (and even national) scale of those characteristics that define the topographic, geological, climatic, and land use conditions by categorizing them and applying algorithms of interaction between these variables. However, in technical literature and in technical reports of state entities that manage natural hazards, new advances are being made in the determination of other aspects or variables that detail the condition of geotechnical susceptibility; at the same time, nowadays there are technological tools for the massive analysis of information and its spatialization. This article presents a new approach to the definition of geotechnically homogeneous zones using these technological tools. A comparison is made against the conventional definition.

Keywords: Geotechnical susceptibility, Machine Learning, .

INTRODUCTION

The geotechnical zoning of rights of way (ROW) is a fundamental tool for the management of existing, or potential, hazardous geotechnical events by establishing those zones that may have the greatest impact on the design, operation, and maintenance of the hydrocarbon transport infrastructure given its stability condition. In turn, computational tools progress to such an extent that it is increasingly possible to analyze technical information, allowing for a better understanding of the condition of geotechnical stability.

This article aims to present a new approach for the determination of geotechnically homogeneous zones through the implementation of an unsupervised machine learning algorithm. The results obtained are analyzed with respect to the information of existing geotechnical findings of several databases, including the list of geotechnical findings of the rights of way of the Cenit infrastructure. Finally, a comparison is presented against the conventional definition of geotechnically homogeneous zones.

1. DEFINITION CONVENTIONAL GEOTECHNICAL SUSCEPTIBILITY IN THE RIGHT OF WAY

Studies carried out in 2011 in conjunction with the Institute of Hydrology, Meteorology and Environmental Studies (IDEAM – Instituto de Hidrología, Meteorología y Estudios Ambientales) related to the definition of geotechnical susceptibility at a country scale in a buffer of 10 km with respect to the ROWs of the systems of Cenit hydrocarbon transport, identify that 20% of the area is between a high and very high condition of geotechnical susceptibility by mass removal movements. These sections are located mainly in the Andean region of the country, where the morphometric and morphogenesis parameters have the main incidence, according to the obtained results (see Figure 1 and Table 1).

The usual definition of geotechnical susceptibility zoning is made by weighting the variables related to the slope, and the physical and structural geology, as detailed in Figure 2. Sometimes it is possible to refine its definition when the characterization of the land use and vegetation cover is available.

---

[1] Contact author: julian.chaves@cenit-transporte.com
[2] Contact author: jaime.aristizabal@cenit-transporte.com
[3] Contact author: carlos.motta@cenit-transporte.com
[4] Contact author: juan.alvarado2105@gmail.com

Something to be considered in this type of zoning definition is that they correspond to methodologies based on expert judgment and the determination of a unique relationship between the variables contemplated in the analysis.

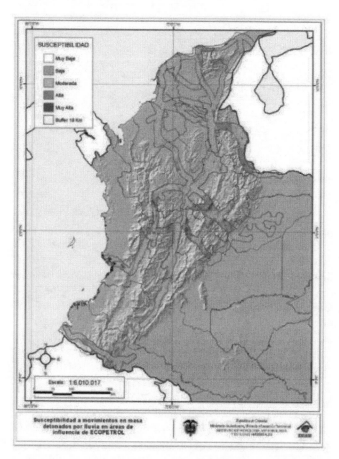

Figure 1. Susceptibility to mass movements detonated by rain in the ROWs of the conduction systems operated by VIT-Ecopetrol. [1].

Table 1. Levels of susceptibility to mass movements detonated by rainfall in the ROWs of the systems operated by VIT-Ecopetrol. IDEAM - Ecopetrol (2011)

Susceptibility	(%)	Length (km)
Low	51,2%	3553
Moderate	29,2%	2026
High	18,3%	1270
Very High	1,3%	90

2. CLIMATE ZONATION

The space-time characterization of the rain regime is a relevant aspect for the management of geohazards, since it allows to identify the portions of the year with the highest probability of occurrence of threatening events, as well as the seasons of execution of geotechnical works and maintenance of the ROW stipulated in the maintenance plans, among other aspects (see Figure 3).

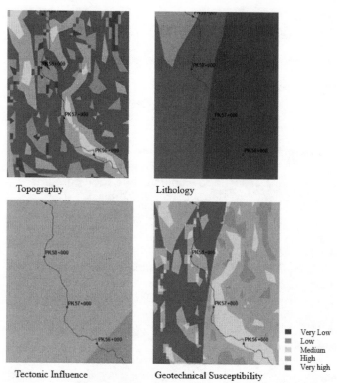

Topography   Lithology

Tectonic Influence   Geotechnical Susceptibility

■ Very Low
■ Low
□ Medium
■ High
■ Very high

Figure 2. Conventional determination of geotechnical susceptibility zoning Own source.

Given that rainfall is considered the main triggering factor for geohazard events, it is necessary to include its characterization in the definition of geotechnically homogeneous zones.

The IPG 2017-2528 article mentions other relevant aspects of the climatic zoning made by the geo-hazard management process of Cenit. The variables that define the climatically homogeneous zones in Cenit transport systems are listed below.

- Rainfall quantity index (IFM)

The rainfall erosivity factor is a specific property of the precipitation behavior that determines its potential capacity to mobilize soil particles under given conditions. The evaluation of IFM is based on historical rainfall records using the following expression:

Where:

$$IFM = \sum_{1}^{12} \frac{p_i^2}{P}$$

IFM: Fournier modified index
p_i: Monthly rainfall (mm)
P: Annual rainfall (mm)

The IFM can be used as a measure of the soil erosion potential of the soil due to a quantity of precipitation and as an input in the Universal Soil Loss Equation.

The monthly IFM is calculated with the previous expression, but considering only the month of interest, as follows:

$$IFM_{mensual} = \frac{p_i^2}{P}$$

- Rainfall frequency index (FLL)

On the other hand, the rainfall duration can be obtained as the probability of rain occurrence during a period. In general, the following expression is used to determine the rainfall frequency:

$$FLL = \frac{n \text{ días}}{N \text{ días}}$$

Where:

FLL: Rainfall frequency factor monthly/annual
n (days): Number of days with rainfall in each period (month/year)
N (days): Number of days in the time period (month/year)

Both the IFM and the FLL are indicators that allow the differentiation of areas with greater or lesser potential for water erosion. Based on statistical analysis of the information, seven (7) categories of each variable were estimated, giving rise to 49 possible combinations as shown in Table 2.

Table 2. Units of the climatic zoning. VIT-Ecopetrol (2016) [2].

Number of days with rain per year	Monthly/Annual Rainfall (mm)						
	Ex. Low	Low	Mod. Low	Normal	Mod. High	High	Very High
Ex. Low	1	2	3	4	5	6	7
Low	8	9	10	11	12	13	14
Mod. Low	15	16	17	18	19	20	21
Normal	22	23	24	25	26	27	28
Mod. High	29	30	31	32	33	34	35
High	36	37	38	39	40	41	42
Very High	43	44	45	46	47	48	49

3. ADVANCES IN THE GEOTECHNICAL CHARACTERIZATION OF THE TERRAIN – STATE OF THE ART

In previous sections, topographic (morphometric), geological, climatic and land-use variables have been considered to formulate geotechnical susceptibility and climate zoning models; its integration would allow to develop a zoning of relative hazard of processes of mass removal triggered by rainfall based on expert judgment methodologies. However, geotechnical zoning applied to ROW of hydrocarbon transport systems requires the integration of these attributes, as well as the inclusion of new factors that allow a more complete description of the nature of the hazard and its sources of uncertainty.

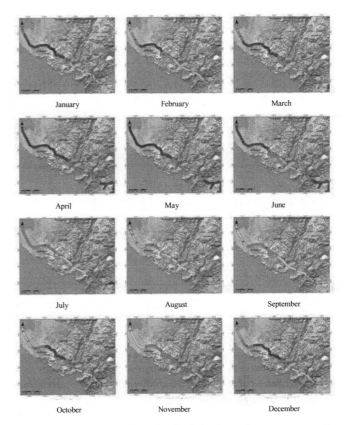

Figure 3. Climatic zoning of a Cenit hydrocarbon transportation system. Source: VIT-Ecopetrol [1].

For this, it is necessary to involve attributes of weather, soil and biota and thus delimit geographic regions to complement the characterization of ROWs and to facilitate the decision-making process inside the company.

Given the extension of the ROWs and the spatial nature of the attributes to be considered, Geographic Information Systems constitute the main tool to carry out this type of analysis and to develop the new zoning models. In conjunction with these systems, several Machine Learning algorithms have been used in the literature to perform landslide prediction [3], assess the susceptibility of rainfall-induced landslides [4], or to estimate the probability of occurrence of shallow landslides [5]. Figure 4 shows a classification of some of these Machine Learning methods and their interaction with other commonly used methodologies.

Likewise, the literature review allows the extraction of variables (or attributes) commonly used to spatially define the geographical regions. Table 3 shows a summary of said attributes. As will be seen in following sections, some of these variables, or similar attributes, were considered in the new geotechnical zoning model.

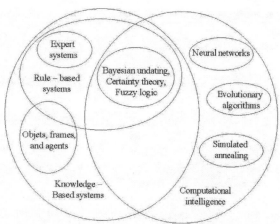

Figure 4: Categories of analysis methodologies. Source Adrian Hopgood. Intelligent systems for scientist and engineers.

Table 3: List of weather-soil-biota attributes used in literature.

Slope
Aspect
Elevation
Lithology
Annual/Monthly rainfall
Land use
Topographic wetness index
Soil type
Sediment transport index
Soil drainage pattern
NDVI (Normalized Difference Vegetation Index)
Accumulated daily rainfall

The work presented in this article aims to put some distance from the expert judgment methodologies to develop a geotechnical zoning using Machine Learning methods through Geographic Information Systems.

4. A NEW APPROACH OF GEOTECHNICAL ZONINGN

The use of the analysis methodologies mentioned above is possible when there is enough technical information on the variables that define the environmental condition of the territory. This new approach to the definition of geotechnically homogeneous zones has been developed given the management of environmental information that the Colombian State integrates into the Colombian Environmental Information System - SIAC (*Sistema de Información Ambiental Colombiano* www.siac.gov.co).

The new approach to geotechnical zoning aims to complement the previous models with new geographic attributes that define the climate system (biosphere, lithosphere, hydrosphere, and

others) focused on the identification of areas susceptible to mass removal processes.

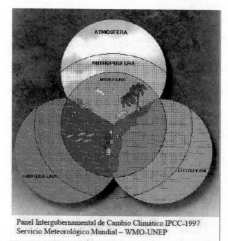

Panel Intergubernamental de Cambio Climático IPCC-1997
Servicio Meteorológico Mundial – WMO-UNEP

Figure 5: Interaction of the components that define the climatic system

For this purpose, a 5km analysis buffer was defined in GIS around the alignment of each one of the transportation systems. The unit of analysis corresponds to a pixel of dimensions 30mx30m delimited by the Digital Elevation Model SRTM30 (Shuttle Radar Topography Mission of NASA). This means that the considered geographic attributes are extracted for each of the 30x30m pixels that make up the entire infrastructure buffer.

4.1 Selected variables

The subsequent sections list the 7 attributes (variables) considered with their corresponding description and source of information

Elevation above sea level

Figure 6: DEM and extraction of elevation values

This attribute was extracted from the SRTM30 Digital Terrain Elevation Model for each of the analysis units.

Slope

The slope was calculated using the same Digital Elevation Model. The values were obtained in degrees and percentages for the corresponding buffer, and subsequently extracted for each of the analysis units.

Figure 7: Slope

Topographic wetness index

This index describes the regions of the terrain where runoff is concentrated, since it is a relation between the area drained in each pixel (A) and its slope (β) as shown in Figure 8 and equation (1).

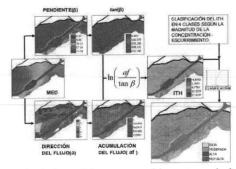

Figure 8: Calculation of the topographic wetness index

$$\lambda = In \frac{A}{Tan\ \beta} \qquad (1)$$

Thus, this index is widely used to quantify the influence of topography on different hydrological processes (Sorensen et al., 2005, cited by Roa et al., 2008). The index was obtained through algorithms included in ArcGis 10.1. A high value of the topographic index indicates that the pixel is prone to saturation since the drained area is large and the slope is low.

Índice pluviografico

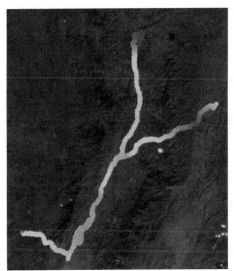

Figure 9: Pluviographic index

This index delimits zones of similar pluviographic behavior and is defined as the relationship between the weighted intensity of rainfall events of each station in each area and the weighted average value for the set of stations analyzed. In total, 72 stations were analyzed, according to the criteria mentioned in section 3. 20 new stations, located within a radius of influence of 20kM, were added to build the new zoning.

To obtain this index, the relative intensity of the stations, used for the interpolations, is initially calculated. This intensity is defined by the following equation:

$$IR(J, D, T) = \frac{I(J,D,T)}{[\frac{1}{NE}]\sum_{J}^{n} I(J,D,T)]} \qquad (2)$$

Where, $I\ (J,\ D,\ T)$ corresponds to the intensity of station J for a duration D and a return period T and NE refers to the number of stations used for the analysis.

Once the Relative Intensities for each of the stations are calculated, the next step is to calculate the Pluviographic Index, defined by the following equation:

$$IP(J) = \sum_{T}^{m} fp(T) \sum_{D}^{n} fp(D)\ IR(J, D, T) \quad (3)$$

Where, $fp\ (T)$ and $fp\ (D)$ are the weighting factors for the return periods and storm durations respectively. The weighting factors used for the zoning are shown in Table 4 and Table 5.

Table 4: Rainfall duration weighting factors

Duration (min)	fp(D)
10	0,45
60	0,1
120	0,05

Table 5: Storm return period weighting factors

Return period (years)	fp(T)
2	0,05
10	0,5
100	0,25

For the construction of the index, the respective relative intensities were estimated considering the intensity values for return periods of 2, 10 and 100 years, as well as durations of 10, 60 and 120 minutes. Initially, an index value was calculated for each station. In order to build a spatially distributed layer, the values of the Pluviographic Index by station were interpolated by applying the Inverse distance weighting technique of the spatial analysis module of ArcGis 10.1. Then, they were linked to each one of the analysis units.

Flow in liters per second

A product of the National Water Study (IDEAM, 2014) is the water performance raster expressed in LPS / km2. Using this raster, and the accumulated flow calculated from the STRM30 model, the flow rate for each pixel in liters per second was calculated.

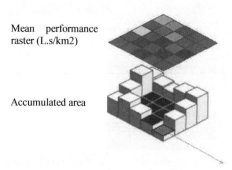

Figure 10: Flow rate calculation diagram

Curve Number

In consideration of the authors, this is a primary variable to keep in mind in the definition of geotechnically homogeneous zones. The Curve Number is a model developed by the Soil Conservation Service (SCS, now the Natural Resources Conservation Service - NRCS) of the United States during the 1950s for application throughout the country (SCS, 1986 cited by Monserrat & Blanco , nd). Its objective was to estimate the runoff in small agricultural basins with certain coverage conditions and soil type, and thus analyze the influence of agricultural treatments and changes in land use (Hawkins, 1978 cited by Monserrat & Blanco, n.d.).

Experimentally, it has been demonstrated that the maximum potential infiltration or runoff threshold depends on the use and type of soil, the slope of the land, the humidity conditions and the ease of drainage. This relationship is not strictly mathematical but relational or tabular, which allows the CN to be deduced from map overlays and applying algorithms based on GIS that allow an automated estimation of this parameter.

Given the versatility of the methodology to estimate runoff, and the incorporation of variables such as soil, slope and vegetation cover for its determination, it was decided to calculate this variable in the influence area of the systems in such a way that the biota-soil factors were reflected in the zoning process. Additionally, it was considered as a strategy to quantify the rainfall-runoff processes that occur in watersheds.

Bearing in mind that the information available at the national level is basically of a discrete or categorical nature, such as Corine Land Cover and the Geopedology cartography containing soil data, predominant slope of the land, geological units and drainage (Figure 11), the processing of these information sources allowed the analysis of the Digital Terrain Model and the pluviographic information of the study area to be complemented.

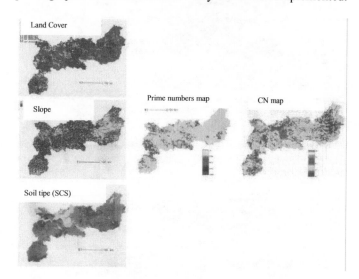

Figure 11:   Calculation of Cn Monserrat et al., 1995

The process implemented to adapt the methodology to the considered thematic inputs (Vegetal Coverage and Geopedology of SIGOT), consists of:

1- Slope map

This product, calculated at the cell level, was recategorized, resulting in a thematic map of two classes, which correspond to cell groups with slopes lower than 3% and higher than this value. This map consists of the first filter for the application of the curve number.

2- Soil type categories

The methodology establishes four soil categories that have drainage characteristics and textures, which were contrasted with the geopedological information. The process consisted of assigning to each unit the corresponding value of soil, either type A, B, C or D. See Figure 12.

3- Land cover assignation

The land cover was contrasted with the categories for uses established by the methodology, this process is very similar to the previous one, with the difference that the number of classes was much higher than the soil categories.

4- Curve Number assignation

Considering the Curve Number calculation tables, (Monserrat et al., 1995; Ibañez, n.d.) the corresponding values were assigned for each type of soil, land cover and slope ranges. This process was carried out by intercepting the covers and establishing conditionals that simulated the triple entry tables recommended in the literature for the assignment of these values that fluctuate between 0 and 100, indicating a higher level of waterproofing of the soil the higher the CN. The intermediate products generated in this process were rasterized with the same spatial resolution of the Digital Terrain Model to maintain the same working scale.

5- Extraction of the Curve Number

As with the other variables, these CN values were incorporated into the database per unit of analysis (Figure 12).

Climatic index

It corresponds to the same index described in section 2.

Finishing the process of extraction of attributes, the result is nearly 30 million units of analysis, each with a value corresponding to each of the 7 variables considered.

4.2 Applied algorithm of zoning

The next step consisted in the application of the K-means algorithm. This is an unsupervised machine learning algorithm, by which the units of analysis are grouped in clusters according to the similarity between their attributes [6]. Each cluster is made up of a group of pixels with similar values for the number of attributes considered.

The clustering algorithm is described below:

- Before starting the clustering, a measure of similarity (for example, the Euclidean distance) between the individuals must be defined. This measure must consider the values of each one of the p variables

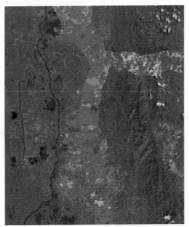

Land cover

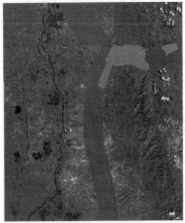

Geopedology

Curve Number

Figure 12: Example of Curve Number calculation.

- K elements are chosen arbitrarily, which represent the first centers of gravity. Keeping these fixed, the distances between the centers and the other individuals are calculated. After that, each individual will be in the group in which the nearest center is located.
- Within each of the groups formed, a new center of gravity is calculated, so that there are K new centers. Following the process analogous to the previous step, the remaining individuals are added around the new K centers.
- The algorithm continues by repeating the previous steps until a partition is reached in such way that it is not better than the previous one, in the sense that the variation between the individuals of the same group does not decrease any more. It can also be stopped when two consecutive iterations lead to the same partition.
- In this way it is possible to group similar pixels together and define areas of homogeneous geotechnical behavior, which is the fundamental objective of a zoning model. At the end of the procedure, 7 clusters were defined using the 7 geographic attributes.

5. DISCUSSION

The clustering algorithm was applied using the 7 variables described above and the results were compared with a large database of geotechnical events collected from various sources. Namely, the sources of information were: Colombian Geological Service SGC (*Servicio Geológico Colombiano*), National Unit of Risk Management of Disasters UNGRD (*Unidad Nacional de Gestión de Riesgo de Desastres*), National Highways Institution INVIAS (*Instituto Nacional de Vías*), Institute of Hydrology, Meteorology and Environmental Studies IDEAM (*Instituto de Hidrología, Meteorología y Estudios Ambientales*) and the baseline list of geotechnical events identified in ROWs of Cenit. In total, information was collected on 5955 events classified as landslides, mudflows, rockfall, debris fall and creep, among others.

These events were superimposed on the results of the zoning using the 7 variables and were also compared with the results of the K-means algorithm using various combinations of the variables. This, in order to determine the best combination of attributes to be used in such a way that there is a better statistical correspondence between the events and the delimitation of the different clusters.

As a result of this characterization based on the statistical significance of the analyzed groups, it was defined that the slope of the terrain, the Climatic Index, the Pluviographic Index and the Curve Number are the attributes that represent the variability of the geotechnical findings in the best way. For the other combinations, it was not observed a category or pattern of occurrence of the events that would allow, from the statistical

and hydrological perspective, to explain which parameters are associated with the events that may affect the stability of the systems.

Table 6 shows the values for each variable and for each cluster, while Table 7 shows the distribution of geotechnical events of Cenit's database in each of the clusters.

Table 6: Range of variation for each variable

Cluster	Average IP	Average slope (%)	CN (min)	CN (max)	Annual CI (min)	Annual CI (max)
1	0,6072	11,11	74	92	23	46
2	0,4986	6,12	74	87	16	24
3	0,6464	4,03	89	98	16	37
4	0,4730	11,52	25	39	16	39
5	0,5269	5,67	45	74	30	46
6	0,6014	3,83	61	71	16	24
7	0,4853	29,62	70	98	23	46
Total	0,5533	15,24	25	98	16	46

TABLE 7: Distribution of geotechnical findings

Cluster	Creep	Erosion	Landslides and debris flows	Rockfall	Subsidence	Total
1	78	264	192	8	1	543
2	21	683	55	1	1	761
3	4	67	7		2	80
4	9	128	15		3	155
5	9	102	19			130
6	7	456	21		9	493
7	32	63	103	16		214
Total	160	1763	412	25	16	2376

6. CONCLUSIONS AND RECOMMENDATIONS

The database described in the previous section allow for identification of critical zoning categories given the frequency of occurrence of the geotechnical events. The data sets were analyzed separately and the predominance of clusters 1 and 7 is evident. Form this, it can be inferred that in these zones there is a relationship between the variables Curve Number, slope, climatic index and pluviographic index, which could explain in a broad sense the occurrence of events associated with landslides among other categories of natural phenomena that directly affect the ROW stability

The preliminary findings in the analysis of the information are described below:

- When analyzing the data set it is evident that 72.5% of the events reported in the area of influence are in the categories or cluster 1 and 7
- When filtering the information sources by type of event, landslides were presented in 71% of the areas categorized as critical (1 and 7)
- The events reported in the areas categorized as critical are characterized by their presence in sectors with high

curve numbers, moderate slopes 11-30 ° and climatic index between 16-48.

Finally, it should be mentioned that the distribution of geotechnical events can be found for the transportation systems individually and, in this way, make a more specific analysis considering the geotechnical, land-use and climatic particularities of each ROW.

As a main opportunity to improve the zoning presented, future analysis is based on a supervised machine learning algorithm.

ACKNOWLEDGEMENTS

A special thanks to the Engineers Nelson Obregón, Carlos Capachero and Leonardo Real for their technical support in the construction and implementation of the proposed analysis methodology, as well as in the analyzes carried out to understand the benefits of this new zoning methodology and the glimpsed opportunities for improvement.

REFERENCES

[1] Chaves, J. et al., 2014. (2014). *"Sistema de Alerta Temprana para la Gestión de Amenazas Meteorológicas en los sistemas operados por VIT-Ecopetrol"* ["Early warning system for the management of meterological threats in systems operated by VIT-Ecopetrol"]. XIV Colombian Geotechnical Congress.

[2] VIT-Ecopetrol (2013 - 2016) "Zonificación Climática para la Infraestructura de Transporte de Cenit que opera y mantiene la Vicepresidencia de Transporte y Logística VIT-Ecopetrol S.A.".

[3] Pham, B.T., Tien Bui, D. & Prakash, I. Bagging based Support Vector Machines for spatial prediction of landslides. Environ Earth Sci (2018) 77: 146

[4] Lin, Gwo-fong., Chang, Ming-Jui., Huang, Ya-Chiao. & Ho, Jui-Yi, Assessment of susceptibility to rainfall-induced landslides using improved self-organizing linear output map, support vector machine, and logistic regression. Engineering Geology (2017) 224: 62.

[5] Nguyen, Quang-Khanh., Tien Bui, D., Hoang, Nhat-Duc., Trinh, P.T., Nguyen, Viet-Ha. & Yilmaz, Isik. A Novel Hybrid Approach Based on Instance Based Learning Classifier and Rotation Forest Ensemble for Spatial Prediction of Rainfall-Induced Shallow Landslides using GIS. Sustainability (2017) 9:5

[6] P. Kainthura, V. Singh and S. Gupta, "Gis based model for monitoring and predition of landslide susceptibility," 2015 1st International Conference on Next Generation Computing Technologies (NGCT), Dehradun, 2015, pp. 584-587.

This page left blank intentionally.

IPG2019-5301

RETROEROSION IN A TBG GAS PIPELINE CROSSING AND ITS REHABILITATION

Cesar Augusto Costa
TBG
Campinas, São Paulo, Brazil.

Walter Schultz Neto
TBG
Campinas, São Paulo, Brazil.

Thiago Wichrestink Zozula
TBG
Rio de Janeiro, Rio de Janeiro, Brazil.

ABSTRACT

This Paper presents a case study of the Jardim Novo Maracanã stream situated in Campinas, São Paulo, in which recent streambed modifications were characterized, aiming to define the rates and the potential erosions along the channel alignment of which have Bolivia-Brazil Gas Pipeline crossing.

Its presents the erosion process analysis and mitigation concepts aimed at the pipeline and fiber optic cables facilities integrity, as well as to indicate the design issues, considering the streambed deepening in this watershed. For this, satellite images and aerial photographs were collected in different periods, soil and subsoil surveys were performed, information on rainfall and watershed characteristics was analyzed, as well as hydrological and hydrotechnical studies were developed. These studies included geotechnical channel and banks analyzes, the spatial and temporal trends of the fluvial geomorphology evolution and the infrastructures safety conditions analysis.

It was concluded that a new channel erosion process occurred after the streambed was filled by recent sediments. This process is associated with an increase floods magnitude, the slopes occupation intensification with the county urbanization and the streambed conditions changes, from an alignment sinuous to rectilinear and from a shallow to deeper channel. Once initiated, the channel erosion process maintained its retroerosion, i.e. its "headcutting" trend, deepening its equilibrium profile to its stratigraphic base level, located about 5.0 m below the 2014 stream bottom, in the pipeline cross section. Alternative concepts for the infrastructure integrity rehabilitation in these new morphological-fluvial conditions were also developed and dimensioned. Among these, the rectangular culverts alternative was adopted. They support a landfill at the crossing with the buried pipe and have to 100-year return period peak flows capacity.

INTRODUCTION

TBG is the owner and operator of the Bolivia-Brazil Gas Pipeline which is 2,593 km long in Brazil. It crosses about five thousand rural properties and 1,900 water crossings of 136 municipalities in the Mato Grosso do Sul, São Paulo, Paraná, Santa Catarina and Rio Grande do Sul states (Figure 01).

Figure 01. TBG Pipeline Route in Brazil.

In 1999, in the southern extension Bolivia-Brazil the pipeline was installed using conventional trenching techniques at the Jardim Novo Maracanã stream cross section its km0029+180S located in Campinas-SP.

TBG has a gas pipeline integrity program that, during the stream inspection activities, was observed changes in pipeline stream crossing with channel bed lowering. This gas pipeline

Jardim Novo Maracanã stream crossing (km 0029+180S) underwent an intense erosive process at 2015, which resulted in a former gabion protection structure collapse and gas pipeline and fiber optic exposure (Figure 02).

Figure 02. Picture TBG gas pipeline in Jardim Novo Maracanã stream crossing, exposed due to an intense precipitation and erosive events in 2015, looking downstream. Source: TBG Collection (2015).

This erosive event, as in others alluvial soils areas subjected to intense stormwater discharges, such as in the Missouri River watershed [1], "the great weight and speed floodwaters can scrape tens of meters of soil and loosen it from the river bed, potentially exposing pipelines".

PIPELINE WATER CROSSINGS

In gas transmission and distribution systems, according to [2], water bodies crossings are pipeline crossover, through the rivers channels, lakes, dams, permanent or possibly flooded regions, as well as ravines and others water streams for three basic options: Underground (Horizontal Directional Drill - HDD); Surface (Aerial) and Submerged (Conventional Burial or Open-Cut).

During the design phase of pipeline routing, the selection of pipeline crossings must take into account, in addition to the limitations imposed by the pipe bending, the appropriate conditions of the pipes, avoiding those with too sharp curves. Also attention additional in this location is the existence of points where during the construction the deviation of the watercourse is possible, as well as the possibility of the pipeline axis being perpendicular to channel alignment, being this stretch straight and level in the bends, in order to obtain the shortest possible length and avoiding inflection points very close to the margins.

If these recommendations can't be met, economic studies should be carried out, comparing alternatives such as diversions and variants, additional ground handling services, as well as special works for the safe execution of the crossing. Also,

information on the river regime, beds occupation, sediment transport, possibility of diversion, navigability, dredging and damming, supported by bathymetry and soundings are required, when the nature, conformation and permanence of the banks and which should be well defined and require the least amount of land movement and restoration services.

The choice of the constructive crossings method, after its position defining, should consider the condition of the beds, especially if deep, rocky, unstable, and safety aspects or constructive difficulties. An analysis of channel degradation and scour should be completed to ensure the pipelines are not exposed and broken during extreme runoff events [3].

For to smaller streams open cut crossing is a dominant pipeline crossing construction method for economic and/or technical reasons.

Although the depth of cover soil to ensures pipeline protection has a regulatory requirement the depth of cover, a new pipeline crossing by open-cut method, should consider the watershed and stretch channel physical characteristics.

If the execution is defined by the open-cut crossing method, the crossing will be the subject of necessary and continuous inspections and maintenance, due to the possibility of changes during the period of operation in the conditions defined in the design, or those verified at the time of the pipeline installation.

THE HYDROTECHNICAL GEOHAZARDS

Depending on the river's ability to alter its shape and slope, the rivers, by the hydraulic engineering classification system, are distinct between alluvial and non-alluvial rivers.

The alluvial rivers flow over and between beds and banks of unconsolidated sedimentary material subject to being transported and deposited by the river. Because the material was deposited by the river and can be eroded by the river, the channel is able to adjust its dimensions, shape, pattern, and slope in response to the discharge rate and the upstream sediment load. The alluvial rivers establish a quasi-equilibrium state where the widths, depths, and slopes adjust to flows conditions [4]).

A fluvial system [5] is divided, along its length, into three zones correspond, respectively, to the stages of youth, maturity and senility.

The shape of the river's cross-section is strongly influenced by the fluvial system stage, the type of soil forming the bed and banks. Channels in cohesive soils tend to be relatively deep and narrow due to the erosion resistant soils that are stable on the banks, and only erode along the bed where the velocity and tractive force is greatest.

Alluvial channels are constantly changing in shape and size in response to short term changes in water and sediment flow rates. The term "regime" is applied to those alluvial channels where the net effect of short term channel changes was a long term balance of equilibrium. The regime channels are still subject to the short term scour, deposition, depth and width changes and slope changes, but the net effect does not result in a long term change.

The stability or changes in the river bed (bed channel and riverbank) is a result of the integration of the controls exerted by the geology, climate and land use aspects of the catchment basin. For this reason, to understand the evolution of a stretch of river, one must evaluate the quantity and type of sediments, the way water is supplied from the drainage headlands, the climate, the geology and also determine The effects of upstream conditions on downstream channel behavior, as well as likely changes in the base level.

According to [6], hazards resulting from stream stability issues can be categorized by the type of channel movement. A common categorization method delineates hydrotechnical hazards into three types, which can be delineated as follows: a) **Vertical Channel Movement**, •Scour •Degradation •Aggradation; b) **Horizontal Channel Movement**, •Bank erosion • Encroachment and c) **Channel Relocation**, •Avulsion • Meander Cutoffs.

How vertical channel movement, scour is the action at the local stream bed in which the water movement erodes the channel soil, due to high local velocities or flow disturbances such as eddies and vortices. Scour is the local deepening of the channel commonly caused by obstructions, constrictions, and/or impingements that re-direct and concentrate the flow pattern of the stream. Aggradation is the increase in streambed elevation due to the deposition of sediment. Degradation is the general and progressive (long-term) lowering of the channel bed due to erosion, over a relatively long channel length. While scour is considered to be an event-based process, channel degradation occurs over a long period of time and along relatively long stream stretches. The causes of channel degradation are complex, but can be caused an increase in water discharge, reduction in sediment supply, lowering in the elevation of downstream base levels. Down-cutting degradation (Figure 03) is a very common fluvial hazard at pipeline watercourse crossings.

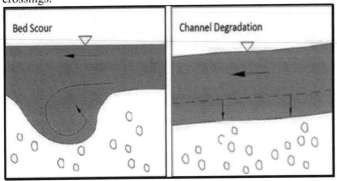

Figure 03. Illustration of types degradation by down-cutting erosion channel. Source: [7] NHC (2011).

Several hypotheses have been suggested to explain the cause of stream degradation [8]: a) a change in the vegetation and that resulted in greater runoff into stream channels; b) a lowered in the base level channel; c) an increase in the stream gradient thereby increasing the stream flow velocity; d) a natural cycle of degradation and aggradation in response to hydrologic or climatic changes; e) the presence of soils derived alluvium.

According to [9], the current or sub actual channels dissection is associated with drainage carving, in some way influenced by surface uplift, that is, with the positive epeirogenic movement responsible for the reactivation of the upstream-propagating erosion and consequently the incision of thalwegs.

Most of the fluvial anomalies are associated with the morphothectonic features produced by neotectonic disturbances. They directly affect the behavior of drainage channels, producing waterfalls, reactivating stabilized erosive processes, catching rivers, abrupt changes in direction, channel fitting to structures (faults and joints), terrain re-entry, valley narrowing, busbars, training, retention pockets, slope refinement, valley entrapment with sediments, changes in groundwater level and others changes. [10].

The "base level" is the lowest level at which erosion of the Earth's surface seeks to attain. It is especially the level below which rivers cannot erode their armoring. The river channels encounter different levels of base on their way towards the regional (or global) base level. Sea level is considered the main base level and the bed level of the current channel of a river stretch serves as a local or temporary base level for its tributaries.

The Channel Vertical Upstream Degradation

A special case of channel vertical upstream degradation is when the linear incision and knickpoint moves headcutting indicating that is occurring a most active entrenchment of the streambed.

Knickpoints are defined as a short, over steepened segment of the longitudinal profile. As a knickpoint moves upstream, the stream cuts vertically into the channel leaving a new, lower bed downstream (Figures 04 to 06).

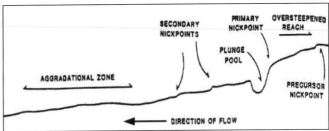

Figure 04. A sketch of headcut (primary knickpoint) and knickpoint (secondary knickpoint) formation. Source: [8] Hadish et al. (1994).

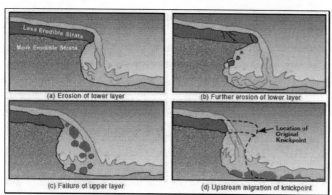

Figure 05. A sketch of the steps involved in knickpoint migration. Source: [11] Papanicolaou et al. (2008).

Once a knickpoint has formed it will continue to advance upstream, eroding the channel bed, lowering the base level for tributary streams, and, if unchecked, eventually affecting the entire watershed. The knickpoint may cease advancing upstream once it reaches a more resistant bed layer, when it has advanced so far upstream that the drainage area does not provide enough runoff to continue the erosional cycle, or if tailwater conditions change downstream.

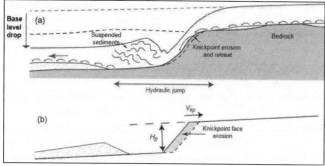

Figure 06. Schematic longitudinal section of a river bed during the propagation of a knickpoint triggered by relative base-level fall. (b) Idealized representation of a knickpoint characterized by its velocity, and the plunge pool depth.
Source: [12] Grimaud et al. (2016).

As the downstream extent of the bed of the tributary channel erodes, the knickpoint is moved upstream.

Several factors that may affect the upstream migration of knickpoints include geological characteristics: channel and knickpoint gradient, channel and knickpoint geometries, scour depth, the presence of joints or cracks, as well as bed material characteristics like cohesion, erodibility, density, and homogeneity and hydraulic variables: water discharge, shear stress, angle of impinging flow into the scour hole, conditions under the nappe, negative porewater pressures, tailwater depth, the presence of upward directed seepage forces on the falling limb of hydrographs [11].

For a bed comprised of sandy alluvium, bed erosion and knickpoint movement occur relatively quickly (Figure 07).

Figure 07. Headcut progression up is shown in the Fox River, Missouri. Source: [11] Papanicolaou et al. (2008).

As might be expected within a given stream reach or small watershed, then these anomalies in slope can reflect changes in lithology and the base-level fall can result in the upstream propagation of knickpoints along tributary channels.

In the same way, gullies also move upstream but especially by the piping headwater erosion.

Under accelerated erosion conditions the gullies, how a piping headwater erosion, is a "retroerosion" that according to [13], (Figure 08) has the following pattern:

a) Initially there is a process of elimination of natural surface retention in the slope, in most cases by use and management anthropic;

b) Concentrated surface runoff, causing soil erosion with soil running to the lower slope;

c) Sedimentation or disruption or artificial excavation on the rising water table vegetation area, in the contact between two infiltration surfaces. The up layer has much more infiltration capacity, than down layer;

d) Death of hydrophilic vegetation root system, with elimination of the natural "water filter";

e) Concomitantly there is the process of high groundwater recharge, due to heavy rains or accumulation of water in facilities including level terracing, increasing the groundwater flow;

f) Beginning of piping headwater erosion in subsoil layers on the slope or deep undermining the laterals wall grooves, by the groundwater flow;

g) Surface collapse or slumping of the region around the new drainage channel (initial gully);

h) Channel erosion in the initial gully;

i) Acceleration of these headwater erosion;

j) Development of branches, i.e. new branches of the main channel;

k) Development of the "pinnacles", among the branches.

These kinds of piping headwater erosion (*retroerosion*) occur where water flows through a layer of loose grains and washes them out. This basic mechanism of erosion can be called extrusion. This is seen when a hole is dug in a sandy beach - once the water table is struck, the sand keeps pouring into the hold. But it is not always necessary to have a clean sandy layer. Many clayey sands can be washed out because the clay disperses finely when wetted and can be winnowed out. Headward advance by any kind of undermining is called "sapping", so if a whole layer is washed out by extrusion, the mechanism is "extrusion sapping". In some instances, only a narrow part of a layer is washed out and a extrusion tunneling or pipping is formed. [14].

Figure 08. Picture gully or headwater erosion in the Rio Verde watershed, Mato Grosso do Sul - Brazil. looking downstream. Source: [13] Costa (1997).

This stream channel erosion mechanism is so environmentally aggressive that in the Iowa state the farmers called it "Hungry Canyons".

The Hungry Canyons is the severe loss of land and damage to transportation infrastructure caused by stream channel erosion in county area of the deep loess soils region of western Iowa. Significant stream channel erosion (channel deepening and widening) has been identified on streams in this region, causing damage to bridges, pipelines, telephone lines, and loss of agricultural land through land voiding [8].

THE HYDROTECHNICAL GEOHAZARDS IN PIPELINE WATER CROSSINGS

Buried pipelines may be exposed by streambed lowering resulting from channel degradation, channel scour, or a combination of the two. Channel degradation occurs over a long stream reach or even the entire drainage network and is generally associated with the overall lowering of the landscape. Degradation also may be associated with changes in upstream watershed or channel conditions that alter the water and sediment yield of the basin [3].

Exposure or suspension of a pipeline at a watercourse crossing could potentially impact the integrity of the pipeline from hydrodynamic loads, impact loads and fatigue caused by vortex shedding. Although pipeline exposures are not desirable and are attempted to be prevented, it is important to recognize that the flow in some smaller creeks and channels may not be sufficient to damage an exposed pipeline [6].

Hydrotechnical hazards associated with watercourse erosion are typically the most common and most active geohazards affecting an operating onshore pipeline. The environmental consequences of pipeline failures are often significant, maintaining integrity of the pipelines continues to be a priority of the industry [6].

Hydrotechnical hazards at pipeline water crossings are related to stretch stream channel changes. Rapid and unexpected changes can occur in streams due to natural disturbances of the fluvial system and/or in response to human activities within the watershed. Natural disturbances such as floods, landsides etc... may result in large changes in sediment load in a stream and changes in the stream channel. Human-induced changes in the drainage basin and the stream channel, such as the installation of bridges, culverts, reservoirs or changes to vegetation cover or land use can have major effects on stream flow, sediment transport and channel geometry and location.

When a buried pipeline crossing is exposed, a mitigation action is required as soon as possible. Lowering the pipeline by natural flexion is sometimes chosen after competing in magnitude, complexity and cost with other alternatives such as river bank and bed erosion control protections [15].

THE JARDIM NOVO MARACANÃ STREAM RETROEROSION

The bed and banks stream Jardim Novo Maracanã crossing underwent an intense erosive process with a rapid evolution of channel ancient degradation, after heavy rains at first quarter of 2015. It was results from a combination of channel degradation, channel scour and a retroerosion process.

The stream bed was lowered at km 0029+180S gas pipeline crossing. The difference between the bank top and the bed, which was approximately 1.0 m in 2014, grew to about 4.0 m by 2015 when the pipeline was exposed.

The TBG Gas Pipeline in the km 0029+180S Water Crossing.

In 1999, the 24" gas pipeline in it km 0029+180S stream crossing after conventional burial was grounded with a minimum coverage of 1,50 m. The banks at the time had 1,0 m high on 40% slopes at the pipeline crossing.

The 24" gas pipeline is 0.487" thick API 5L X70 steel with Double Coal Tar cover and 35.3 m pipeline Concrete Jacket (JC) protected along the alluvial valley length, including positions beyond the channel banks.

Studies and Surveys of the 2015 Erosive Process.

The stream pipeline crossing the Jardim Novo Maracanã stream section located in west county of Campinas-SP, Brazil (Figure 09).

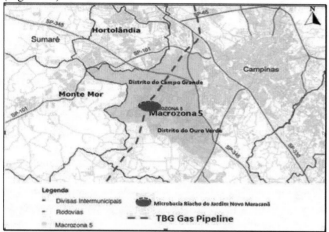

Figure 09. Location of the Pipeline Crossing at Jardim Novo Maracanã stream in Campinas-SP County. Source: Internal Report of TBG (2015).

The Jardim Novo Maracanã watershed of the pipeline stream cross section was delimited considering its location and physiographic and geomorphological characteristics.

It is a small catchment in which its terrain is represented by a rolling hills region, interspersed with sedimentary ramps forming recent alluvial fans with low slope and sinuosity fluvial channels. This catchment is a Capivari river watershed tributary which is a component of the Tiete river system, in the great Parana watershed. The watershed area at the km 0029+180S cross section is about 0,81 km² (Figure 10).

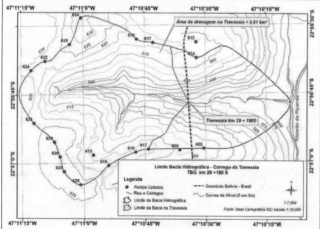

Figure 10. Jardim Novo Maracanã Stream Watershed Boundary. Source: Internal Report of TBG (2015).

From the Digital Terrain Model (Figure 11), the longitudinal profile shows the water stream length to the ridge at the study section of 982 meters, with a mean slope of 0.00316 m/m.

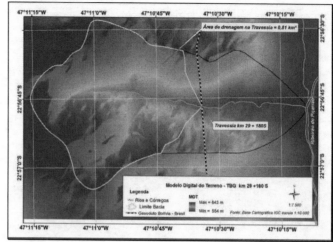

Figure 11. Digital Terrain Model of Jardim Novo Maracanã Stream Watershed. Source: Internal Report of TBG (2015).

The watershed soil characterization, concluded that the region soils, obtained by Brazilian Soil Map (IBGE, 2001) information's (1:5,000,000 scale), is predominantly the soils Red - Yellow Argisol. These soils are classified as type "C" (SCS, 1986). Among the hydrological characteristics of this soils group, that it is soils with low infiltration rate and low resistance and low erosion tolerance. The superficial and subsurface texture can be: sandy / medium and medium / clayey, showing abrupt textural change; sandy / loamy and sandy / very clayey.

The watershed had, estimated based on the ArcGIS "World Imagery" image, updated in March 2015, 63% of urban areas and 37% with pasture coverage (Figure 12).

Figure 12. Soil Uses at Jardim Novo Maracanã Stream Watershed. Source: Internal Report of TBG (2015).

With the aid of soil type and soil cover maps it was possible to analyze the infiltration coefficient watershed for the determination of effective or excess rainfall using the method SCS method [16]. As previously described, the watershed soil "Red-Yellow Argisol" is shallow and homogeneous, presenting a hydrological classification of type C in SCS - CN curve number. Thus for those conditions of the soil watershed type "C", in urbanized area CN number was estimated at 75 and for the use and coverage pastures the CN 71 was admitted.

In order to obtain the effective rain in this conditions CN for this watershed was adopted CN 75. To future conditions, assuming that the trend of the county is the intensification of urbanization, CN 90 was adopted.

For the purpose of obtaining the coefficient C of the rational method, 0.50 was accepted for pasture and 0.90 for urban area, resulting in a weighted average coefficient C of 0.75 for the current conditions. For future conditions a coefficient of 0.90 was adopted, which characterizes a densely urbanized area.

The region under study is located in the Deposition Basin (Paraná Basin), through the samplings it was possible to define the lithological characteristics of yellowish sandstones as having relative rhythmicity. Placing the watershed area in regional geological maps can found that the rock belongs to Itararé Paleoenvironments Depositary Fluvial-deltaic Group and Platform Marine Neocarboniferous, included in the Eopermian (60 million years approximately).

In the explored area, were carried out six drills by SPT percussive methods to evaluate soil strength and depth as well as geotechnical and geological characteristics.

In the sampling points, a profile was observed initially with sandy soil of shallow rock alteration, very compact of yellowish color, followed by rock of arenite alteration very compact and yellowish, enclosing with sound rock of very poor quality, but with good resistance.

Thus indicated that a sandstone rock was relatively close to the surface between three and five meters of depth that can support any type of foundation.

This shallow rock layer is overlaid by a peat layer on the new eroded streambed. On the left bank this soil layer is straighter than the right bank (Figure 13).

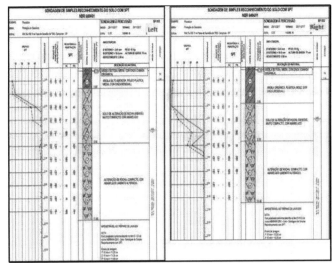

Figure 13. Diagrams of two SPT Samplings in the km0029+180S Pipeline Crossing at the Left and Right Stream Bank. Source: Internal Report of TBG (2016).

In all the six drilling holes the water table level was observed around four meters, probably this one is limited and conditioned by greater resistance of the rock.

Concepts for the Erosive Process Mitigation.

For the establishment of a stable crossing condition it is necessary that there is a river profile balance. This equilibrium profile is the expression of its slope, or gradient, represented by the relationship between altimetry and length, at various points, located between the headwaters and the mouth. The slope of the equilibrium profile is a function of river discharge and sediment load [9].

The mitigation measures and treatment options [6] employed at a particular site will be dependent on the nature of the hydrotechnical hazard, the river morphology and the root causes of the hydrotechnical hazard changes, but the main goal of the mitigation is to reduce the risk of pipeline damage or failure while minimizing the impact on the environment. Some examples of mitigation include: a) Installation of erosion protection for the bank or bed of the watercourse; b) Lowering the pipeline; c) Deploy a landfill over culverts, with the buried pipe, above the new stream bed level; d) Building a new crossing by directional drilling or constructing an aerial crossing, and e) Rerouting to a new pipeline section to avoid that hazard watercourse section.

The choice of crossing method depends on costs, the dominant geomorphic processes at the stream crossing, as well as environmental constraints.

The key design data for conventional crossings includes estimates of scour and bank erosion for the design flood as well as the potential for channel degradation and avulsion.

For aerial crossings additional data required include the peak flood discharge for the design flood and an estimate of the type of debris that will be transported during floods to ensure that the infrastructure is located outside of the debris impact zone.

To cross pipelines above the channels surface, the structure axis should be above all that cross stream channels on the surface should be located above all possible floodflows that may occur at the site. At a minimum, pipelines must be located above the 100-year flood elevation and preferably above the 500year flood elevation [3].

In order to position the buried duct above the bed, it must be surrounded by structure soil over bridges or culverts.

Surveys of the Erosion Process Evolution.

In order for the stream bed to deeping until at cross-section km 0029+180S, exposing the pipeline in 2015, there was a sequence of events that were recorded in successive images or pictures.

In 2010, the height between the top of the bank and the bed was approximately 1,0 m (Figure 14).

Figure 14. Picture Jardim Novo Maracanã stream crossing, in 2010, looking upstream. Source: Internal Report of TBG (2015).

After 2015 extreme flood this difference advanced to about 4.0 m height (Figure 15).

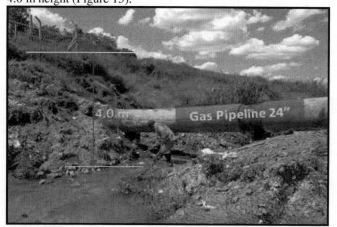

Figure 15. Jardim Novo Maracanã stream crossing, in 2015. Source: Internal Report of TBG (2015).

Approximately 400 m downstream of the pipeline crossing, under the 11th Street crossing, there is un culvert of approximately 2.0 m by 2.0 m (Figure 16).

Figure 16. Picture Jardim Novo Maracanã Stream 11th Street Crossing, in 2015, looking downstream. Source: Internal Report of TBG (2015).

This culvert is located above the rigid substrate, and thus is the predominant factor in the stabilization of bed erosion i.e. it is the local base level.

In the 2001 satellite image, the culvert of 11th Street is already seen crossing the creek, 400 m downstream of the pipeline crossing. At that time a small incision of the stream can already be noticed, indicating that there was a lowering of the bed and erosive process in the margins, in the stretch from the pipeline up to 11th Street (Figure 17).

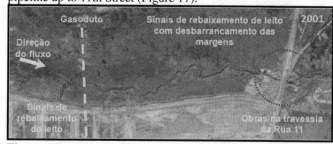

Figure 17. 2001 Satellite Image of Jardim Novo Maracanã Stream. Source: Internal Report of TBG (2015).

The alignment of the Jardim Novo Maracanã stream maintained slightly sinuous until then became, in the image of 2006 (Figure 18), more rectilinear downstream of the pipeline crossing, indicating that there was an accelerated process of bedding and banks erosions.

Figure 18. 2006 Satellite Image of Jardim Novo Maracanã Stream. Source: Internal Report of TBG (2015).

From 2006 to 2014 there was a significant evolution of the collapse of the banks and back erosion processes with retroerosion characteristics in the stream bed, in the stretch between the pipeline crossing and the 11th Street.

However, the existence of the buried gas pipeline and its protective structures contributed to the temporary stabilization of the erosion process, limiting it to the section of this crossing and avoiding (until 2015) the lowering of the bed in the stretch upstream of that section (Figure 19).

Figure 19. 2006 Satellite Picture of Jardim Novo Maracanã Stream. Source: Internal Report of TBG (2015).

During the 2015 stream floods the retroerosion had the contribution of hydraulic excavation (with supercritical flow velocities) and bed deepening of about 3.0 m (Figure 20) in the downstream bed protection structure section, installed in the pipeline cross section, that resulted in this bed protection collapse and the exposure of the pipeline with a free span of approximately 12 m.

This phenomenon continued its evolution until the final erosion stabilization, in 2018.

This phenomenon continued its evolution, with channel deepening and increase of erosion width, until the definitive stabilization of the erosive process in 2018.

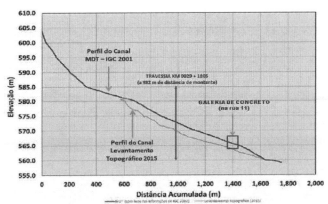

Figure 20. Jardim Novo Maracanã Stream Channel Profile. Source: Internal Report of TBG (2015).

From there, the channel bed, upstream and in the gas pipeline crossing, was quickly taken up by the erosive process, causing the exposed pipeline (Figures 21 and 22).

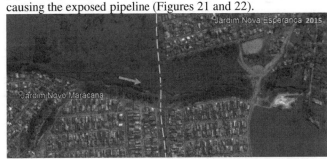

Figure 21. 2015 Satellite Image of Jardim Novo Maracanã Stream. Source: Internal Report of TBG (2015).

Figure 22. 2015 Aerial Picture of Jardim Novo Maracanã Stream. Source: Internal Report of TBG (2015).

SELECTED MITIGATION ALTERNATIVES

After all the studies carried out, it is concluded by adopting the most viable technical and economical solution of "Culvert Inlet Protection with the pipeline enveloped crossing", instead Aerial, HDD and Check Dam protection crossings alternatives.

The stretches of the channel immediately upstream and downstream of the work were adjusted to the new bottom channel dimension and configured with a transition zone between the culverts and the upstream natural channel for a distance of approximately 7.0 m downstream maintaining a slope of 0.5% until the encounter with the natural channel.

These culverts were designed and constructed comprising three parallel series of parts of 2.5 m by 2.5 m, supporting a landed gabion "channel" in which was buried the pipeline (Figures 23 and 24).

Figure 23. Picture Jardim Novo Maracanã stream crossing works, in 2018, looking downstream. Source: TBG Collection (2018).

Figure 24. Picture Jardim Novo Maracanã stream crossing, in 2018, looking upstream. Source: TBG Collection (2018).

This alternative was designed with extra protections, as additional measures to prevent retroerosion. A metal barrier buried upstream from the culverts entrance and a filter system under the culverts were installed. The extra subsurface drainage was oriented by gabions structures.

In addition, a debris barrier installed in the canal at the entrance of the culverts to prevent its blockage.

REFERENCES

[1] Nicas, Jack. (2012). **Floods Put Pipelines at Risk**: Records Suggest Erosion of Riverbeds Jeopardizes Oil and Gas Infrastructure. Wall Street Journal, Updated Dec. 3, 2012.

[2] ABNT- Associação Brasileira de Normas Técnicas. (2002). **NBR 12712** – Projeto de Sistemas de Transmissão e Distribuição de Gás Combustível.

[3] Fogg, J. and H. Hadley. (2007). Hydraulic considerations for pipelines crossing stream channels. **Technical Note 423**. BLM/ ST/ST-07/007+2880. U.S. Department of the Interior, Bureau of Land Management, National Science and Technology Center, Denver. 20 pp. http://www.blm.gov/nstc/library/techno2.htm.

[4] MacBroom, James Grant (1981). Factors Affecting the Stability of Structures Erected Along Water Courses: **Applied Fluvial Geomorphology. Report No. 31**, University of Connecticut: Institute of Water Resources.

[5] García López, M. (2013) **Estudios para el Diseño de Cruces de Cuerpos de Agua**. ASME 2013 International Pipeline Geotechnical Conference (IPG2013). Bogota, Colombia, Tutorial A - Parte 2.

[6] CEPA - Canadian Energy Pipeline Association. (2014). Pipeline **Watercourse Management. Recommended Practices**, 1st Edition. Recommended Practices for Development and Implementation of a Pipeline Watercourse Management Program for Operating Pipelines. Calgary.

[7] NHC – Northwest Hydraulic Consultants. (2011). Apresentações: **Pipeline River Crossing Workshop**. Treinamento Interno. Universidade Petrobras. Rio de Janeiro.

[8] Hadish. Gregg A., Braster. Martin, Lohnes. Robert A., Baumel. C. Philip. (1994). Stream Stabilization in Western Iowa. Final Report. Iowa **DOT HR-352**. Golden Hills Resource Conservation and Development. Oakland, 249p.

[9] Casseti, V. (2006) **Geomorfologia**. (Access in: www.funape.org.br/geomorfologia).

[10] Monteiro-da-Costa, P.S. (2009). **Interações Sistêmicas em Ambientes Naturais sob Efeito de Neotectônica, mediadas por Sistemas Fluviais**: Observações no Município de Atibaia (SP, Brasil). In.: Resumos - XII Congresso da Associação Brasileira de Estudos do Quaternário. La Plata.

[11] Papanicolaou, Thanos A.N.; Wilson, Christopher G.; Dermisis, Dimitrios C.; Elhakeem, Mohamed & Thomas, John. (2008). **The Effects of Headcut and Knickpoint Propagation on Bridges in Iowa**. IIHR- Hydroscience & Engineering. Iowa City. http://publications.iowa.gov/20055/1/IADOT_tr_541_Effects_Headcut_Knickpoint_Propagation_Bridges_IA_2008.pdf.

[12] Grimaud, Jean-Louis; Paola, Chris; Voller, Vaughan. (2016). **Experimental migration of knickpoints**: influence of style of base-level fall and bed lithology. Earth Surface Dynamics, European Geosciences Union,

[13] Costa, C.A.; Cupertino, J.L. & Ardenghi, A.F. (1997). Projeto de Conservação Recuperação Ambiental da Bacia do Rio Verde, no Município de Rio Verde -MT - MS. **Anais do I Encontro das Águas**. Fortaleza.

[14] Milton, L. E. (1971). **A Review of Gully Erosion and Its Control**. SCA – Soil Conservation Authority. Victoria.

[15] Carnicero, Martín and Ponce, Manuel. (2015). River Crossings: Lessons Learned from Lowering Pipelines by Natural Flexion. Paper No. **IPG2015-8512**, ASME 2015 International Pipeline Geotechnical Conference. Bogota. http://www.wsj.com/articles/SB100014241278873236229045 78128884280719580.

[16] SCS - Soil Conservation Service. (1986). Urban Hydrology for Small Watersheds. **Technical Release 55**. Washington DC.

This page left blank intentionally.

IPG2019-5314

WATERCOURSE CROSSING PROGRAM: 10 YEARS PERFORMANCE

Gerald Ferris
BGC Engineering Inc.
Calgary, Alberta, Canada

Sarah Newton
BGC Engineering Inc.
Calgary, Alberta, Canada

Minh Ho
Plains Midstream Canada
Calgary, Alberta, Canada

ABSTRACT

Plains Midstream Canada (PMC) completes a watercourse crossing program as part of its overall integrity management program. The approximately 9,900 kilometers of operating and discontinued pipelines are evaluated within the watercourse crossing program. The pipelines are located throughout the Canadian Provinces of Alberta, Saskatchewan, Manitoba and Ontario. The terrain traversed ranges from relatively steep near the Rocky Mountains to extremely flat in northern Alberta and Southern Ontario. Since 2008, PMC's systematic watercourse crossing program has evolved and now consists of approximately 5,000 individual watercourse crossings. The bankfull width of the watercourses ranges from less than 1 m for intermittent streams to more than 700 m at major rivers.

The watercourse crossing program is subjected to a continuous improvement process, with a focus on key learnings from pipeline failures, free spans and exposure. This paper describes the results from the program over the last 10 years and highlights program improvements. In addition, data from a failure and three free spans on the pipelines now owned by PMC, but where the exposure, free span or failure occurred prior to PMC purchasing the pipelines were added to expand the available data for the key learnings.

INTRODUCTION

Plains Midstream Canada (PMC) completes a watercourse crossing program as part of its overall integrity management program. The approximately 9,900 kilometers of operating and discontinued pipelines are evaluated within the watercourse crossing program. The pipelines are located throughout the Canadian Provinces of Alberta, Saskatchewan, Manitoba and Ontario. The terrain traversed ranges from relatively steep near the Rocky Mountains to extremely flat in northern Alberta and Southern Ontario. Since 2008, PMC's systematic watercourse crossing program has evolved and now consists of approximately 5,000 individual watercourse crossings. The

bankfull width of the watercourses ranges from less than 1 m for intermittent streams to more than 700 m at major rivers.

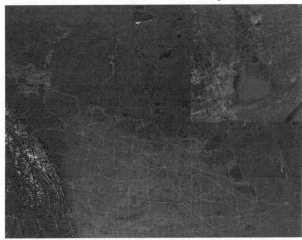

Figure 1 Location of PMC pipelines in Prairie Provinces, insert shows area of Ontario from Windsor to Sarina.

PIPELINE FAILURE MODES IN WATERCOURSE CROSSINGS

Failure modes typically considered for pipeline failure (release of product) in watercourse crossings are water loading, impact loading, and vortex induced vibrations (VIV) [1]. The impact loading can be considered either as part of the water load, where the impact adds to the water load, or it could be debris that causes puncture. The pipeline failure modes are distinct from river erosion processes namely degradation, scour, bank erosion, encroachment and avulsion [1, 2]. The river erosion processes may lead to exposure, free span and failure of the pipeline, depending on the loading type and magnitude that results due to the water action. Except for puncture, the pipeline needs to be free spanning before water loading can cause a pipeline failure [3].

WATER LOADING

A free-spanning pipeline will be subjected to stress from the combined effect of self-weight, buoyancy, operating loads, overburden loads, and lateral loads from the flow of the water. The hydrodynamic loads can be amplified or reduced by debris pile-ups, particular trees with root bulbs. The root bulbs can increase the cross-sectional area of the pipeline that is subjected to flow or, if embedded in the river bed, they can act to reduce the effective free span length. This depends on the nature of the debris. If the size of the free span and flow velocity of the river is sufficient, the combined loading may result in unacceptable plastic strain levels in the pipeline. If a pipeline is not free spanning, the lateral loading from the water flow is generally resisted by the soil, in section, or in plan as if the pipeline is only exposed at a single location the lateral extend of the exposure is limited.

The hydrodynamic loads and resulting stresses can be assessed utilizing the River-X software associated with the PRCI report L51854 *"Enhancement of Integrity Assessment Models/Software for Exposed and Unburied Pipelines in River Channels"* [3]. The River-X software simulates sections of an exposed pipeline being anchored in the river bed or banks and plastic material behavior of a free spanning pipeline. A quasi-static analysis of the pipeline exposed to the river flow is performed using advanced non-linear structural modeling to determine the maximum values of plastic strain, stress, displacement, bending moment and tension.

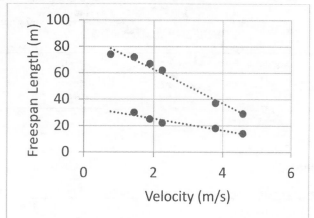

Figure 2 Envelope, above or to the right of the line indicates failure below or left indicates no failure, of critical freespan due to VIV (lower line) and water loading (upper line).

An analysis was completed using River-X and a conservative plastic strain limit of 1.5% for the "failure" condition, noting that pipelines can sustain higher strains than this, so the analysis is somewhat conservative. The results of these analysis are plotted in Figure 2 for; nominal pipeline size (NPS) 12, 7.8 mm wall thickness, X-42 pipeline, 25 mm gunnite weight coated, crude oil pipeline.

VORTEX INDUCED VIBRATIONS (VIV)

The vortex shedding frequency caused by a flow normal to a free span is governed by the Strouhal's number, which is a function of the pipe outer diameter and the flow velocity [3, 4]. As the flow velocity increases and thereby the shedding frequency reaches one of the natural frequencies of the span, the span starts to vibrate. If the vortex shedding frequency and associated vibrations get locked-in with the natural frequencies of the span the vibrations 'lock-in' and the magnitude of the vibration increases. This 'lock-in' occurs over a certain range of flow velocities. If such vibrations are excited over a long enough duration, the span would fail due to fatigue, i.e. if the flood lasts longer than the predicted fatigue life.

Failure in fatigue is typically associated with the growth of pre-existing flaws at the pipeline girth welds. In addition to the shedding frequency that changes with the flow velocity, the natural frequency of the free span is one of the essential parameters. This frequency drops with an increase in the span length, which in turn means that as the span length increases a lower water velocity can induce vibrations matching the natural frequency. This relationship can be used to define a "critical" envelope of free span lengths and velocities [4, 5].

The fatigue life as a function of flow velocity and free span length can also be assessed utilizing the River-X [3]. Using a fatigue life on the order of 1E-04 years as a criterion, a "critical" envelope between no failure and failure was developed for the same NPS 12 pipeline as for water loading. The results are shown in Figure 2.

IMPACT LOADING

Impact loading causing denting that would fail a pipeline typically requires large particles (rocks) moving at minimum velocities in the 8 to 9 m/s range [4]. No watercourses within PMC's inventory are capable of producing velocities in this range; therefore, impact loading failures are not mentioned further in this paper.

10 YEAR PERFORMANCE SUMMARY

The watercourse crossing program is applied to all pipelines owned by PMC. The pipeline characteristics are highly variable, as the pipelines were constructed from the 1950's through to the 2010's with differing:

- design criteria,
- diameter, steel grade, coatings, and operating pressures,
- terrain, geomorphology and hydrology conditions,
- regulatory requirements, and
- flooding conditions that depend on the weather conditions following installation.

PMC's pipelines that cross watercourses range in diameter from NPS 2 to NPS 24 with NPS 4, NPS 6 and NPS 10 having lengths of: 2,600 km, 2,700 km and 1,300 km, respectively. Included in the analysis presented are results for operating and discontinued pipelines. The integrity program requires a site inspection of all pipeline watercourse crossings at least once for operating and discontinued pipeline statuses. For abandoned pipelines the watercourse crossings are identified but no further action is taken unless the need is identified by other methods.

EXPOSURES

During the 2008 to 2018 period there were 107 unique pipeline watercourse crossings where the pipeline was found to be exposed. This total includes watercourse crossings where the pipeline was exposed during the first inspection completed and those where the pipeline became exposed after one or multiple previous inspections. This total number of exposures is not a list of current exposures, as it does not reflect subsequent repairs or natural deposition. For example, a pipeline that became exposed in 2008 and was successfully repaired in 2009 with no later exposure is included as one of the pipeline watercourse crossings that became exposed. Also, a pipeline exposed for multiple years at a watercourse crossing is only counted once.

The rate of pipeline exposure over this 10-year period was 1.21 per 1000 km-year. This compares well with the rate of pipeline exposures previously reported of 1.2×10^{-3} per kilometer per year [6]. The rate calculated herein was for one client, and the rate reported by Leir was based on 8,800 individual watercourse crossings for a diverse client group.

A comparison of the rate of pipeline exposure for different size of pipeline was completed by dividing the total number of pipeline exposures in the 10-year period by the total length of operating and discontinued pipeline with the same NPS. The results are plotted in Figure 3, where the rate of pipeline exposure was found to be between 0.6 to 1.1 per year per 1000 km. The rate of exposure was thus shown to be largely independent of the pipeline diameter.

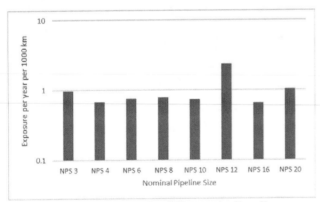

Figure 3 Rate of exposure for different pipeline diameters.

The rate of exposure increases with increasing bankfull width. This result is shown in Figure 4, where number of exposed pipelines was divided by the total number of watercourse crossings in a particular bankfull width range. The widest watercourses have a rate of exposure that is 8 to 10 times greater than the narrowest watercourses. A possible explanation might be related to past construction practices where a single

depth of cover (e.g. minimum of 1.2 m) was utilized for all watercourse. This overall result of increasing rate of exposure on wider watercourses was not previously encountered [5] when a similar analysis was completed across multiple clients. This maybe an indication that PMC owns more pipeline installed with the minimum DoC than the all clients dataset.

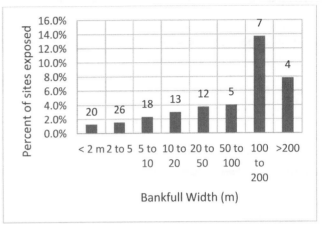

Figure 4 Percentage of watercourse crossings that became exposed in different bankfull width range. The number on the top of the bar indicates the total number of exposures for the bankfull width range.

Figure 5 is a plot of all PMC watercourse crossings that had been exposed during the 10-year period as a function of bankfull width and longitudinal gradient. Figure 5 shows that exposures can occur on all widths and gradients of watercourse crossed by pipelines.

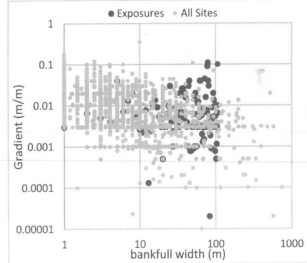

Figure 5 Exposed watercourse crossings plotted based on the watercourses bankfull width and gradient.

The PMC watercourse crossing program requires that all watercourse crossings on operating and discontinued pipelines be inspected. Other companies either may not plan to inspect all watercourse crossings, or due to the large number of sites want a method of optimizing the inspection program to find as many exposed crossings as quickly as possible. As part of the continuous improvement process, a method was recently developed comparing the expected water velocity with a threshold water velocity (which is based on the erosion rate of a particular soil type) to enable the program to focus on sites that are more likely to have either minimal DoC or be exposed [7]. The method was calibrated based on the results of more than 15,000 individual sites that have been inspected in the past.

FREE SPANS AND FAILURE

Although 107 pipelines became exposed in the 10-year period only 12 were confirmed to be free spanning and only one failed (loss of containment). Therefore, during the 10-year period under study the rate of pipeline failure per exposure was 1/107 and the rate of free span per exposure was 12/107.

Pipeline failure per exposure has been termed vulnerability [5]. During the last 10 years, PMC experienced rate of failure per exposure similar to what was proposed in the development of a statistic-based vulnerability model. In the statistics based vulnerability model, implemented by PMC in 2013, properties of the watercourse and the pipeline are considered in order to make an estimate of the rate of pipeline failure if the pipeline became exposed based on the properties of an individual crossing. The controlling factor in the statistics based vulnerability model is the bankfull width [5], with narrow watercourses (1 to 2 m) having a 1/2,000 chance of failure while wide watercourses have a 1/2 chance of failure. In the mechanistic based vulnerability model the bankfull width of the watercourse was compared to the critical free span length due to VIV, Figure 2.

The one failure occurred in 2012, during the spring freshet, on the Red Deer River [8]. The investigating regulator reported that: "At the time of the release, the river flow was about ten times the seasonal flow. It was determined that the pipeline failed at a circumferential (girth) weld located along the west bank of the Red Deer River. The Plains third party investigation indicated that the pipeline failed due to high-cycle fatigue, likely caused by vibrations induced by river flow. The investigation also indicated that the failed portion of the pipeline must have been exposed during the failure and was likely uncovered by scour. Furthermore, the failed section met all applicable manufacturing requirements at the time of installation. Corrosion, a deficient weld, or other material property failures of the section of pipeline are not considered to have contributed to the break."

A photo taken while the Red Deer River was flooding is shown in Figure 6, with the approximate location of the failure marked. A photo of the failed pipe is shown in Figure 7.

During investigations of the pipeline failure, surveys were completed about 1 day after the failure and found that 27 m of the pipeline was free spanning, with a gap of more than 0.5 m beneath the pipeline. During the flood, the approximate water velocity in the main channel at the free span location was approximately 3 m/s. The River-X analysis shown in Figure 2 was for the pipeline at the Red Deer River crossing. When the data from the free span length and velocity is compared to the

'critical free span', this crossing would be predicted to fail due to VIV, but not fail based on water loading.

Figure 6. Photo of the Red Deer River days after the 2012 flood peak that caused failure. The green line shows the location of the pipeline while the star marks the location of the failure.

Figure 7 – Photograph of the failed end of the pipe section at the 2012 Red Deer River failure. [9]

The Red Deer River location had previously been exposed, and potentially free spanned during a 2005 flood which was twice as large as the 2012 flood. Following the 2005 flood and exposure, a groyne was installed on the bank of the main channel [9], which had the purpose of protecting that location from lateral bank erosion by increasing sedimentation over the pipeline. While it prevented bank erosion, the groyne narrowed the water channel and concentrated the erosive power of the fast-flowing water during the 2012 flood which caused a large scour hole to develop underneath the pipeline.

Although there were only 12 free spans encountered during the 10-year period, they can be separated into three "types" of free spans: those that were constructed as free spans, those that are located in ponded areas, and those that were formed and loaded during flooding. There was one of the constructed (Figure 8) type, one of the ponded water types (within a beaver pond) and the remaining ten locations were exposed during a flood, one of which failed. Typically, the free spans are found by ground and pipeline profile surveys during or after large floods (during if concern about possible free span was pre-identified or after as part of a follow-up action identified in a high flow action plan) or found once the flood waters recede and visual inspection is completed. It is possible that additional undocumented free spans might have been formed during flood events within the 10-year period for which the exposed pipeline did not fail and was subsequently covered with sediments following the flood. The 2012 Red Deer River failure experienced re-sedimentation such that the post-flood survey channel base was nearly identical to the pre-flood elevations, although the during-flood survey showed a large free span.

Figure 8 Constructed and supported free span crossing an unnamed stream. Note that the pipeline is discontinued.

The one ponded water free span was located in the base of beaver pond and the reason for the free span is mostly likely due to lack or loss of buoyancy control on the pipeline. The free span was located in northern Alberta. Prior to the influence of beaver activity, the watercourse was approximately 4 m, whereas the width of the pond was about 100 m due to backwater effects from the beaver dam. The mechanical analysis would indicate that this free span and other similar free spans are not likely to fail, as the velocity of water is near zero if the beaver dam is intact. If the beaver dam fails, the water velocities will be limited in the ponded area due to flow concentration in the narrow outflow channel.

Comparison of the free spanning pipelines (including the 2012 failure and two historical failures) based on bankfull and gradient is included in Figure 9. The data plotted in Figure 9 shows that the free spanning pipelines occurred throughout the range of gradients and bankfull widths. The 2012 failure occurred at a wide watercourse crossing, but not every free span at wide watercourses has failed.

Although the PMC data does not provide confirmation of the ideas presented as part of the statistical vulnerability [5], due

largely to the limited number of failure sites, which was that watercourses with wide bankfulls where more likely to fail. The PMC is consistent with the "statistical vulnerability" approach. When the two historical failures (see next section) are added to the dataset, Figure 9, the wide bankfull approach of statistical vulnerability has more support. Detailed mechanical analysis, as shown in Figure 2, indicates that the failure of a pipeline depends on the water velocity and the free span length, not necessarily the bankfull width.

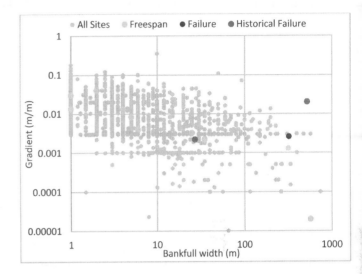

Figure 9 Comparison of the bankfull width and gradient of the watercourse crossings where either free spans or failure occurred (historical failure are included). All PMC watercourse crossings are also included.

Figure 10 plots the bankfull width of the watercourse and the free span length that was measured at each of the locations, when it was possible to measure them. For the majority of the free spans, the failure and non-failure status are understandable based on the analysis shown in Figure 2. The non-failure occurs when the free span length and velocity combination are to the left or below the 'critical free span' limits shown in Figure 2 (modified for the particular pipeline). However, two free spans in the dataset that did not fail had similar or larger bankfull widths and free span lengths than the Red Deer River failure site.

One of these two free spans that is an exception to the rule occurred at a watercourse with a width of 575 m, which has an extremely low gradient. The watercourse is part of the St. Lawrence Seaway in Canada, which has controlled (0.9 m/s) water velocities so that the combination of the free span length and velocities are less than the VIV and critical free span length combination. In addition to this factor, the free span is not continuous; rather it has multiple points where the pipeline touches down on the base of the channel, reducing the affected length of the free span from the plotted length shown in Figure 9.

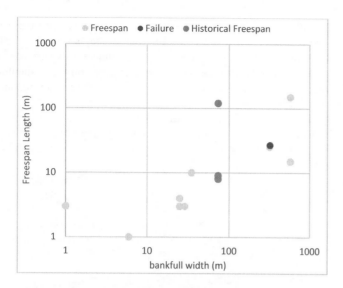

Figure 10 Bankfull width and the measured free span length of free spanning pipelines, including the 2012 failure. Historical freespans have also been included.

The other exceptional free span occurred at a watercourse crossing having a 320 m bankfull width. In that case, the free span length and the velocities that the pipeline experiences should have resulted in failure according to a similar analysis as that shown in Figure 2. Detailed studies of this crossing have not resulted in a satisfactory explanation. It is speculated that the free span was too large and VIV was no longer a viable failure mode, and at the same time, the free span was not large enough to cause failure due to water loading. This speculation is based on similar analysis previously presented [10].

HISTORICAL FREE SPANS

To supplement the number of free span case histories available, the exposure and free spans that occurred at the James River crossing during the 2005 flood were added. During the estimated 100-year flood, bank erosion occurred and moved the location of the main channel approximately 40 m. This resulted in free spanning of three pipelines (Table 1) at this location. The NPS 8 pipeline experienced the largest exposure/free span of approximately 120 m length. Numerous trees became caught on the pipeline, Figure 11, and the pipeline was floating near the top of the water during the flood. As shown in Figure 11, the majority of the water flow was conveyed through the main channel, which was approximately 50 m wide. The two NPS 12 pipelines were undermined (Figure 12), but their free span length was limited to 8 m and 9 m and they were not visible during the peak of the flood, Figure 11. The NPS 12 pipelines also had trees / woody debris caught on them during the flood, but much less than the NPS 8 pipeline that was near the surface of the flowing water during the flood.

The Water Survey of Canada gauge for the James River is only 3 km upstream of the pipeline crossing, so the estimated discharge represents the crossing fairly well. Based on measured river gradients, the estimated average velocity during the flood event was 2.2 m/s using Manning's equation. Based on the photographs and discussion with staff attending the site during the flood, the velocity was concentrated in the new main channel and would have had a velocity of 3.5 m/s. That estimate was consistent with the size of the bed and bank material eroded by the water action.

These three additional free spans were included in Figure 10. The two NPS 12 pipelines matched the majority of records, with the combination of the water velocity and free span length being less than the VIV 'critical' zone. The NPS 8 pipeline was an outlier as the total length of the free span exceeded both the VIV and water loading 'critical zones'.

Figure 11. View of NPS 8 pipeline free spanning in the James River during 2005 flood.

Figure 12. James River - View of the NPS 8 (foreground) and NPS 12 (background) pipelines at lower flow.

Table 1. Pipeline properties – James River.

Site Attribute			
Diameter	NPS 8	NPS 12	NPS 12
Steel Grade, API 5L	X52	X52	X46
Wall Thickness (mm)	4.78	6.35	7.92
Coating type	Tape	Extruded PE	Tape
Concrete Weight Coating, thickness (mm)	None	None	None

HISTORICAL FAILURES

A pipeline failure occurred a pipeline that were owned by previous operating companies prior to their purchase by PMC, were also considered in this study. In 2008 a failure of an NPS 6 crude oil pipeline in the Red Deer River [11] occurred.

The Red Deer River failure occurred on June 15, 2008. The failure investigation concluded that the failure occurred as the result of one-way bending fatigue [11]. The stated reason for this fatigue failure was that the supporting soil was eroded by increased water flow. The pipe was noted to be freely exposed in the current of the Red Deer River. No indications of any pipe material or welding flaws could be found that would have contributed to the failure.

The pipeline at the Red Deer River crossing had previously become exposed in 2004 and 800 m of pipeline had been deeply buried across most of the floodplain of the braided river. During the 2008 flood the main channel of the river avulsed into a section of the floodplain where the channel had not been deeply buried and caused a large section of the channel to become free spanning.

The regulator incident report did not report the length of pipeline that was exposed or free spanned. The location of the incident could be found and information was available to plot the two failures on a bankfull width versus gradient plot, shown on Figure 9, but could not be plotted on Figure 10.

Based on the failure type information contained in the reports, it is apparent that the failure was a VIV type fatigue failure, similar to the 2012 Red Deer River failure. The limited number of failures on the PMC system fits the general pattern discussed previously [5], where the watercourse crossings of most concern for an integrity program are the ones with large bankfull widths. The variation in the bankfull width of these watercourses also shows that the measurement that matters is the freespan length, which needs to be combined with the water velocity to give the detailed cause of failure.

PROGRAM IMPROVEMENTS

This section summarizes all the program improvements already noted and additional activities performed to date, including the following:

A method to focus inspections to find the locations that are more likely to have low DoC or become exposed [7]. This method uses past inspection performance to calibrate a prediction of those expected to become exposed. The method uses the predicted velocities that will cause the soil to become mobilized.

A vulnerability screening level method to focus efforts on those watercourse crossings that are more likely to fail [5]. This 'statistical vulnerability" method assigns high probability of failure (if exposed) to wide watercourse crossings.

A detailed assessment of the failure modes [3, 4] that accounts for the pipeline properties, presence of defects and weight coating, and the expected water velocities. A 'critical zones' where a pipeline could be expected to fail due to VIV or water loading failure modes. This needs to be combined with estimates of the expected water velocity and free span length for larger floods [4, 12], such as shown in Figure 10.

A flood monitoring program that uses predictions of the initiation of exposure, freespan and the growth of freespan to define discharge levels where actions could be taken to avoid pipeline failure [12]. The flood monitoring program needs to include a plan that defines actions to take at different warning levels for watercourse crossings susceptible to a potential VIV failure. The monitoring program and the defined action to take during the flood is a high flow action plan.

These program elements have been implemented as part of PMC's water crossing program since the 2012 failure at the Red Deer River. The results have been used to:

- Prioritize mitigation based on probability of failure due to VIV.
- Employ flood monitoring to manage the risk at crossings that might fail prior to completing mitigations, with actions such as shut-ins and purging implemented when a high flood occurs.
- Complete engineering assessments that concluded that some exposed pipelines can be monitored through regular site inspections without impacting pipeline integrity.

SUMMARY

PMC's formal watercourse management program evolved during the first ten years of implementation especially following a pipeline failure in 2012. The program continues to improve based on experience gained in-house and lessons learned from practices implemented by other operators. The two main lessons are that; at narrow watercourse crossings exposure is unlikely to lead to pipeline failure, and with a high flow monitoring plan watercourse crossings that might fail if a large enough flood occurs can be proactively managed using flood monitoring.

ACKNOWLEDGMENTS

The authors would like to acknowledge the helpful discussions with past and current colleagues.

REFERENCES

[1] CEPA 2014 Pipeline Watercours Manual, Recommended Practices, 1st Edition, CEPA, December 2014

[2] Baumgard, A., Coultish, T. and Ferris, G. 2014. Implementing a geohazard integrity management program – Statistics and lessons learned over 15 years, IPC2014-33559, in Proceedings of the 2014 10th International Pipeline Conference, Calgary, Alberta

[3] Bryndum, M.B., "Enhancement of Integrity Assessment Models/Software for Exposed and Unburied Pipelines in River Channels," Pipeline Research Council Intitute (PRCI), 2000

[4] Heggen, H.O., Fletcher, R., Fyrileiv, O, Ferris, G. and Ho, M. 2014 Fatigue of Pipelines Subjected to Vortex-Induced Vibrations at River Crossings, 2014 Brazil Oil and Gas, Rio, Brazil, IBP1941-14

[5] Dooley, C., Prestie, Z., Ferris, G., Fitch, M. and Zhang, H. 2014. Approaches for Evaluating the Vulnerability of Pipelines at Water Crossings. 2014 International Pipeline Conference, Calgary, Alberta, Canada

[6] Leir, M., 2012. Geohazard Management Program for Onshore Pipelines. Proceedings, Environmental Concerns in Rights-of-Way Management: The 9th International Symposium, Portland, Oregon, September 27 to October 1, 2009. Utility Arborist Association 617 pp. Editors, James M. Evans, John W. Goodrich-Mahoney, Dean Mutrie, and Joe Reinemann.

[7] Ferris, G. and Newton, S. 2018 Measured depth of cover in a watercourse crossing as a measure of degradation and/or scour. Proceedings of the 9th International Scour and Erosion Conference, Tiapei, Tiawan

[8] AER 2014 Plains Midstream Canada ULC, NPS12 - Pipeline Failure and Release into the Red Deer River, AER Investigation Report, March 4, 2014

[9] Det Norske Veritas 2012 Failure Investigation of Plains Midstream Canada's 323 mm Rangeland South Pipeline. Report part of reference [8].

[10] Samcheck, A., Beckstead, G. and Zhou, J. 2001 Case Studies of scour and erosion at water crossings. Proceedings of the ASCE Pipeline Division Specialty Conference. San Diego, California.

[11] ERCB 2009 Pembina Pipeline Corporation, Crude Oil Pipeline Failure, Licence No. 1386, Line No. 003, June 15, 2008 ERCB Investigation Report, February 11, 2009

[12] Ferris, G., Newton, S., Ho, M., Bear, D. & Eichhorn, G. 2015 Flood monitoring for pipeline crossings, 2015 Rio Pipeline, Brazil

IPG2019-5321

COST OPTIMISATION IN RISK REDUCTION MANAGEMENT BASED ON GROSS DISPROPORTIONATION CONCEPT

Alejandro Marín, Jon Hernández
Oleoducto Central S.A. (OCENSA)
Bogotá D.C, Colombia

ABSTRACT

Gross Disproportionation concept is used as indicator once risk reduction measures are required. This indicator shows that a measure must be implemented if its cost (i.e. Capital Expenditure), is not grossly disproportionate if compared to benefits –represented by casualties suppression- reached by the measure. Due to this, a risk reduction measure is reasonable feasible unless its cost is highly disproportionate in comparison to its benefits.

In hydrocarbon transportation industry, benefits represent the avoided cost if threats take place; on the other hand, for risk mitigation cost estimation, the cost per casualty averted must be accounted. The latter, provides a global cost of the mitigation measure adopted in relation to the direct cost of construction, with the reduction of the level of risk (i.e. social risk) and with the expected design period for that measure. In this last concept, the higher the reduction in the level of risk or the longer the design period of the mitigation measure, the lower the cost per casualty averted, a fact that reflects an effective mitigation measure in terms of risk reduction and its durability.

This document shows, from a case study, how the application of the concept of grow disproportionation allows to select the type of optimal intervention over Ocensa's pipeline, with the most favorable relation between cost and benefit, and the effective risk reduction level.

Keywords: Weather, Outside Forces, Societal Risk, Gross Disproportionation, Mitigation, Threats, Integrity.

NOMENCLATURE

HCA	High Consequence Area
QRA	Quantitative Risk Analysis
Δ RS	Delta of Societal Risk
API 5L	Specification for Line Pipe
FN	Frequency vs. Number of Casualties.

INTRODUCTION

The Ocensa's Pipeline extends through the Colombian Andes, from Cupiagua in the Eastern Plains to Coveñas on the north coast of the country. This, generates that its profile presents elevations that vary between sea level and the 3000 meters above sea level, where mountainous grounds of this Cordillera have high moisture levels and precarious stabilities, standing out extensive colluvial deposits in movement. Figure 1 shows Ocensa's pipeline elevation profile.

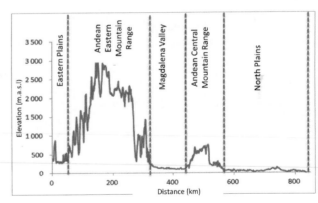

FIGURE 1. OCENSA'S ELEVATION PROFILE.

Among identified threats on the pipeline operated by Ocensa, Climate and Outside Forces (*i.e.* Geohazards) embraces risk factors over the integrity of the system, associated to geotechnical, hydrological and tectonic conditions, inherent to the geographical location and topography on which the route of the pipeline extends.

Terrain movements associated with these factors of geotechnical and tectonic instability, have the potential to induce stresses on the pipeline and structures, causing their displacement and consequent deformation. However, although the threat of Climate and Outside Forces exert influence within risk and pipeline integrity, eight additional threats must be taken into account once a realistic determination of the probability of failure is required, classified as:

- Internal Corrosion;
- External Corrosion;
- Stress Corrosion Cracking;
- Incorrect Operations;
- Manufacturing Defects;
- Construction Defects;
- Fatigue;
- Third Party Interference.

Once the nine threats that increase the pipeline probability of failure have been identified, it is possible to perform Quantitative Risk Analysis (QRA) of pipeline segments that present anomalies or critical strain levels, based on the estimation of the associated Failure Frequency of the predominant threat, and consequence estimation.

When a Quantitative Risk Analysis shows an unacceptable risk level if compared to tolerability thresholds, it is necessary to implement mitigation measures to reduce aforementioned levels of risk to a tolerable one. To ensure that capital investment when implementing these mitigation measures is reasonable, taking into account delta of risk reduction level, Cost-Benefit analysis is usually carried out in order to select the suitable risk mitigation alternative, which represents the optimal balance between capital investment and the acquired benefit.

As a practical example, the application of a Quantitative Risk Analysis applied to the Ocensa pipeline is exposed, where due to pipeline´s strain levels associated with soil displacement, need of cut and replacement of a segment of pipeline was found. For this, the implementation of two solution alternatives was evaluated, where a Cost-Benefit analysis was developed and the concept of Gross Disproportionation was applied, in order to define the best solution alternative in terms of investment and risk reduction.

1.1 Methodology

For the Gross Disproportionation application concept to both solution alternatives proposed, once the pipeline segment was cut, a Quantitative Risk Level was estimated first. Generally, a Quantitative Risk Analysis is conducted for those threats to which the pipeline operator does not have enough control, despite having integrity and monitoring programs, such as the threats of Climate and Outside Forces and Damage associated with a Third Party; on the other hand, remaining threats have a number of controls and monitoring that facilitate the operator to maintain minimum levels of probability of failure.

For the particular case of study, materialised threat on the pipeline is based on geotechnical instability (*i.e.* Climate and

Outside Forces), reason why is the Failure Frequency associated with this threat which is taken into account for the analysis. The above does not mean that factors associated with possible mechanical anomalies, operating conditions or geometric parameters have not been accounted in the determination of Failure Frequency, since they are an integral part of this factor in the risk equation.

For Failure Frequency estimation, it is common practice to adopt historical data of hydrocarbon transportation pipelines failures, reported by several groups of operators around the world. However, Ocensa has statistics of its pipeline associated with each recognized threat, so the frequency of particular failure for Climate and Outside Forces results from the cross between the number of reported damages, the length of the pipeline, and operation years. Regarding the consequences, factors associated with volume and density of product released, probability of ignition, potential affectation radius, radiation and existence of High Consequence Areas (*i.e.* HCA), were taken into account for the estimation of this factor.

Knowing that pipeline failures for crude oil transportation are classified as low frequency-high consequence events, it is more representative to evaluate risk levels with respect to social vulnerability rather than the individual one, since acceptability of design of a new pipeline or realignment of an existing one, or the planning of an urban settlement will be viable with respect to this criterion that encompasses collectivity. Due to this, the definition of suitability of the alternative to be selected is determined by the level of Societal Risk estimation.

In the performance of the Cost-Benefit analysis, the concept of cost per casualty averted is included, which represents the relationship between the direct cost of intervention and the factor resulting from the risk delta between the level of social risk of the initial scenario or without modification and each alternative, with the design life of the latter, expressed as follows:

$$Cost\ per\ Casualty\ Averted = \frac{Alternative\ Cost}{\Delta SR * Design\ Life}$$

(1)

As observed, the higher the risk reduction or the longer the estimated design life of the mitigation measure, the lower the value of cost per casualty averted will be, which represents an effective mitigation measure in terms of reducing risk level and its durability.

Regarding benefit determination, this represents the avoided cost if the threat takes place, by applying the proposed mitigation measure. Among evaluated aspects to determine the value of benefit, paid costs by insurance companies once casualties associated with pipeline failure takes place are included, sanctions and environmental fines, damage to infrastructure, loss of profit, deterioration of the corporate image, due to negative reactions of society, among others.

Since there is no regulatory definition of the financial value of human life, for Benefit value establishment within the equation should be taken into account the expertise and judgment of the risk assessor, which takes as a guide the average value of compensation before an accident, multiplied by several billions of pesos, in order to take into account the uncertainty associated with the occurrence of a pipeline failure, and the negative reactions that this entails.

Finally, the optimal solution alternative is determined in terms of Cost-Benefit, represented by Gross Disproportionation Factor. This concept makes possible to show whether the proposed mitigation cost (reflected by the cost per casualty averted) is substantially high if compared to the degree of benefit obtained by its implementation, which is measurable on the risk reduction level and consequently, in casualties reduction. In these terms, the concept of Gross Disproportionation is applied when obtaining the disproportionation factor, which shows how many times the value of the cost is to the value of the benefit.

Usually, once this factor exceeds a value of 10 (*i.e.* cost of investment to mitigate risk greater than ten times the cost of the benefit), the implementation of such mitigation would be disproportionate. The mathematical representation of the concept of Gross Disproportionation is given by:

$$\frac{Cost}{Benefit} \leq 10 \qquad (2)$$

Therefore, it is expected that any risk mitigation alternative is less than or equal to 10, to find investment justifiable and proportionate with acquired benefit.

1.2 Analysis and Results

To carry out the Quantitative Risk Analysis (QRA), the representative pipeline operation parameters of the area where strains over the pipeline were accounted, due to soil displacement, were taken into account. These parameters are shown in Table 1.

TABLE 1. PIPELINE PARAMETERS ADOPTED FOR THE ANALYSIS.

Parameter	Value
Steel Grade	API 5L X70
Diameter	30"
Thickness	19.05 mm

Societal risk levels were calculated for the initial scenario, for mitigation alternative 1 and alternative 2. The analysed alternatives correspond to the replacement of the existing pipeline, which is located on the same alignment as the original one; conversely, alternative 2 includes a realignment, which represents varying the length of the existing pipeline and the achievement of additional property permits. It is noteworthy that the realignment of the pipeline is considered within the existing RoW of the pipeline that has an environmental licensing, so it is not necessary to obtain a new license of this nature.

The FN Societal Risk curve for the initial scenario, as for the proposed alternatives is shown in Figure 2. There, red continuous line represents the criterion of Societal Risk acceptability, represented by a value of 1×10^{-3} fatalities per year. This value is widely used by pipeline operators around the world, as acceptance threshold for levels of Societal Risk, where any level that is greater than this, is unacceptable. The green dotted curve represents the original or initial risk level, while the gray dotted curve corresponds to the Societal Risk level calculated for the pipeline replacement alternative; blue dotted curve corresponds to the pipeline realignment alternative.

As shown, risk level of the original or initial scenario justifies the need for cutting and replacement of pipeline segment, because it is above the acceptability criterion, while both Societal Risk levels calculated for the proposed alternatives reduce Societal Risk levels to a broadly acceptable one, below the acceptability envelope.

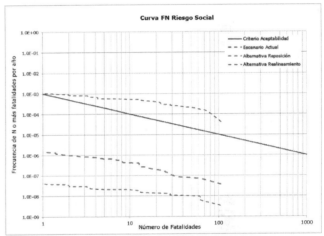

FIGURE 2. SOCIETAL RISK FN CURVE FOR CUT AND REPLACEMENT OF PIPELINE SEGMENT.

Taking into account that both alternatives meet Societal Risk levels required by regulation, a Cost-Benefit analysis was carried out, and the concept of Gross Disproportionation was applied, in order to determine the optimal solution in terms of investment and benefit.

For cost per casualty averted determination, estimation of related costs of construction of each alternative, delta or decrease of the level compared with the initial risk level was made, and the design life or useful life of each alternative was estimated. On the other hand, the benefit value was calculated taking into account abovementioned factors in the methodology, finding a value of $ 40,000 million pesos, aligned with income and main factors of the Colombian economy.

In terms of design life or useful life of each alternative, the experience and background of the problem within hydrocarbon transportation sector was taken into account, so that the replacement of the pipe segment on the same original route possesses a high probability of generating large strains of the pipeline, associated to geotechnical factors and to the bending geometry of the pipeline. Due to this, the replacement alternative has been granted a design period of 20 years, similar to the useful life of the original pipeline segment when it requires replacement; useful life or design period of the realignment alternative is equal to 40 years. Table 2 summarises cost and benefit obtained values.

TABLE 2. COST-BNEFIT VALUES.

Scen.	Risk Level	Cost (Thousa nds of Millions COP)	Δ SR	Cost per Casualty Averted (Thousands of Millions COP)
Initial	2.1×10^{-3}			
Replac.	8.9×10^{-6}	$ 8.5	2.06e-3	$ 206
Realign.	6.4×10^{-7}	$ 10.2	2.07e-3	$ 123

As previously shown, although both the direct costs of construction of both alternatives are similar and Societal Risk delta are approximate, cost per casualty averted value between alternatives differ significantly, corresponding to the replacement alternative a cost per casualty averted of $ 206,000 million pesos, and for realignment alternative a cost of $ 123,000 million pesos. The above reflects the influence of the design period factor assigned to each alternative, justified in the aforementioned background.

Consequently, disproportionation factor was obtained as the quotient of the relationship between cost and benefit acquired when implementing each alternative, as summarised in Table 3.

TABLE 3. DESPROPORTIONATION FACTOR FOR ASSESSED ALTERNATIVES.

Scen.	Risk Level	Cost per Casualty Averted (Thousan ds of Millions COP)	Benefit (Thousan ds of Millions COP)	Desproportio -nation Factor
Initial	2.1×10^{-3}	-	-	-
Replac.	8.9×10^{-6}	$ 206	$ 40	5
Realign.	6.4×10^{-7}	$ 123	$ 40	3

Once the concept of Gross Disproportionation has been applied, it is important to note how both alternatives satisfy established criterion by this concept, represented by values lower than 10, which indicates that if implemented, associated cost to the benefit acquired would not be disproportionate. However, a lower value obtained for the realignment alternative is the indicator or tool for the risk assessor, which serves as a criterion for decision making, and justification as to the alternative to be implemented.

1.3 Conclusions

After carrying out a Quantitative Risk Analysis and a Cost-Benefit analysis to two alternatives for mitigating the risk associated to Climate and Outside Forces threat, it is evident how the alternative comprised by the realignment, despite having a direct cost of construction greater than that of the alternative corresponding to the replenishment of the pipeline, is more convenient for its application. The foregoing, as a result of the adoption of the concepts of cost per casualty averted and the concept of Gross Disproportionation.

Obtained values of cost per casualty averted, benefit and Gross Disproportionation factors for this paper, are aligned and within order of magnitude of similar QRAs and Cost-Benefit analyses carried out by pipeline operators around the world. As of this, it is demonstrated once again the convenience of application of the methodology, since it works as a decision making tool for risk reduction measures selection, capital expenditure and integrity management.

When applying this last concept, the replacement alternative obtained a value of 5, which indicates that the cost of its implementation is five times the cost in which the operator would have to incur due to pipeline failure, this is, the acquired benefit. Although this cost is five times its benefit, according to the Gross Disproportionation concept is acceptable.

On the other hand, the alternative corresponding to pipeline realignment obtained a value of 3, an indicator of an investment cost of three times the acquired benefit; in the same way as for the replacement alternative, this value is below the acceptance criterion established by the concept of Gross Disproportionation, but having a lower value, it is this alternative of realignment that is suitable to be implemented.

Gross Disproportionation concept allows, as in this particular case, to understand why a direct cost of capital investment is not necessarily more unfavorable for the operator, and how a more economical solution alternative in terms of direct costs of construction, does not correspond to the ideal to implement.

Finally, it is important to bear in mind that related to capital investment optimisation when carrying out mitigation and risk management activities, associated with threats´ materialisation over hydrocarbon transportation pipelines, it is necessary to carry out rigorous analyses where variables directly obtainable as construction costs are not only accounted, but it is strictly necessary to have criteria and experience to define variables such as benefit, which involves controversial issues such human life cost.

REFERENCES

[1] ASME B31.4-2012, Pipeline Transportation Systems for Liquid Hydrocarbons and Other Liquids, Amerincan Society of Mechanical Engineers, 2012;

[2] ASME B31.8-2010, Gas Transmission and Distribution Systems, Amerincan Society of Mechanical Engineers, 2010;

[3] ASME B31.8S-2010, Managing System Integrity of Gas Pipelines, American Society of Mechanical Engineers, 2010;

[4] CZA Z662-11, Oil and Gas pipeline systems, Canadian Standards Association, 2011;

[5] IGEM/TD/2, Application of pipeline risk assessment to proposed developments in the vicinity of high pressure Natural Gas pipelines, Communication 1737, Institution of Gas Engineers & Managers, 2008.

[6] PD 8010-1:2004, Code of practice for pipelines, The British Standards Institution, 2004;

[7] PD 8010-3:2009+A1:2013, Steel pipelines on land-Guide to the application of pipeline risk assessment to proposed developments in the vicinity of major accident hazard pipelines containing flammables, 2009-2013;

This page left blank intentionally.

IPG2019-5325

AN ANALYTICAL APPROACH FOR PIPELINE GEOHAZARD MANAGEMENT

Otto Huisman
ROSEN Group
Lingen, Germany

Moness Rizkalla
Visitless Integrity
Assessment
Calgary, AB,
Canada

Matt Tindall
Visitless Integrity
Assessment
Calgary, AB,
Canada

Alejandro Reyes
Rosen Technology and
Research Centre
Lingen, Germany

Erika Santana
Rosen Technology and
Research Centre
Newcastle, United Kingdom

ABSTRACT

Contamination of waterbodies as a result of hydrocarbon releases is one of the most undesirable events in our industry. Unfortunately, over the past few years, several major events have occurred around the globe, and geohazards have played a major role in many of these. Indeed, Pipeline Geohazard Management is a complex, multi-disciplinary process, heavily dependent on data integration and expert judgment. The current work presents a methodology that allows the identification of critical zones by assessing potential hydrocarbon release mechanisms that could affect waterbodies and adjacent areas, including: channel section pipeline failures, approach slope pipeline failures and spill path effects. The geological model is constructed based on datasets such as a digital elevation model (DEM), surficial geology and route geometry form. Additional datasets can also be derived to represent features such as drainage basins and slopes. The entire framework is being implemented on a data and integrity management platform that not only supports the integration of spatial, geological and general integrity management data (including multiple ILI data sets) but can also execute processes, such as stability analysis, and provide visualizations of results within a GIS (Geographic Information System) environment. Execution of semi-quantitative and quantitative risk assessments is also facilitated, as well as the elaboration of rehabilitation plans. To illustrate the methodology application and the platform capabilities, an anonymized, but real, case study is presented.

1. INTRODUCTION

Globally, the contamination of waterbodies associated with pipeline ruptures are often high profile incidents typically leading to among the most adverse environmental and in-turn business consequences to operators. When particularly significant, such incidents may impact the operator's shareholders in terms of very high direct and indirect costs. This places a heightened priority for leading operators to continuously improve their operational and integrity management practices to avoid such incidents.

A complete risk mitigation approach should address all credible potential mechanisms that may lead to the contamination of waterbodies may they be due to a pipeline failure in the channel section (Figure 1.1a and b), a pipeline failure in an unstable approach slope adjacent to the waterbody (Figure 1.2) or a spill path connecting a pipeline ruptures in uplands to the waterbody even if such a rupture is not geohazards induced (Figure 1.3).

Unfortunately, over the past few years, several major events have occurred around the globe, and geohazards have played a major role in many of these (Porter et al., 2016). Several categories of geohazard mechanisms may lead to the pipeline ruptures that may impact waterbodies predominantly including:

- Mass wasting mechanisms e.g. landslides, slope creep, debris flow and possibly rock mass instability
- Seismic mechanisms e.g. fault displacement and liquefaction
- Hydro-technical mechanisms e.g. vertical scour, channel migration and avulsion.

Figure 1.1a: Pipeline Exposure Due to Channel Migration. Figure 1.1b: Pipeline Rupture in Waterbody.

Following a brief review of the industry's state of practice and opportunities for improvement, an emerging analytical approach (Intelli-Riv) powered by a powerful and flexible computing platform (NIMA[1]) are described. An anonymized case study applying the methodology is then presented before highlighting the key points of the paper.

2. OPPORTUNITIES FOR IMPROVEMENT IN A DYNAMIC STATE OF PRACTICE

Pipeline geohazard management is a rapidly advancing field with continuously improving practices. Pipeline companies undertake such integrity management and damage prevention programs as prudent operators and to manage the expectations of their internal and external stakeholders. The state of practice varies from one operator to another depending on the extent of exposure to these particular integrity hazard mechanisms and the philosophy adopted by the operator. For some operators, a largely reactive approach is adopted on a case-by-case basis. Other operators adopt a more proactive approach of some variation of regularly updated system-wide risk-based assessments that inform annual integrity management programs of both monitoring and mitigation interventions.

For the operators striving towards the best practices of proactive analysis-based assessments, the following areas present common challenges to varying degrees:

1. Managing effective data acquisition, updating and management
2. Undertaking a disciplined systematic analyses and associated version control with regularly updated inputs while demonstrating the use of traceable information and data
3. Modelling the effect of the geohazards on pipeline response integrity
4. Overcoming a prevailing discipline-by-discipline work flow to better integrate the potential effects of interactive non-geohazard integrity threats (metal loss)
5. Maintaining situational awareness and utilization of look-ahead analyses to inform scoreboards and proactively trigger notifications for timely interventions.

The systematic characterization and assessment of geohazards in relation to pipelines requires a disciplined interfacing between geotechnical and pipeline engineering to properly account for the interaction between the operating pipeline and the natural environment to produce and compare successive risk profiles. The analytical approach and supporting enabling tools presented herein offer several advantages to the community of pipeline geohazard management practitioners.

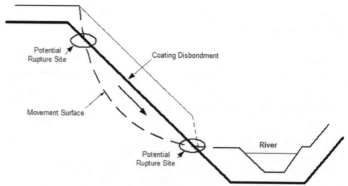

Figure 1.2: Pipeline Failure in Unstable River Approach Slope.

---

[1] NIMA is commercial software offered by the ROSEN Group.

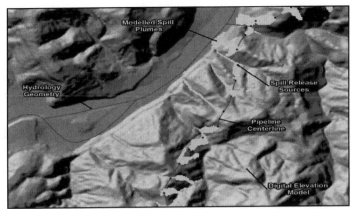

Figure 1.3: Example Spill path connecting a pipeline ruptures in uplands to the waterbody.

3. ASSESSMENT OF GEOHAZARDS: PROCESS FORMALIZATION

In order to get closer to a systematic approach to the assessment of geohazards, it is imperative to formalize the process from the data integration up to the analysis processes, aiming to guarantee its repeatability and fidelity.

A systematic way of breaking down integrity management activities has been introduced into as an Integrity Modelling Language (IML) by Reyes and Huisman (2018), who introduce the syntax and semantics required to model well-known processes, drawing upon Business Process Modelling Notation (BPMN) and XML. The aim of IML is to promote standardization and comparability of Integrity-related activities and minimize the opportunities for misinterpretation.

IML is built upon the notion that Integrity Processes can be represented by a series of clearly defined actions, each of which can be broken down into a series of "Process Steps" (Figure 3.1).

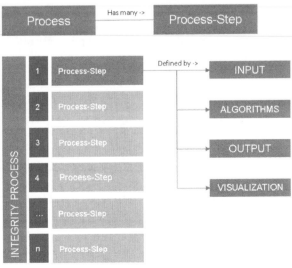

Figure 3.1: Integrity Process Description in IML

Much like mathematical functions, process-Steps can be defined/modelled by experts by defining the datasets required within the step, the algorithms used to process the data, how the structure of the output dataset is and the way how the data should be visualized:

a) INPUT: the defined dataset structures such as the Soil Properties, Topology or In-line Inspection Results.
b) ALGORITHMS: the calculations, transformations and processing that should be applied.
c) OUTPUT: The defined location for the output of the calculation or transformation (e.g. publishing of river crossings back to geodatabase).
d) VISUALIZATION: the presentation of specific inputs and output datasets in the form of tables, charts, maps and statistics

In practice, Geohazard Management processes are interpreted differently all over the world, and the workflows that make up these processes are defined by individual engineers and experts. Successful Geohazard management is about enabling transparent decision-making through clearly defined process-steps, while maintaining a degree of flexibility to tailor the process to the specific organizational needs. Therefore the process specification should account for the possible variations that may raise during the usage of the model such as data sources, algorithms and reporting.

The following figures depict the proposed geohazard process that determines which pipeline water crossings become at risk during a 25-year rainfall event using IML to describe the process. Figure 1 represents the high level BPMN of the overall Assessment of Geohazards Integrity Process (Figure 3.2).

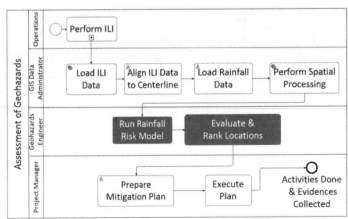

Figure 3.2: Assessment of Geohazards BPMN Model

From this high level definition, the two blocks highlighted in blue in Figure 1 can be taken for the breakdown into process steps. Figure 3 presents the process-step definition for the Rainfall Risk Model Process (Figure 3.3)

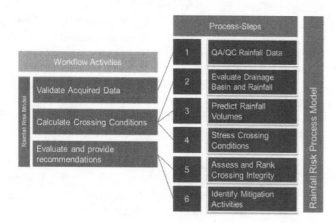

Figure 3.3: Rainfall Risk Model Breakdown into Process-Steps

The resulting definition when further specifying the Predict Rainfall Volumes process-step using the Inputs, Algorithms, Output and Visualization can be seen in Figure 3.4.

4. THE PROPOSED ANALYTICAL APPROACH FOR PIPELINE GEOHAZARD MANAGEMENT

The technical nature, scope, rising business environment expectation and now available digital data along with the means to effectively integrate and analyze all data sets lend an opportunity for a break-through improvement of traditional practice. The pipeline geohazards integrity management demands are well suited for applying an approach of intelligent data mashing towards actionable insights as opposed to detailed high precision calculations.

Data should not be an obstacle to getting started and adopting a continuous improvement approach. The initial, ongoing acquisition, integration and data management is a critical element of applying the proposed approach. In certain cases, start-up can be largely based on externally sources data and progressively transition to a incrementally larger fraction of data converted from the operator's historic as-built drawings and or collected during future operations as would be informed and prioritized by the implementation of the proposed approach.

The main elements and key considerations of the approach are briefly discussed below in-turn.

4.1 Underlying Geological Model and associated Regional Inputs

The geological model may contain data from some or all of the following categories:
- Pipeline route
- Physiographic region
- Surficial geology
- Landform profile
- Soil properties

- Bedrock
- Geothermal conditions
- Topography
- Watercourses and waterbodies
- Faults
- Seismicity
- Landslides
- Environmental conditions
- Pipeline design details (i.e. diameter, wall thickness, grade, pipe manufacturing etc.)
- Construction as-built details (cut and fill)
- In-line inspection results
- Observations from specialized geotechnical field visits
- Conclusion from 3rd party reports
- Geohazards
- Mines, roads and other developments
- Cadastral boundaries

4.2 Map Scale and Resolution

Map scale refers to the ratio between the distance on a map and the distance on the earth. On a 1:50,000 scale map, every centimeter represents 500 meters on the ground. Data is often identified as small-scale or large-scale data and it is a common source of confusion. Large-scale data (or map) shows an area at high detail while small-scale data shows low amount of detail. A map of a country would be small scale whereas a map showing a town would be large scale. Free data tends to be of smaller scale but very large-scale datasets are not always needed or even wanted in some cases.

There is also a relationship between scale and accuracy. Since smaller scale data is coarser, the accuracy will be lower than a large-scale dataset. That being said, it is entirely possible for a large-scale dataset to have poor accuracy. The scale tends to define the upper bounds of the potential accuracy of the dataset.

For raster-based datasets such as orthophotos the resolution of the dataset becomes important. Resolution refers to how much ground each pixel covers. For example, an aerial photo with a 1 m resolution means that each image pixel is 1 m x 1 m. The smaller the resolution, the greater the detail available for the analysis

4.3 Data Sources

An enormous amount of spatial data has been made freely available online that can be used to build a geological model. All the data needed to build a geological model can likely be sourced from Government agencies. Canadian and American governments make the data freely available on the internet but other countries may sell the data and/or make it only available by request. Governments are typically the custodians of:
- Digital Elevation Models (DEMs)
- Ortho-imagery and stereo imagery
- Base vector data

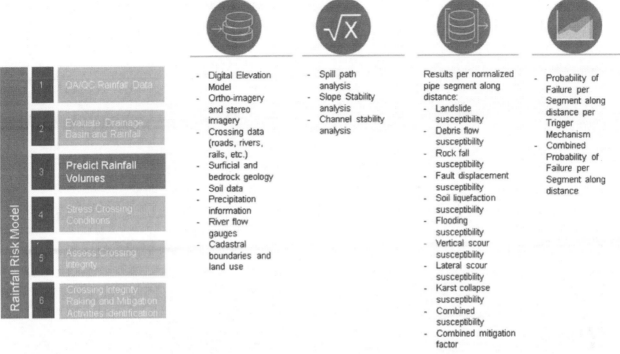

INPUT   ALGORITHMS   OUTPUT   VISUALIZATION

Rainfall Risk Model

1. QA/QC Rainfall Data
2. Evaluate Drainage Basin and Rainfall
3. **Predict Rainfall Volumes**
4. Stress Crossing Conditions
5. Assess Crossing Integrity
6. Crossing Integrity Ranking and Mitigation Activities Identification

INPUT
- Digital Elevation Model
- Ortho-imagery and stereo imagery
- Crossing data (roads, rivers, rails, etc.)
- Surficial and bedrock geology
- Soil data
- Precipitation information
- River flow gauges
- Cadastral boundaries and land use

ALGORITHMS
- Spill path analysis
- Slope Stability analysis
- Channel stability analysis

OUTPUT
Results per normalized pipe segment along distance:
- Landslide susceptibility
- Debris flow susceptibility
- Rock fall susceptibility
- Fault displacement susceptibility
- Soil liquefaction susceptibility
- Flooding susceptibility
- Vertical scour susceptibility
- Lateral scour susceptibility
- Karst collapse susceptibility
- Combined susceptibility
- Combined mitigation factor

VISUALIZATION
- Probability of Failure per Segment along distance per Trigger Mechanism
- Combined Probability of Failure per Segment along distance

Figure 3.4: "Predict Rainfall Volumes" Process-Step in Rainfall Risk Model

- o Roads, rails, rivers and lakes, etc.
- o Often assembled into "Digital Atlases"
- Geology data
  - o Surficial geology
  - o Bedrock geology
  - o Soil sciences data
  - o Seismic data
- Environmental data
  - o Restricted areas
  - o Endangered species
  - o Fisheries data
  - o Precipitation data
  - o River flow gauges
- Cadastral data
  - o Boundaries
  - o Cities and towns

If Government data is not of sufficient resolution, accuracy or temporality, then the data may need to be purchased from a commercial vendor. Off the shelf, LiDAR and imagery (Aerial & Satellite) is widely available for areas with high commercial interest (oil sands, crowded pipeline corridors, etc.) but for most places a new collection will need to be contracted, which can be costly.

Some types of thematic vector data can only be found through commercial vendors. Pipeline and facilities data for places in North America would need to be purchased from a vendor such as IHS Markit or GDM Pipelines, for example.

Industry specific spatial data tends to be very expensive and is often sold through a subscription service since the data rarely remains static. Other types of thematic vector data cannot be purchased anywhere and will need to be derived from other datasets or collected in the field by appropriate personnel. A good example would be surficial geology. If the project area does not have suitable Government surficial geology data or perhaps none at all, then either a qualified geologist will need to create it by interpreting stereo imagery or determine it by visiting the project area in the field.

4.3 Data Usage

The datasets stored in the geological model can be leveraged in multiple analyses. As can be seen in Table 4.3.1, there is considerable commonality in the data sets required to support the assessments of the three sources of risk that may lead to pipeline integrity incidents causing impacts to river crossing and water bodies. This lends to efficiencies in acquiring and managing these data sets although they are utilized in different analyses by different engineering and geomatics disciplines.

4.4 Enabling Algorithms and Analyses

A wide range of analytical tools is available for use to support defendable results and recommendations. As an example, Table 4.4.1 (Rizkalla and Read 2019) compiles a comprehensive listing of published methods that may be cast as algorithms to assess landslide stability and deformation as well as the associated pipeline's structural response. Analytical methods are also available to assess water channel scour and lateral migration processes as well as the associated pipeline's structural response.

Datasets	Intelli-Riv Core Functions		
	Spill Path Analysis	Slope Stability Analysis	Channel Stability Analysis
Pipeline route	✓	✓	✓
Physiographic region		✓	✓
Surficial geology			
Digital Vector Maps	✓	✓	✓
Raster Maps (PDs, TIFFs, etc.)	✓	✓	✓
Landform profile		✓	✓
Soil properties	✓	✓	✓
Bedrock			
Digital Vector Maps		✓	✓
Raster Maps (PDs, TIFFs, etc.)		✓	✓
Geothermal conditions		✓	✓
Topography			
Digital Elevation Model (DEM)	✓	✓	✓
Contours or Breaklines	✓	✓	✓
Spot Elevations	✓	✓	✓
Triangulated Irregular Network (TIN) (External)	✓	✓	✓
Triangulated Irregular Network (TIN) (DEM Derived)		✓	✓
Hydrology			
Watercourses (External)	✓	✓	✓
Watercourses (DEM Derived)	✓	✓	✓
Water Crossing Location (DEM Derived)		✓	✓
Water Crossing Location (External)		✓	✓
Waterbodies	✓	✓	✓
Climate			
IDF Curves		✓	✓

Table 4.3.1 Data Sets required to support key analyses.

4.5 Assessment Confidence

The confidence in the results of the assessment is determined by the relationship between the quality of the data and the conservativeness of the algorithm's estimated parameters inputs. Invariably, applying the established analytical methodologies of both the geotechnical and hydro-technical disciplines requires data and engineering judgement. The need for extensive data and practitioner judgement is perhaps even more in the context of long linear assets in largely isolated locations such as pipelines.

A simple transparent assessment confidence approach is proposed herein that would be well suited for both customization based on the practitioner's expert judgement and to documentation for due diligence. The proposed assessment confidence approach is presented in Figure 4.5.1. The approach captures the practitioner's expert judgment of the sources of uncertainty of the analysis inputs

4.6 The role of in-line inspection

A broader multi-disciplined view beyond strictly geotechnical and hydro-technical analyses is critically important. Consideration of the pipeline structural capacity and interaction with other co-located integrity hazards such as corrosion features offers an accurate assessment of risk. In fact, and as has been observed and anecdotally reported in some operational cases of pipelines with asphalt- or tape-coating, the indication of corrosion features may be a surrogate indicator to creeping ground movement.

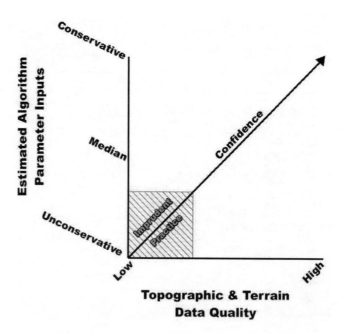

Figure 4.5.1: Approach to assessment confidence

As such the integration of in-line inspection data is a key feature of the proposed approach in a two-way synergy:

- ILI data informs the geohazard assessment
- The geohazard assessment supports the analysis of the ILI data.

5. APPLICATION TO A GENERAL CASE STUDY

5.1 Area overview

The idealized project consists of a medium diameter pipeline, 16.4 km in length that traverses rugged terrain. The pipeline carries refined petroleum products, and is buried with no above ground segments. Several pipeline incidents during its operation have been caused by geotechnical events. Consequently, geohazard assessment of the pipeline route was undertaken.

One major water crossing is of particular concern since it consists of a valley prone to seasonal flooding and has a history of slope instability on the west approach slope (Figure 5.2 and 5.3). Additionally, the river is upstream from a major population center that relies on it for drinking water.

Initial Data Inventory/Review

The data used for the assessment was provided by the operator, and supplemented where required with information from publicly-available sources. Soil properties data required for analysis was derived using approximate correlations with soil, bedrock and surficial geology descriptions. Data provided by the operator consisted of:

Stability Analysis	Reference
General	
Description of landslide mechanisms	Varnes (1978)
Typical geometric dimensions of rotational and translational failure features	Skempton and Hutchinson (1969)
Rotational Failure	
Generic failure circle explicit equation for static factor of safety	Easa and Vatankhah (2011)
Toe failure circle design chart and table for static factor of safety	Barnes 1991
Customized circular failure multi-variate relation for static safety ratio (Camisea Pipeline, Perú)	Velásquez Martinez and Robles Robles, (2009)
Translational Failure (With or Without Tension Crack)	
Infinite slope with seepage parallel to slope closed-form solution for static factor of safety	Craig (1980)
Infinite slope with seepage non-parallel to slope design chart for static factor of safety	Duncan and Wright (2005)
Infinite slope with seepage parallel to slope closed-form solution for pseudo-static factor of safety	Matasovic (1991)
Translational sliding with tension crack closed-form solution for static and pseudo-static factor of safety	Wyllie and Mah (2004)
Customized translational sliding multi-variate relation for static safety ratio (Camisea Pipeline, Perú)	Velásquez Martinez and Robles Robles, (2009)
Complex Slope Stability	
Complex slope numerical modeling of static factor of safety using software codes	Gharti et al. (2012)
Frequency Analysis	**Reference**
Critical Rainfall Intensity and Associated Return Period	
Coupled infinite slope and infiltration model for rainfall-induced shallow landslide	Montgomery et al. (1998)
Coupled infinite slope and infiltration model for rainfall-induced shallow landslide (South America)	Fontes Guimarães et al. (2003)
Empirical relations for rainfall intensity-duration-frequency triggering of shallow landslides	Guzzetti et al. (2008)
Critical Seismic Peak Ground Acceleration Return Period	
Critical seismic acceleration return period from regional probabilistic seismic hazard data	Chen et al. (2014)
Vulnerability Analysis	**Reference**
Runout Distance and Impact Zone Delineation	
Empirical landslide runout distance estimation	Hutchinson (1988); Corominas (1996)
Numerical modeling of landslide runout and material redistribution using software codes	Guthrie (2009); Aaron et al. (2016)
Seismically-Induced Slope Displacement	
Empirical Newmark slope displacement from earthquake-induced peak ground acceleration	Jibson (2007); Ambraseys and Menu (1988)
Empirical Newmark slope displacement from earthquake-induced spectral acceleration parameters	Bray and Travasarou (2007)
Numerical modeling of earthquake-induced dynamic slope displacement using software codes	Lenti and Martino (2012)
Critical Slope Dimensions	
Empirical relation to estimate critical longitudinal slope length for pipeline elastic strain	Yoosef-Ghodsi et al. (2008); Fredj et al. (2008); Fredj and Dinovitzer (2014)
Empirical relation to estimate critical transverse slope breadth for pipeline rupture	Sweeney et al. (2004)

Table 4.4.1: Typical approaches and algorithms for Landslide geohazard assessment and associate pipeline vulnerability analysis (With permission Rizkalla and Read, 2019)

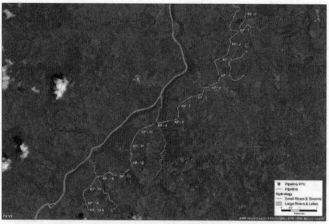

Figure 5.1: Pipeline system map

Figure 5.2: Crossing of concern

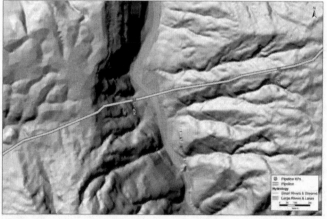

Figure 5.3: Crossing of concern - Digital elevation model hillshade

- Pipeline horizontal alignment
- Pipeline stationing
- 5-meter Digital Elevation Model
- Surficial geology Mapping 1:20K
- Soil parameters.
- Seismic peak ground acceleration data
- IDF rainfall curves
- ILI results

Data mining and acquisition – Informed by gap analysis
Datasets that weren't provided by the operator but were still needed to run the geohazard assessment were sourced from Government agencies at no cost. Satellite imagery was acquired as were some base datasets such as roads, rails and towns. The datasets were of varying scales and were determined to be appropriate for use in the geological model before loading.

Data Pre-processing
Some input datasets required fit for purpose pre-processing before being ready to use. Pre-processing included such steps as projection and datum conversions, tiling or clipping, format conversions and merging.

Master database (MDB) Populating
All of the project data undergoes a quality assurance and completeness check to ensure it is ready to be consumed in the geohazard assessment model.

Master database (MDB)
The master database consists of a relational database that stores all of the spatial data needed to run the geohazard assessment and ensures data integrity. An ESRI File Geodatabase served as the database to house the geological model. A more complex project may require a more capable database platform such as SQL Server.

Derived Data Creation
The derived data required for the pipeline geohazard assessment included soil properties, hydrological networks as well as topographic information and other spatial data. Additionally, surrogate parameters may be needed to stand-in for datasets or attributes that may not be available. All derived data was stored in the master database.

Run Geohazard Assessment Model
Information used as input for the analysis included a digital elevation model (DEM), bedrock geology shapefile, soil depositional mode 1D takeoff with descriptions of coarse and fine soil components along the route, seismic peak ground acceleration (PGA) shapefile for a return period of 475 years, several precipitation related contour plots (maximum 24 hour rainfall, maximum hourly rainfall intensity, mean annual precipitation, and number of rainy days), regional rainfall Intensity-Duration-Frequency (IDF) curves, hydrological shapefiles for single and double line watercourses, and the route centerline and associated slack chainage measures.

The analysis primarily applied two algorithms: Coupled infinite slope and infiltration model for rainfall-induced shallow landslides and Infinite slope with seepage parallel to slope closed-form solution for pseudo-static factor of safety (Rizkalla and Read, 2019).

Geohazard assessment produced values that indicate annual probabilities of slope failure and annual frequency of pipeline loss of containment.

5.2 Sample Results

Pipeline geohazard assessment typically is focused on probability of geohazard occurrence and the pipeline vulnerability.

The product of these two terms is referred to as susceptibility, which is an estimate of the annual probability of loss of containment (or probability of failure, PoF) within a pipeline segment due to a geohazard occurrence.

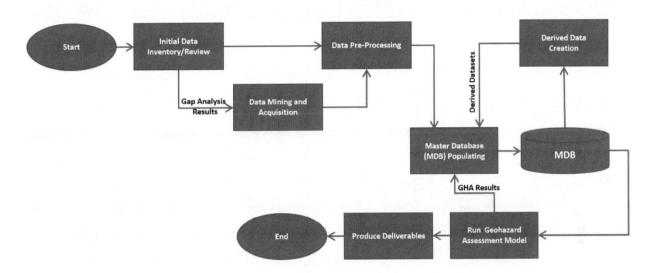

Figure 5.2.1: Assessment workflow

A semi-quantitative pipeline geohazard assessment methodology offers the framework to identify and susceptibility rank geohazard sites. Generally subtle variations have been reported in the details of applying such methodologies.

Some advances have been presented to allow factoring-in the interaction of triggering and combining geohazards mechanisms for a give site. Figure 5.2.2 shows a generalized graphical representation of geohazard assessment results showing geohazard occurrence locations (in light background color), individual geohazard pre-mitigation susceptibility profiles (in darker foreground colors), and the combined pre- and post-mitigation susceptibility profiles (Rizkalla and Read, 2019). It is important to reiterate, that data limitations should not preclude quantitative estimates of risk, but do affect confidence and uncertainty in such estimates. As the underlying principal of the proposed approach, it is admissible and often necessary to conduct quantitative assessments of risk with relatively limited data using expert judgment as long as the associated limitations and estimated uncertainty are also

communicated in terms of assessment confidence to avoid the appearance of undue precision. An example is presented for applying the assessment confidence evaluation to site-specific susceptibility values for the slope and channel sections in the case study (as shown in Figure 5.2.3).

Credible data improvement or mitigation intervention scenarios are considered for the low confidence high susceptibility slope site. Documentation of the defendable and transparent assessments is an example of the operator's due-diligence.

Integration of Near-real Time Satellite Imagery and Weather Reports
The digital and in some cases near-real time accessible nature of remote sensing data and weather reports lends to their utilization within the proposed approach in either non-time-sensitive water channel migration monitoring applications or for near-real time prioritized critical event monitoring as part of high water action plans.

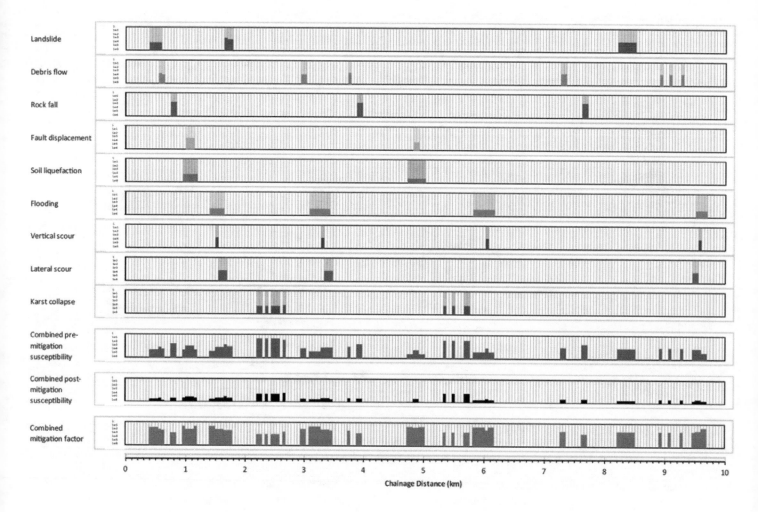

Figure 5.2.2: Generalized graphical representation of geohazard assessment results.
The vertical axis represents relative orders of magnitude. Light colored bars on bar chart represent the presence of the respective geohazard,
while dark colored bars chart lines represent pipeline susceptibility at the given location.
(With permission Rizkalla and Read, 2019).

Considering potential risk mitigation interventions for the site introduced above with a hydrotechncial geohazard induced high susceptibility, and as noted in the API Recommended Practice 1133 on managing Hydrotechnical hazards for pipelines (API, 2017), plans and procedures should be developed to address and mitigate risks to pipeline integrity for high risk areas which would be triggered by reaching pre-established threshold indications.

Weather watch and satellite imagery can be integrated in the integrity management decision process. In such cases, automated ingestion of customized real time weather watch and forecasts for the area of interest can be integrated. Leading to and after the triggering threshold condition, the acquisition of before and after near-real-time satellite imagery can contribute

to understanding the potential integrity impacts and for planning the response.

In such critical cases of potentially adverse impacts to water bodies, the risk mitigation intervention options may include one or more of the following (API, 2017):

- Pipeline focused interventions: Isolation of the effected section, reduced pipeline operating pressure, shutdown and purging the pipeline contents (with due consideration of buoyancy)

- Water crossing focused interventions: Diverting flow from the water crossing, emergency placement of pipeline supports for unsupported sections and emergency bank armoring.

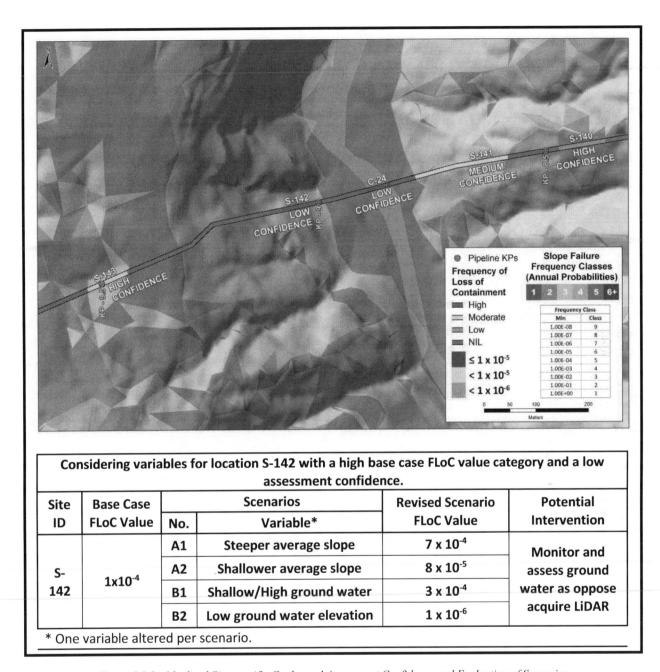

Considering variables for location S-142 with a high base case FLoC value category and a low assessment confidence.					
Site ID	**Base Case FLoC Value**	**Scenarios**		**Revised Scenario FLoC Value**	**Potential Intervention**
		No.	**Variable***		
S-142	1×10^{-4}	A1	Steeper average slope	7×10^{-4}	Monitor and assess ground water as oppose acquire LiDAR
		A2	Shallower average slope	8×10^{-5}	
		B1	Shallow/High ground water	3×10^{-4}	
		B2	Low ground water elevation	1×10^{-6}	
* One variable altered per scenario.					

Figure 5.2.3: Idealized Site-specific Geohazard Assessment Confidence and Evaluation of Scenarios

6. CLOSURE

Through a data and expert driven approach, the implementation of the Intelli-Riv powered by the NIMA platform delivers a total solution for managing high profile risks of pipeline water crossings.

A disciplined, transparent and traceable approach to manage pipeline geohazards is introduced to demonstrate a pipeline operator's due-diligence. The approach enables data (as may be available at a given juncture) and algorithm based analyses to guide geohazard management allowing expert judgement by users and the utilization of specialist inputs.

The approach offers an improvement of current practices because of the totality of its scope, efficiency in data utilization and management and ability to support operator decision making workflows by:

- Managing all potential sources of impacts on water crossings
- Readiness to start with any status of operator data
- Utilization of "Look-ahead Analyses" to inform scoreboards and notifications for timely interventions

It is demonstrated that the integrated approach can deliver transparent (and traceable) integration of all of the required data to perform the assessment, as well as consistently repeatable results for a multi-hazard environment. The latter should not be underestimated, particularly in larger organizations or – in a broader view – in terms of the potential for benchmarking or evaluating the sensitivity of specific mitigations or other parameters.

The proposed approach enables not only effective due-diligence demonstrations and demonstrable compliance with relevant codes and standards, but also the careful management of continuous improvement processes.

7. REFERENCES

API 2017, Recommended Practice 1133, *Managing Hydrotechnical Hazards for Pipelines Located Onshore or Within Coastal Areas.*

Porter M., et. Al. 2016, Updated Estimates of Frequencies of Pipeline Failures Caused by Geohazards, Calgary AB: International Pipeline Conference. IPC2016-64085, ASME.

Reyes A. and Huisman O. 2018, *Formalizing Integrity Management Workflows: Towards Integrity Process Modeling,* Calgary, AB: International Pipeline Conference. IPC2018-78512, ASME.

Rizkalla M and Read R. 2019, *Pipeline Geohazards: Planning, Design, Construction and Operations.* ASME Press.

IPG2019-5327

RISK MANAGEMENT OF PIPELINE BREAKAGE AT RIVER CROSSINGS THROUGH QUANTITATIVE ANALYSIS OF THE THREAT, VULNERABILITY AND CONSEQUENCES

Carlos Debandi[1]
NEPTA S.A.
Mendoza, Argentina

Fernando Martearena
YPF S.A.
Neuquén, Argentina

Natalia Roth
NEPTA S.A.
Mendoza, Argentina

1 ABSTRACT

The floods of rivers and streams are among the threats that most frequently cause technological accidents. A quantitative analysis of the risk of breakage of pipelines in crossings with channels is presented.

The proposed methodology evaluates the risk of rupture of the pipeline quantifying both the threat of being discovered and its vulnerability to hydrodynamic forces and those due to vortex shedding.

Decision-making for risk mitigation is complemented by the evaluation of the consequences that breakage can produce in the environment and in the activity of the operator, that is, the assessment of the severity of the risk. To this end, the impact is quantified in terms of the extent of the damage caused and the economic losses due to the stoppage of production and the remediation costs.

Finally, risk management is developed, which includes actions to mitigate the hazard and vulnerability, the priority of each of them and the implementation and monitoring plans.

The application of the proposed methodology achieves the early identification and reduction of risk of breakage, knowledge of the state of the crosses, objectivity and reliability in the assignment of risk levels and the correct allocation of resources for mitigation.

Keywords: Pipeline, quantitative risk management, flood.

2 INTRODUCTION

The floods of rivers and streams are among the threats that most frequently cause technological accidents, since the pipes are very vulnerable to the effects of this type of events [19]. A quantitative analysis of the risk of breakage of pipelines in crossings with channels is presented, developed for the punctual evaluation of these or to complement comprehensive evaluations that analyze all the possible failure mechanisms of the pipeline [5].

The proper management of risk requires applying a methodology that meets the following requirements:

- Must be documented, as technical and legal support.
- It must be able to be reproduced, so that it can be used by different analysts with minimum error margins.
- The results must be quantifiable, in order to maximize objectivity.
- Must be able to create a historical database that allows analyzing the behavior of the risk over time and that is updated periodically.
- It must endure over time, allowing the information to be transmitted efficiently to new members of the technical staff.

3 BACKGROUND

Risk is the probability of occurrence of an unwanted event with economic, social or environmental consequences in a particular site and during a given exposure time. The risk of spillage or leakage of oil, gas or formation water due to floods is analyzed.

The threat is a latent danger associated with a physical phenomenon of natural, technological or human-made origin that may manifest itself in a specific place and at a certain time, producing adverse effects on people, goods, services and / or environment [4]. The characterization of the hazard requires

---

[1] Contact author: cdebandi@nepta.net

defining the frequency of the flood event. The parameter used for this is the recurrence time, usually 25, 50 or 100 years. Special characteristics of the analyzed crossing or forecasts about climate change can raise the value assigned to this variable.

Vulnerability is the internal risk factor of a subject or system exposed to a threat, corresponding to its intrinsic predisposition to be affected or to be susceptible to suffering damage.

The risk severity takes into account the consequences due to the occurrence of an unwanted event.

4   PROPOSED METHODOLOGY

The methodology for the quantitative analysis of the risk of breakage of pipes at crossings with channels follows the following steps:

1. Preliminary activities:
   - Delimitation of watersheds and channels.
   - Pipelines inventory.
   - Review of previous inspections.
   - Identification of duct crossing points with channels.
   - Determination of flood flows according to the recurrence adopted.
2. Risk analysis:
   - Preliminary risk analysis applying the available data.
   - Field inspections.
   - Risk analysis applying the available data and those surveyed in the field.
3. Risk assessment:
   - Definition of acceptable risk thresholds.
   - Analysis of the economic and environmental consequences.
   - Evaluation of the severity of the risk.
4. Risk management.
   - Preparation of the Mitigation Plan.
   - Application.
   - Monitoring.

5   RISK ANALYSIS

1.1   Assessment of the Threat

General scour occurs by increasing the energy of the flow. It is a common phenomenon in channels with high energy and steep slopes, where the flood peaks are brief and infrequent [14], [18].

During the flood, the mobilization of the sediments can change the cross section of the channel, either by lowering the level of the bed and / or modifying the position of the thalweg. The phenomenon appears when the flow reaches a speed called critical, which depends on the conditions of the runoff. Erosion increases as the difference between the speed of runoff and the critical increases. In the cross section of the channel there is not

only an increase in the level of the surface of the water as the flow increases, but also a decrease in the level of the river bed, this decrease being approximately maximum in the center. This erosion can reach the level of burying the pipe and discover it totally or partially. When the flow of the flood begins to decrease and the speed of the current is below the critical speed, the process is reversed and part of the entrained material begins to be deposited. At the end of the process, the final level of the river bed may be the same as at the beginning, so that an inexperienced observer can conclude that the channel has remained stable and that the pipelines have not been exposed.

The depth of the general scour can be estimated using the method of Lischtvan - Levediev modified by Maza - Álvarez, for which the geometry of the crossing, the values of flow and granulometry of the bottom material of the channel at the crossing point are necessary.

In Figure 1, the degree of threat is classified according to the percentage of general scour calculated with respect to the minimum existing cover on the duct in the cross section [13].

Level	Symbol	Threat Assessment
Very Low	L-	The calculated scour is less than 20% of the minimum burying depth
Low	L+	The calculated erosion is between 20% and 35% of the minimum burying depth
Moderate	M	The calculated erosion is between 35% and 65% of the minimum burying depth
High	H-	The calculated erosion is between 65% and 80% of the minimum burying depth
Very High	H+	The calculated scour is greater than 80% of the minimum burying depth

FIGURE 1: CRITERIA OF VALUATION OF THE THREAT BY GENERAL SCOUR

The erosion control works for the protection of buried pipelines are executed downstream of these, in order to keep the riverbed stable upstream of its location, mitigating the action of general scour upstream of the considered point and establishing a barrier for the advance of headward erosion.

To assess the threat in crosses that have erosion control works, the following criteria apply:

- Works with an adequate design and in good condition: The assessment of the threat is reduced by one level.
- Works with adequate design in regular condition: The level of threat assessment is maintained considering the non-existence of the work.
- Works with adequate design in poor condition or works with inadequate design: The threat assessment is raised by one level.

1.2   Quantification of Vulnerability

In crossings with channels, the pipes can be exposed as a result of erosion and therefore subjected to spatial deformations due to the combined effects of flow dynamics, buoyancy, gravity and soil strength.

The most common breaks occur in the body, in the threads or in the welds of the pipe, due to stresses in the materials above the admissible, or by cracks by impact in fragile materials such as the glass fiber-reinforced epoxy pipes, by abrasion of the different types of coating, etc.

To the problem of the breakage of the structure should be added the spillage of polluting fluids within the runoff under conditions that are extremely unfavorable for their control and containment, due to the magnitude of the flows and the volumes of water that circulate through the channel, to the state of the access roads, communication difficulties, etc. The above can lead to a contamination situation of extensive downstream areas, which must be avoided at all costs.

The vulnerability estimation of pipes at water crossings is based on the comparison of the maximum allowable free span length that a given pipe can withstand in a watercourse with respect to the maximum exposure length [12]. The maximum allowable free span length is evaluated taking into account the stresses in the material due to the hydrodynamic loads and the fatigue produced by vortex shedding. In this method of analysis it is considered that the exposed length of the pipe corresponds to the width of the channel at the crossing site.

The main advantages of considering channel width as exposed length are the following:

- The channel width is generally greater than the actual exposed length, obtaining conservative estimates.

- It is a parameter of easy measurement, through satellite images or field survey.

To characterize the relative vulnerability at the intersection, the Free Span Ratio (FSR) is calculated, defined as the ratio between the maximum allowable length Lmax and the maximum exposure length Lexp (channel width):

$$FSR = \frac{L_{máx}}{L_{exp}}$$

The vulnerability of the pipeline Vul is inversely proportional to FSR:

$$Vul \propto \frac{1}{FSR}$$

If the value of FSR is ≤ 1.0, the crossing is potentially vulnerable. Conversely, if FSR> 1.0, then it is unlikely that the duct will fail even if exposed to the full width of the channel.

Hydrodynamics Loads on Exposed Pipelines

At river crossings, the pipelines are subjected to hydrodynamic, buoyant and gravitational forces [2], [9], [16], [17]. Assuming a stable flow with uniform velocity, the loads on the pipeline can be simplified in the following distributed loads:

- Hydrodynamic loads, which include the transverse drag load F_D, the inertial load F_I and the up-lift load F_L.
- Bouyancy load F_f.
- Load by own weight of the pipe and the fluid transported W.

The acting forces are shown in Figure 2.

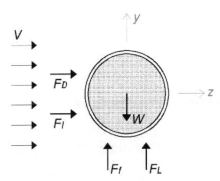

FIGURE 2: HYDRODYNAMIC LOADS ON EXPOSED PIPELINES

Distributed loads are calculated according to the following equations:

- Horizontal forces

$$F_D = \frac{1}{2}\rho_w D C_D v_e^2$$

$$F_I = \frac{1}{4}\rho_w \pi D^2 C_M \left[\frac{dv}{dt}\right]$$

- Vertical forces

$$F_L = \frac{1}{2}\rho_w D C_L v_e^2$$

Where ρ_w is the density of the fluid, D is the outside diameter of the pipe, Ve is the average velocity of the fluid, C_D is the drag coefficient, C_L is the elevation coefficient, C_M is the transverse fluid inertia coefficient and dv/dt is the transverse component of fluid acceleration. The coefficients C_D, C_L and C_M depend on the Reynolds number.

The buoyancy and self-weight load on the pipeline are calculated by the following expressions:

$$F_f = \rho_w g \frac{\pi D^2}{4}$$

$$W = \pi g \left[\rho_p t D + \rho_i \left(\frac{D}{2} - t\right)^2\right]$$

Where ρ_p is the density of the material constituting the pipe, t is the thickness of the pipe wall, ρ_i is the density of the transported fluid and g is the acceleration of gravity.

The hydrodynamic loads can be amplified by floating elements entangled in the pipe, since they increase the cross section of the pipe in the direction of flow. The production of floating material and its subsequent transport is a common situation in most rivers and streams, which depends on the degree of instability of the margins of its tributaries and the main channel.

The channels with adequate depth and width characteristics efficiently transport the floating material, which, for the most part, consists of trunks, branches and roots [8]. The greatest amounts of floating material accumulate in the places where the flow separates from an obstacle, such as open pipelines or piles of bridges. Field studies show that the length of the trunk is the factor that most influences the thickness of the trapped material. To calculate the latter, the lowest of the following values is taken:

- The width of the channel upstream of the section analyzed.
- The length of the trunks of the vegetation in the basin.

The possibility that the floating material is trapped by the pipeline increases as it is closer to the surface.

The forces generated by the accumulation of floating material depend on its thickness, its porosity and its internal structure. In order to contemplate the effect of the drag material retained by the pipeline, the following relationships are proposed:

$$F_D = \frac{1}{2} \rho_w D' C_D v_e^2$$

$$F_I = \frac{1}{4} \rho_w \pi D'^2 C_M \left[\frac{dv}{dt} \right]$$

$$F_L = \frac{1}{2} \rho_w D' C_L v_e^2$$

Where D' is the diameter of the assembly formed by the pipe and the material trapped by it. To estimate D', the following expression is used:

$$D_e' = k D_e$$

Where

$$k = 0.94 \left(\frac{L_t}{D} \right)^{0.708}$$

L_t being the average length of the trunks of the vegetation of the basin. The loads acting on the pipeline can be classified into two types: those that act in the direction of flow and those that act in vertical direction. Under the combined effects of the mentioned loads, the pipe undergoes a spatial deformation of vertical and horizontal flexion. For the analysis of the stress in the pipeline, the resultant of the loads distributed in both directions is calculated and applied to the analysis model, which is, in a conservative way, a simply supported beam. See Figure 3.

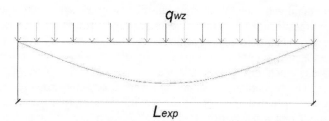

FIGURE 3: ANALYSIS MODEL OF PIPELINES EXPOSED TO FLOW

The distributed load turns out to be:

$$q_{wz} = \sqrt{q_v^2 + q_h^2}$$

Where q_{wz} is the distributed load on the pipe, q_v is the vertical distributed load and q_h is the horizontal distributed load.

From the analysis of the bending and shear stresses on the proposed model, the stress acting on the material is obtained.

The axial stress in the material is calculated by the following expression

$$\sigma_{LP} = \frac{M}{W_x} + \frac{pD}{4e} \leq \sigma_{adm}$$

Where M is the bending moment and W_x is the section modulus of the pipe. The section modulus of a hollow circular section is:

$$W_x = W_y = \frac{\pi}{32 D_e} \left(D_e^4 - D_i^4 \right)$$

Being D_e and D_i the outer and inner diameter of the pipe respectively. Considering the model as a simply supported beam with distributed load, the value of the moment acting on the pipe is:

$$M = \frac{q_{wz} L_{\exp}^2}{8}$$

The axial stress in the pipe is:

$$\sigma_{LP} = \frac{\dfrac{q_{wz} L_{\exp}^2}{8}}{\dfrac{\pi}{32 D_e} \left(D_e^4 - D_i^4 \right)} + \frac{pD_e}{4e} \leq \sigma_{adm}$$

The maximum allowable exposed length is given by:

$$L_{máx} = \sqrt{\frac{\pi}{4 q_{wz} D_e} \left(D_e^4 - D_i^4 \right) \left(\sigma_{adm} - \frac{pD_e}{4e} \right)}$$

The maximum length obtained is compared with the exposed length L_{exp}, corresponding to the width of the channel and the free span ratio (FSR) is obtained.

Vortex Shedding

Vortex shedding occurs when a fluid flows around a stationary object. During movement, the flow separates and the object experiences a drag force in the direction of flow. The shear layers formed at the points of separation on the surface of the object create vortices which are shed into the flow from alternate sides. Each time a vortex is shed from the object, the local pressure distribution is altered, so that it undergoes varying pressure cycles over time. If the object, in this case the pipe, is flexible or flexibly mounted, interactions may arise between the vortex shedding mechanism and the deviation of the object. Under certain conditions, the object can oscillate at a frequency close to its natural frequency, resulting in potentially large and destructive forces [6], [14], [15].

The methodology for the evaluation of the effect of the vortex presented is based on the comparison of the natural frequency of the pipe with the load conditions expected during the flood.

In the shear layers formed at the points of separation on a cylindrical surface, vortices are shed into the flow from alternative sides at a frequency that is calculated by the number of Strouhal S_t.

$$ S_t = \frac{f_s D}{U_c} \approx 0.2 $$

The natural frequency of the pipeline can be calculated using the following equation:

$$ f_n = \frac{k\pi}{2L^2} \sqrt{\frac{EI}{M}} $$

Where E is the modulus of elasticity of the pipe, I is the moment of inertia, L is the exposed length and M is the dynamic mass of the submerged pipe.

It is assumed that the natural frequency of the pipe is similar to the transverse vibration of a simply supported beam with symmetrical links, so it is adopted $k \cong 1$.

The condition for the pipeline to be hydrodynamically stable is

$$ \left| f_s - f_n \right| \gg 0 $$

This condition ensures that resonance does not occur.

If the vortex shedding frequency f_s around the exposed length of the pipeline remains below 70% of its natural frequency f_n, the risk derived from the vibration induced by vortices will be low.

Esta condición asegura que no se produzca resonancia.

Si la frecuencia de corte por vórtices f_s producidos a lo largo de la longitud libre de la tubería se mantiene por debajo de un 70% de la frecuencia natural de la misma el riesgo derivado de la vibración inducida por vórtices (VIV) será bajo.

$$ f_s \leq 0.7 f_n $$

Combining equations, the maximum allowable free span length can be determined by solving for L:

$$ L = \sqrt{\frac{3.5 C_f D}{U_c}} \sqrt{\frac{EI}{m}} $$

Vortex shedding does not constitute a risk for all pipes. This mechanism can be eliminated when the following conditions are met:

- Incomplete exposure of the pipeline. The vibrations associated with the formation of vortices will not occur unless the pipe is exposed to its full height.
- Small free span length. When the L/D value <30, it is unlikely that the pipe will experience vibrations due to vortex shedding.

6 RISK QUANTIFICATION

1.1 Preliminar Analysis

In those situations where a significant number of points must be analyzed, it may be useful to carry out a preliminary analysis to determine which ones present, a priori, higher levels of threat or vulnerability. To do this, for the calculation of the threat and the vulnerability, all the available data are applied and those that do not are estimated approximately.

It is advisable to inspect all points with moderate to high potential risk. To define the survey priority of each of them, the following criteria can be used:

- Crosses with estimated values of cover and general scour that result in medium or high threats.
- Crossings with discovered pipelines.
- Crosses where an FSR $\leq$ 1.0 is estimated.
- Crossings of pipelines whose constituent material is vulnerable to the impacts of the sediments transported by the runoff.
- Crossings where the rupture of the pipeline results in environmental impacts, economic impacts and / or mitigation costs are medium or high.
- Crosses with history of breakage or damage.

1.2 Field Inspections

This activity seeks to obtain the following data [7]:

- Location of the crossing.
- Channel identification.
- Identification of the pipeline.

- Existence of pipeline protection works (None, Anchors, Counterweights, Concrete, Other), with indication of status (Good, Regular, Bad) [4].
- Existence of erosion control works (Weirs, Revetments, Groynes, Sheet Piles, Other), with status indication (Good, Regular, Bad) [4].
- Angle between the axis of the channel and the axis of the pipe.
- Channel width at riverbed.
- Channel width between margins.
- Height of the margins.
- Estimated Manning coefficient for the section of analyzed channel.
- Uncovered pipe (Yes / No). If so:
  - Unevenness between the bottom point of the outer surface of the pipe to the riverbed.
  - Length of uncovered pipe.
  - If not, the minimum existing cover.
- Outside diameter and material of the pipe.
- Type and condition of the pipe coating.
- Fluid transported.
- Estimated granulometry of the riverbed material. At crossings where the risk resulting from the preliminary analysis is high, it is recommended to take samples for subsequent granulometric analysis.
- Type of surrounding vegetation and average length of branches or trunks that may get stuck in the pipeline.
- Visual analysis of water hazards present:
  - General scour.
  - Erosion of margins.
  - Lateral migration of the channel or active meanders.
  - Dredging of the channel riverbed.
  - Presence of debris.
  - Accumulation of vegetation.
- Sketch of the planimetry and the cross section at the crossing point.
- Photographs.

At crossings with high risk or severity of risk it may be necessary to carry out detailed investigations, such as:
- Location and depth of the pipe across the width of the riverbed and on the margins of the crossing.
- Detailed topography of the place.
- In permanent channels, bathymetry in the crossing sector.
- Historical behavior of the crossing through the analysis of aerial photographs and satellite images.
- Review of plans according to the work of the structures executed in the place.

1.3 Assessment of the Threat and Vulnerability Factors

Once all the data required for the analysis has been obtained, the individual calculation for each point of the threat and vulnerability is carried out.

7 RISK AND RISK SEVERITY EVALUATION

The decision making for risk mitigation requires not only assessing the risk of breakage but also the consequences that breakage can produce in the environment and in the activity of the operator, that is, assess the severity of the risk. These consequences will be the ones that guide the process of selecting mitigation actions and their implementation over time [20], [21], [25].

The proposed analysis seeks to determine the consequences of a spill caused by the rupture of a pipe. This approach considers the environmental and economic effects generated by the damage of the affected facilities. In this respect, the following variables are considered:

- Existence of leak detection systems and automatic shut-off valves. They have an influence on the speed with which the loss of fluid is resolved and therefore on the volume spilled and the extension of the pollution plume generated
- Diameter. In case of damage, a pipeline with a larger diameter may be associated with a larger spill volume.
- Fluid pressure in the duct. In case of damage, a higher pressure can be associated with a greater volume of spillage.
- Fluid transported. The effects caused by each fluid transported in the event of a spill are analyzed, according to its toxicity and persistence (oil, dry gas, humid gas, formation water, etc.)
- Download point. It implies considering where the spill will drain in case of occurrence. The impacts for spills with potential access to courses and bodies of water are analyzed.
- Time of year in which the spill occurs. The behavior of the spilled fluid can be influenced by atmospheric conditions.
- Type of soil affected. The more permeable soils absorb the spilled fluids faster, making recovery more difficult and presenting the possibility of contaminating groundwater.
- Affected resource. It considers the impact of natural resources, such as grazing lands and native flora and fauna.
- Economic loss. It considers the economic loss as a result of the repair of damage to facilities, the loss generated as a result of the stopping of activities derived from the lack of electrical power due to breakage of transformers, power lines, flooding, etc.

1.4 Risk as Probability of Exposure vs. Vulnerability

The FSR ratio considered to establish the risk index is the one that is lower among those obtained for hydrodynamic forces and for vibrations induced by vortex shedding [12].

To illustrate the relative probability of failure, the probability of exposure and the value of FSR -that is inversely proportional to the vulnerability- are plotted. The relative probability of failure is shown in Figure 4, in which 5 zones have been delimited. Zone 5 has the lowest probability of failure while zone 1 indicates the highest probability.

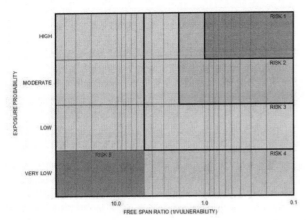

FIGURE 4: PROBABILITY OF EXPOSURE VS VULNERABILITY

Vulnerability values combined with the probability of exposure are used to assess the risk of breakage at intersections of pipelines with channels and to establish the plan for control and mitigation activities, prioritizing those sites that present a higher risk.

1.5 Consequences Due to Oil Spill

Impacts

The physical, chemical and biological impacts are analyzed [3], [25].

Physical impacts include:
- Asphyxiation of living organisms.
- Coverage of feathers or fur, reducing its insulation efficiency and generating hypothermia.
- Incorporation of extra weight to living beings, which, therefore, cannot move naturally or maintain balance.
- Coverage of soils and sediments, which reduces the exchange of liquids and gases (oxygen and carbon dioxide) affecting the underground organisms.
- Coverage of beaches, water surfaces, wetlands and other resources used by people, which can result in annoying odors, visual impact and dirt in livestock, crops, clothing, recreation equipment, pets, etc.
- Erosion or soil washing.
- Spill fires that occur near sites where ignition of spilled fluid may occur.

The chemical or toxicological impacts are the result of chemical and biochemical reactions in biological processes of individual organisms. Effects may include:

- Several toxic effects in animals and birds when they try to remove the hydrocarbons from their feathers or fur.
- Direct mortality.
- Interference in food and reproductive health.
- Reduction or loss of senses of perception.
- Tumors
- Interference in biochemical, genetic and metabolic processes.
- Other acute chronic effects.
- Fish and underwater organisms in stagnant water habitats such as swamps, lakes, ponds, etc., can be poisoned by the dissolved fraction.

Biological and ecological impacts may manifest themselves in local populations, communities or entire ecosystems, depending on the location, size, type, season, duration and persistence of the spill, as well as the type of habitats and biological resources exposed to spilled oil.

The impact is assessed based on the extent of the damage caused by a failure in the pipeline and the release of the product it carries. It is calculated by giving a value to each of the following factors:
1. Environmental pollution:
   a. Superficial water.
   b. Underground water.
   c. Atmosphere.
2. Mechanical effects.
3. Fire / explosion scenarios

Consequences Quantification

For the quantification of the consequences, the criterion proposed by K. Muhlbauer [1] is used to calculate the Event Consequence Index. The impact is assessed according to the extent of the damage caused by a failure in the pipeline and the release of the product that it transports. The economic consequences refer to:
- Direct damage to the facilities. Refers to damage caused to objects and property as a result of direct contact with runoff.
- Direct damages due to the interruption of operations. It refers to the commercial losses caused by the loss of production.
- Indirect damages. It includes the affectation on suppliers and clients outside the affected area. To assess the economic impact due to the rupture of a pipeline, direct damage is considered in the present analysis.

Remediation Costs

The remediation costs are valued according to Table 1 [22].

Score		Description
Very High	1	Very high implementation costs (more than US$ 500.000)
		Implementation requires more than 200 days
High	2	High implementation costs (Between US$ 100.001 and US$ 500.000)
		Implementation requires between 101 and 200 days
Intermediate	3	Intermediate implementation costs (Between US$ 10.001 and US$ 100.000)
		Implementation requires between 51 and 100 days
Low	4	Low implementation costs (Between US$ 1.001 and US$ 10.000)
		Implementation requires between 11 and 50 days
Very Low	5	Very low implementation costs (Less than 1.000)
		Implementation requires less than 10 days

TABLE 1: VALUATION OF REMEDIATION COSTS

8 APPLICATION OF THE METHODOLOGY

The proposed methodology was applied to evaluate the risk of failure of the pipelines that form the water, gas and oil networks, at the intersections of these with the channels that drain the Loma La Lata concession area, between the Neuquén River to the North and the Los Barreales reservoir to the south, in the province of Neuquén, Argentina.

148 potential risk points were surveyed. In each of them the information indicated in section **1.2 Field Inspections** was revealed, which was turned into a spreadsheet structured by columns of income data and by result columns.

The results were grouped taking into account the transported fluid (water, gas, oil) and active and inactive. It was observed that, in many cases, the probability of pipeline rupture is low even though its probability of exposure is high. See Table 2. The information obtained was turned into maps, where the analyzed crosses were identified and the risk evaluated for each one of them.

Cauce		Ducto		Vulnerabilidad		Riesgo
Probabilidad de Exposición		Estado	Fluido Transportado	Valor FSR	Causa	
Calificación	Corregida					
Alta	Alta	Activo	Gas	3.17	Fuerzas Hidrodinámicas	Bajo
Alta	Alta	Activo	Gas	2.16	Fuerzas Hidrodinámicas	Bajo
Alta	Alta	Activo	Gas	2.16	Fuerzas Hidrodinámicas	Bajo
Alta	Alta	Activo	Gas	3.16	Fuerzas Hidrodinámicas	Bajo
Baja	Baja	Activo	Gas	2.13	Desprendimiento de Vórtices	Bajo
Baja	Baja	Activo	Gas	1.44	Desprendimiento de Vórtices	Bajo
Baja	Baja	Activo	Gas	1.71	Fuerzas Hidrodinámicas	Bajo
Alta	Alta	Activo	Gas	4.39	Fuerzas Hidrodinámicas	Bajo
Alta	Alta	Activo	Gas	4.39	Fuerzas Hidrodinámicas	Bajo
Baja	Baja	Activo	Gas	1.56	Fuerzas Hidrodinámicas	Bajo
Baja	Baja	Activo	Gas	1.56	Fuerzas Hidrodinámicas	Bajo
Alta	Alta	Activo	Gas	2.46	Fuerzas Hidrodinámicas	Bajo

TABLE 2: SUMMARY OF THE RESULTS OF THE RISK EVALUATION FOR SOME OF THE ANALYZED DUCTS

9 RISK MANAGEMENT

Risk management involves reducing the contribution of the factors that intervene in its formation, that is, the threat and vulnerability [23].

9.1 Mitigation Priority

The priority in mitigation considers the following factors:
- Risk of occurrence of an event
- Potential impact of the event
- Estimated cost to implement mitigation actions

Each of these factors is weighted according to the Table 3.

Probability	Impact	Cost
Very Hig= 10	Very Hig= 10	Very Hig= 1
High= 8	High= 8	High= 2
Average= 6	Medium= 6	Intermediate= 3
Low= 4	Low= 4	Low= 4
Very Low= 2	Very Low= 2	Very Low= 5

TABLE 3: WEIGHTING THE FACTORS TO DEFINE THE PRIORITY OF MITIGATION

Higher values are assigned to the Probability and Impact factors with respect to the Mitigation Cost Factor to reflect the greater importance of those in the overall analysis of the risk mitigation priority. The values of the Mitigation Cost factor are listed from lowest to highest to indicate that the implementation of low-cost mitigation measures should be prioritized over those of higher costs.

The mitigation priority is evaluated for each risk by adding the risk scores of occurrence, potential impact and mitigation cost. Higher scores indicate higher priorities for the implementation of mitigation measures.

9.2 Mitigation Actions

The main objective of mitigation is to reduce the risk of damage or failure of a pipeline and minimize the environmental and economic impact that these can cause.

It includes actions that usually require engineering designs. Its execution is preceded by tasks such as topographic and bathymetric surveys, engineering, permits, environmental studies, etc. Its preparation may require from weeks to months.

Threat Mitigation

The degree of threat due to general scour is determined by the percentage of general scour with respect to the minimum soil cover over the pipeline in the cross section. The reduction of the value of the general scour can be carried out by means of any of the following procedures:
- Decrease the runoff flow.
- Decrease the speed of runoff.
- Modify the granulometry of the material of the riverbed.
- Reduce hydraulic depth.
- Modify the pipeline route to avoid crossings with sections of channel with high values of general scour.
- Build works that keep the river level stable upstream
- Burying the pipeline deeper.
- Crossing the river by pipe bridge

Mitigation of Vulnerability and Consequences

Mitigating the vulnerability of a pipe at a crossing with a channel involves increasing the FSR value, that is, reducing the maximum exposure length and/or increasing the maximum allowable span length. The first alternative can increase the threat level by reducing the width of the channel and therefore increasing the hydraulic depth in the section, so its implementation must be carefully analyzed.

To increase the maximum allowable span length, the mechanical characteristics of the pipe must be modified, which can be foreseen in the design stage of the pipeline.

It should be analyzed to have an early warning system by means of information sent by rain gauges distributed in the basin or by stations of flow measurement in sections of the channel located upstream of the crossings that activate actions such as reduction of pressure or reduction or interruption of the fluid flow in the pipes.

9.3 Planning of Mitigation Actions

The main consideration in the planning of mitigation actions is to reduce the risk below the threshold defined by the operator. However, considerations such as the season of low flow or dry climate should be considered.

9.4 I Periodic Inspections and Monitoring

The ability of the water threat to affect a pipeline is not static. The factors causing the threat, their activity and the state of the defense works executed in the place can be modified with time. It is therefore advisable that periodically an analysis be made of the components of the risk, that is, of the threat and vulnerability, in order to keep the inventory of points or sections at risk updated.

The frequency of inspections at a given point will be given by the risk calculated for it. The following periods are recommended according to the zoning shown in Figure 4:

- Risk in Zone 1: Periodic inspections every six months, which will be complemented with inspections prior to and following the rainy season.
- Risk in Zone 2: Annual inspections.
- Risk in Zone 3: Inspections every two years.
- Risk in Zones 4 and 5: Inspections every three years.

The mentioned intervals can be reduced considering factors such as the following:
- Situations of severe floods or other unusual hydrological phenomena.
- Field staff observations.
- Observations resulting from crossing monitoring.
- New data.

9.5 Monitoring

Monitoring involves the reading and analysis of data to verify the behavior and progression of the threat and its impact on the pipeline. This activity may include topographic surveys, bathymetric surveys, installation of instruments for the measurement and recording of flows and erosion, installation of markers to measure erosion of margins, etc.

9.6 Maintenance

The maintenance tasks correspond to actions in the field that do not require engineering designs, such as:
- Bridges and culverts maintenance.
- Construction of ditches or small embankments.
- Replacement of markers.
- Access maintenance.

10 CONCLUSIONS

The proposed methodology significantly improves the reliability and integrity of the pipes analyzed. Among the advantages of its application can be named:

- **Risk Reduction**. It is possible to reduce the ruptures in the pipes or the interruptions in the transport of fluids through systematized observations at regular intervals, the storage of the data and a greater degree of knowledge of the state of the crosses.
- **Information availability**. The accessibility to the database allows knowing the status of the crossings to the operator's personnel.
- **Savings of Resources**. Periodic inspection of crossings at risk-dependent intervals optimizes resources in the field.
- **Early Identification of Risks**. The periodic inspection allows identifying risks in their early stage of development and improves the overall integrity of the lines.
- **Objectivity**. The standardized survey and processing of the crossing data improves the objectivity of the risk analysis and therefore the allocation of resources for the mitigation of risks.
- **Knowledge at the Corporate Level**. The generation of a database improves the retention and availability of historical information over time.

In the analyzed case of the Loma La Lata area, the methodology allowed to identify and quantify the different levels of risk in each of the inspected crossings and to establish priorities for risk mitigation.

11 REFERENCES

[1] "Pipeline Risk Management Manual", W. Kent Muhlbauer, Gulf Professional Publishing.
[2] "Oil and gas pipeline design, maintenance and repair", Dr. Abdel-Alim Hashem, Cairo University.
[3] "Onshore pipeline quantified risk assessment", Allseas Engineering BV, Corrib Field Development Project (Phase II), 2001.
[4] "Scour risk assessment at river crossings", Roca & Whitehouse, HR Wallingford, ICSE6, Paris, 2012.
[5] "Geohazard management trends in the onshore pipeline industry", Savigny, Porter y Leir, Geoline, 2005.

[6] "Fluid mechanics aspects of a buried natural gas pipeline at a river crossing", Shrisvastava, 11vo Congreso Panamericano de Mecánica Aplicada, 2010.

[7] "Field inspection module for hydrotechnical hazards", Leir, Reed y Yaremko, International Pipeline Conference, 2004.

[8] "Potential drift accumulation at bridges", Timothy Diehl, U.S. Department of Transportation, Federal Highway Administration, 1997.

[9] "Determination of maximum span between pipe supports using maximum bending stress theory", Vakharia y Mohd Farooq, International Journal of Recent Trends in Engineering, 2009

[10] "Channel crossing erosion and scour hazard assessment Chevron San Ardo to Coalinga heated oil pipeline, Monterey and Fresno counties, California", Golder Associates, 2007.

[11] "Analisys of natech risk for pipelines: A review", Roberta Piccinelli and Elisabeth Krausmann, Publications Office of the European Union, 2013.

[12] "Approaches for evaluating the vulnerability of pipelines at water crossings", Dooley, Prestie, Ferris, Fitch & Zhang, 10th International Pipeline Conference, ASME, 2014.

[13] "Propuesta metodológica para la evaluación del riesgo aluvional en cursos efímeros atravesados por conductos subterráneos – Estudio de casos en Mendoza, Argentina", Hector Daniel Farias, Instituto de Recursos Hídricos, FCEyT-UNSE, Santiago del Estero, 2009.

[14] "Fluid Mechanics Aspects of a Buried Natural Gas Pipeline at River Crossing", Gyan S. Shrivastava, 11th Pan-American Congress of Applied Mechanics, 2010.

[15] "Vortex Induced Vibrations of Free Span Pipelines", Kamran Koushan, 2018.

[16] "Analytical Methodology for Evaluating Stress and Strain of Pipeline Exposed in Flood", Xialin Wang, Jian Shuai, Xiamin Guo, 8th International Pipeline Conference, ASME, 2010.

[17] "Dam failure: Assessing the risks to pipeline infrastructure", Simon Impey, DNV.GL, 2013.

[18] "Identifying soil erosion risk for onshore pipelines", Keith Winning, Principal Pipeline & Geomatics Engineer, CB&I, ESRI European User Conference, 2014.

[19] "Semi-quantitative risk assessment", Northern Gateway Pipelines, Worley Parsons, 2013.

[20] "Pipeline risk assessment: New guidelines". Hopkins, Goodfellow, Ellis, Haswell & Jackson. WTIA/APIA Welded Pipeline Symposium. Sydney, Australia, 2009.

[21] "Pipeline risk management". Mountain House Specific Plan III, San Joaquin County, California.

[22] "Quantitative risk assessment for crude oil pipelines". H. Cekirge.. International Journal of Environmental Monitoring and Analysis. Vol. 3, No. 3, 2015.

[23] "Pipeline watercourse management". Recommended Practices, 1st Edition, Canadian Energy Pipeline Association, 2014.

[24] "Pipeline associated watercourse crossings", 3rd Edition, Canadian Energy Pipeline Association, 2005.

[25] "Oil spill risk assessment and environmental consequence analysis". Keystone XL Pipeline Project. Canada - Estados Unidos, 2009.

IPG2019-5328

ASSESSING AND MANAGING GEOLOGIC HAZARDS IN THE APPALACHIAN REGION OF THE UNITED STATES

Martin P. Derby, P.G., CPG
Golder
Buffalo, New York, USA

Bailey Theriault, P.G.
Golder
Manchester, New Hampshire, USA

ABSTRACT

Geohazards have the potential to adversely affect the operation or integrity of an existing pipeline, or the routing, design, and construction of a proposed pipeline. Identifying, characterizing, evaluating, and if necessary, mitigating and monitoring geologic hazards have become critical steps to successfully and safely building and operating pipelines in the Appalachian Basin region of the United States. The recent, rapid expansion of pipeline construction and operation in the region, along with natural geologic and geographic conditions which are conducive to landsliding and ground subsidence, have resulted in a recent increase in geohazard-related incidences both during and post-construction of pipelines. As such, there is an increasing need to recognize, understand, and closely manage geohazards in this region, prior to, during, and post-construction of pipelines. This paper will provide an overview of essential tools that have proven most useful in this region, to identify, characterize, and ultimately mitigate and monitor potential geohazards. This paper will also provide insight on how to evaluate specific project needs and best-fit approaches and solutions for the project at hand, to reduce the operator's risk. A case study will be presented from the Appalachian Basin region, including how a phased approach was used to assess and manage geohazards. The phased approach includes (1) Phase I Assessments, which consist of a regional-scale desktop assessment to identify, initially characterize, and qualitatively classify (e.g., low, moderate, high hazards) geohazards; (2) Phase II Assessments, which consist of a non-intrusive ground reconnaissance completed at targeted sites; and (3) Phase III Assessments, which consist of subsurface investigations such as drilling, test pitting, or geophysical surveys to further characterize specific hazards.

The information obtained from the phased approach can be used for the design of mitigation and/or monitoring, if deemed necessary. Overall approaches to selecting and utilizing best-fit mitigation and monitoring options, both during and post-construction, fit for the regional conditions and to the individual project, will also be discussed.

INTRODUCTION

Landslides and ground subsidence are two types of geologic hazards (geohazards) that are prolific in the Appalachian Basin region of the United States, which generally incorporates portions of New York, Pennsylvania, Ohio, and West Virginia. Geohazards have the potential to adversely affect the operation or integrity of an existing pipeline or the construction of a proposed pipeline. The recent rapid expansion of pipeline construction in the Appalachian Basin region is associated with oil and gas upstream/midstream activities in the Marcellus Shale Formation.

Though the systematic characterization of geologic hazards is sometimes perceived as an added project expense, failure to recognize and mitigate hazards at an early stage can lead to schedule delays, substantial liability, repair, and business interruption costs [1]. Understanding the complex geology of the Appalachian Basin region, the triggers for and dynamic nature of landslides and ground subsidence and performing a systematic approach to geohazard assessment is key to reducing risks to pipeline operators.

BACKGROUND OF THE APPALACHIAN BASIN REGION

The Appalachian Basin region consists of several physiographic provinces; however, most of the Marcellus Shale Formation is within the Appalachian Plateau physiographic region. The Appalachian Plateau physiographic region is characterized by rugged, hilly terrain, heavily dissected by streams and tributaries. The bedrock geology is comprised of mostly flat-bedded alternating sequences of sedimentary units that include sandstone, siltstone, claystone, shale, limestone, and coal.

The Marcellus Shale Formation is in the northeast/mid-Atlantic area of the Appalachian Basin region (Figure 1). The Marcellus Shale, also referred to as the Marcellus Formation, is a middle Devonian-age, black, low-density, carbonaceous (organic rich) shale that occurs in the subsurface beneath much of Ohio, West Virginia, Pennsylvania, and New York. Small areas of Maryland, Kentucky, Tennessee, and Virginia are also underlain by the Marcellus Shale [2].

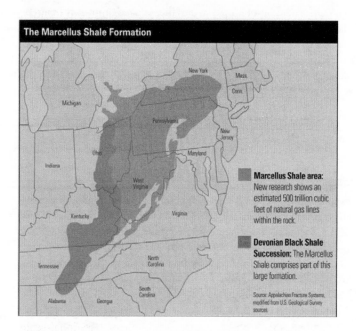

FIGURE 1 – Marcellus Shale Formation located within the Appalachian Basin region (USGS).

The Marcellus Shale Formation is one of the largest shale formations in the United States and was estimated initially to contain over 80 trillion cubic feet of natural gas. Operators have known for decades that the shale was a high yielding formation, but extracting the natural gas was very difficult.

In the early 2000s, advances in drilling technology enabled rigs to drill deep into the shale layer and then drill horizontally along fracture lines. The gas is recovered using a technique called hydraulic fracturing (or "fracking") in which large quantities of water, sand, and chemicals are forced in the well, causing the shale layers to break apart along fracture lines, releasing the gas contained within the rock [3].

The addition of new natural gas wells in the Marcellus Shale Formation brought the construction of new pipelines. The wells and pipelines are located in difficult, hilly terrain which makes for difficult accessibility and construction. Existing landslides and subsidence areas created additional burdens for pipeline construction. Improper pipeline slope designs caused additional slope failures and have exasperated well and pipeline owners.

GEOHAZARDS IN THE APPALACHIAN BASIN REGION

A geohazard is generally defined as a natural geologic condition, ongoing geologic process, or potential natural event that may pose a threat to humans, properties, and infrastructure including pipelines. Geohazards may also occur from human activities (i.e., underground mining). Naturally occurring geohazards include: unstable slopes such as landslides and rockfalls; seismic or co-seismic events; hydrotechnical (water erosion from streams and floods); expansive or collapsible soils; karst; permafrost/frost heave; shallow groundwater; meteorological events (i.e., tornadoes and hurricanes); and volcanic hazards. Human activities that induce geohazards may include mining operations or fluid withdrawal, which can result in ground subsidence and settlement.

The major geohazards that pose a threat to the Appalachian Basin region include: unstable slopes/landslides and rockfalls; hydrotechnical; and ground subsidence from coal mining operations.

Unstable Slopes/Landslides – A landslide is the "movement of a mass of rock, debris, or earth down a slope," and encompasses geologic processes such as debris or mud flows, rotational slides (slumps), translational slides, earth flows, rockfalls, or debris slides [4][5]. Landslides can adversely affect pipelines by bending the pipe along the lateral limits or failure planes of the landslide, by compressing and tensioning the pipe during downslope movement of soil and rock, by undercutting and exposing the pipe (in the event that material flows out from underneath the pipeline), or by physically impacting the pipe in the event of a rapid debris flow or rockfall. Due to the slope steepness and the overburden soil structure; the slopes of the Appalachian Basin region (see Figure 2) are conducive to slope movement, which can range from slope creep to instantaneous failures. Slope failures are generally triggered by saturated soil and the lack of drainage systems to remove surface water and groundwater. Additionally, landslides may be triggered by human activity during construction (e.g., excavations).

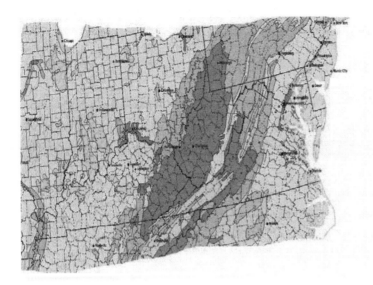

FIGURE 2 – Map of landslide prone areas within the Appalachian Basin region. The mapped red color indicates high incidence of landslides (greater than 15% of the area). From the Digital Compilation of "Landslide Overview Map of the Conterminous United States" (USGS).

Subsidence – Collapse or subsidence of underground voids left by underground mining can produce sinkholes or regional subsidence similar to those produced by karst. These sinkholes can result from collapse of overlying overburden into an underground mine cavern/void or the sudden or gradual collapse of the cavern itself [6]. Deep coal mining performed in the past utilized the "room and pillar" method. Longwall mining, where essentially all coal is removed from mining panels, leaving behind only limited pillars as necessary to protect access and airways, became more common during and after the 1960s. Subsidence occurs relatively quickly with longwall mining, typically being largely complete within a year, but total subsidence can approach the total thickness of the coal seams extracted, and is largely independent of the depth of the coal seams (Figure 3). Both room and pillar mining (historical) and long wall mining (current) for coal extraction are prevalent throughout the Appalachian Basin region. Pipelines may be impacted due to subsidence of the ground [7], which can either pull the pipe downward with the subsiding ground or leave the pipe unsupported.

Hydrotechnical – Hydrotechnical related hazards such as erosion and scour at watercourse crossings can pose a threat to pipelines both during and post-construction. During construction, challenging ground and site conditions and equipment limitations can result in reduced pipeline burial depth and thereby increase the likelihood of future hydrotechnical threats. Post-construction, the loss of cover resulting from scour of the channel bed (i.e., vertical changes) can expose the pipeline, erosion of the channel banks (i.e., horizontal changes) can threaten sagbends, and larger scale

channel migration can threaten burial depth and sagbends in longer segments of the pipeline.

FIGURE 3 – A surface tension crack (subsidence) in a pipeline ROW due to a long wall mining (coal) operation.

APPROACH TO GEOHAZARD ASSESSMENT IN THE APPALACHIAN BASIN REGION

The assessment of geohazards along a pipeline alignment needs to be through a systematic approach, in order to identify, characterize, evaluate, and if necessary, mitigate and monitor hazards that may have the potential to impact pipeline infrastructure and assets. The Appalachian Basin region has undergone a major oil and gas resurgence since the mid-2000s which is primarily due to the natural gas reserves of the Marcellus Shale Formation. Geohazard assessment for new construction of pipelines is paramount to reducing potential impacts to the pipelines, both during and post-construction, in the Appalachian Basin region.

The phased approach to the assessment of geohazards for pipelines is a cost-effective, systematic process that begins with a desktop assessment (Phase I Assessment) and, when required, proceeds to a site-specific level (Phase II [Characterization] and III [Mitigation] Assessments, as needed) in order to identify, characterize, evaluate, and if necessary, mitigate and monitor hazards that may have the potential to affect a pipeline. Details for each phase in the process are provided below:

- Phase I Assessment: preliminary, regional-scale identification and assessment of potential hazards that may affect a pipeline(s). This assessment is generally desktop in nature and involves review of data and research to develop an inventory of potential hazards for further consideration.

- Phase II Assessment: site-specific but non-intrusive field investigations of select sites identified during the Phase I Assessment. Typically consists of a geomorphic and geologic ground reconnaissance and/or more detailed research to gain a better understanding of the location, nature, extent, and potential effect of a hazard to a pipeline.

- Phase III: Detailed site-specific investigation and analyses to develop monitoring and mitigation designs and support implementation. May include intrusive investigation techniques (e.g., drilling or test pitting/trenching) or non-intrusive techniques (e.g., geophysics), and may include detailed engineering analyses and design.

Detailed descriptions of each phase are provided below.

Phase I Assessment

A Phase I Assessment consists of a regional-scale desktop assessment to identify, initially characterize, and qualitatively classify geohazards.

The Phase I Assessment is carried out to provide broad constraints on route selection and construction feasibility, or for existing pipelines, to develop an inventory and identify areas for additional assessment. A Phase I Assessment is primarily an office-based desktop study to evaluate conditions such as extreme terrain, earthquake and fault activity, volcanic activity, slope failure, flooding, river crossings, etc. The objective of the Phase I Assessment is to provide general geologic constraints that can be used to facilitate future planning, route selection, and conceptual design [1].

Typical geohazard data sources for the Appalachian Basin region include:
- Soil Conservation Service (SCS) or USDA maps for types of soils including typical depths
- Engineering or State soils/geomorphology maps
- State bedrock geology maps
- Historical aerial photography
- Light Detection and Ranging (LiDAR) data
- Coal Mining Maps
- Flood zones maps

Soils and bedrock geology maps can be easily obtained from state agencies along with coal seam mapping databases. Historical aerial photographs can be obtained from commercial vendors, as well as state and federal agencies.

LiDAR data is collected through an airborne method that measures distance by illuminating a target with a laser and analyzing the reflected light. The LiDAR obtains x. y, and z data points, and through data processing, tree canopy and vegetation data points can be filtered from ground points. Repeated LiDAR surveys allow documentation of location and comparison of amounts/rates of slope change (Figure 4).

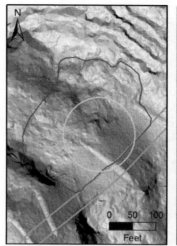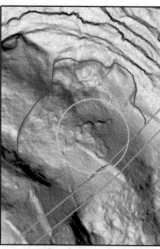

FIGURE 4 – LiDAR data showing topography changes from 2016 to 2018. The pipelines are shown in green, the landslide boundary is shown in red, and the area of new ground movement is circled in yellow.

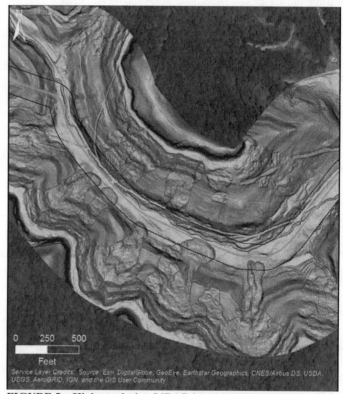

FIGURE 5 – High-resolution LiDAR imagery (displayed as percent slope in blue-scale) of a pipeline (green line), mapping corridor (black line, 200-feet-wide), and intersecting landslides (outlined in pink).

LiDAR data is particularly useful in areas with dense vegetation cover, where a clear view of the ground is difficult through other traditional methods (e.g., from the ground or air, or from aerial photographs) (Figure 5). LiDAR is a fairly new technology and is becoming more of an accepted method for geohazard assessments by oil and gas operators in the

Appalachian Basin region. Specialized expertise with backgrounds in geology, geomorphology, and remote sensing are necessary to properly interpret and identify key slope/landslide movement features.

Once identified, a qualitative hazard classification (e.g., low, moderate, high) is generally assigned to each possible hazard, based on several criteria such as activity level of the geologic process, the aerial extent and proximity of the hazard, the estimated likelihood of the hazard to affect a pipeline during its service life, and the types of potential consequences of the hazard to the respective pipeline. The classifications are often then tied to recommendations for additional assessment and/or response and mitigation or monitoring [8].

For many Phase I Assessments, a helicopter aerial reconnaissance is included, after the desktop assessment is completed. The reconnaissance is intended to provide a current view of the ground conditions, as some of the data reviewed during the desktop assessment may be outdated, and also to cross-check the desktop results with actual ground conditions. An aerial reconnaissance is best completed when the ground is free of snow, and when vegetation is low (i.e., early spring in the Appalachian Basin region).

The Phase I Assessment data are then complied into a GIS database. The GIS database allows new datasets (from the Phase II and II programs) to be merged into one formal database.

Low	Moderate	High
- Dormant or relict landslide (older than a few hundred years) crossed by ROW with low potential for renewed activity. - Shallow, small stream bank slump on ROW that does not intersect pipeline(s).	- Dormant landslide crossed by ROW with potential for renewed activity. - Active landslide within 30 m of ROW with lateral limits or failure surface that do not intersect a pipeline. - Debris flow run-out crossed by ROW.	- Active landslide crossing the ROW, or closely adjacent to the ROW that may pose a hazard to a pipeline. - Debris flow source area or channel that crosses ROW. - Rockfall in close proximity to ROW.

TABLE 1 – Example of a Phase I classification for landslide hazards.

Phase II Assessment

The next step in the phased approach is the Phase II Assessment. The Phase II Assessment is a non-intrusive field program that includes a visit to either the proposed ROW or an existing pipeline ROW. The purpose of the Phase II Assessment is to confirm and further characterize select geohazards identified during the Phase I Assessment (e.g., possibly those assigned as high hazard sites, that may potentially pose the most significant threat to the pipeline).

FIGURE 6 – Phase II Assessment site in the Appalachian Basin region, where the activity level of the landslide and the location of the headscarp compared to the location of the pipeline are confirmed.

The Phase II Assessment technical team should include geohazard specialists and pipeline/geotechnical engineers. The technical team should have extensive experience with Appalachian geology, geohazards, and pipeline design (for new construction) for mountainous regions.

The tasks of a typical Phase II Assessment in the Appalachian Basin region include:

- Characterization of the feature based on surface conditions and the potential threat to the pipeline. For landslides, observations of features such as headscarps, internal scarps, tension cracks, etc., allow for evaluating potential activity level, movement rate, thickness, and aerial extent of the landslide, which can be used to evaluate current or potential threat to the pipeline.
- Investigation of surface features that are typical of slope creep (see Figures 7and 8).
- Investigation of surface mine features such as highwalls and trenches that may not be visible in the ROW during the aerial reconnaissance review.
- Investigation of surface water features and erosional features.
- Confirmation of geohazards identified in the Phase I Assessment and adjustment of the assessment classifications, if needed.
- Development of recommendations for geohazards to be further investigated during a Phase III Assessment. This may also include recommendations for pipelines routes adjustments.
- Discussion with pipeline engineering and geotechnical design team for potential geohazard impacts.

FIGURE 7 – Evidence of slope creep – bowed pine trees.

Figure 7 is an example of slope creep. The bowing of trees is a common example of creep which is prevalent throughout the Appalachian Basin region. Figure 8 shows a tension crack below a tree which caused the tree trunk to spilt in two. Both examples can be observed during a Phase II Assessment.

FIGURE 8 – Slope/landslide tension crack which split the tree. Phase III Assessment.

A Phase III Assessment is a focused program on specific sites that require additional surficial and/or subsurface (geotechnical) information. The purpose of this program is to perform detailed geotechnical/geohazard studies to assist in final pipeline design and/or site mitigation measures.

It is critical at this stage to ensure open communication and consensus among the geohazard team and the pipeline design team to define the parameters required for detailed design, the engineering tolerances, and potential range of solutions dictated by the initial pipeline design, cost, and value-of-information. [1].

The tasks of a typical Phase III Assessment may include:

- Design of a geotechnical investigation program that will define the subsurface soils and or bedrock.
- Completion of a test pit and soil boring program. Program may include the installation of geotechnical instrumentation (i.e., inclinometers, piezometers, extensometers, tilt meters, etc.).
- Completion of geophysical investigations (i.e., seismic refraction) to determine subsurface information between borings and for HDD design.
- Installation of strain gages to monitor pipeline stress/strain (existing pipelines within or near a landslide or subsidence feature).
- Soil mapping for soil resistivity (corrosion).

FIGURE 9 – Phase III Assessment borehole investigation along a pipeline ROW in the Appalachian Basin region.

Following identification and completion of a Phase III Assessment, mitigation and/or monitoring should be developed and implemented, in accordance with and prioritized based on perceived threat the pipeline and surroundings (e.g., other infrastructure, people, environmental concerns, etc.).

MITIGATION APPROACH FOR EXISTING PIPELINES IN THE APPALACHIAN BASIN REGION

The selection of the type and/or combination of possible mitigation and/or monitoring options, as well as the priority and timing of their implementation, may vary from hazard site to site, even within the same hazard class. Priorities will depend upon many factors, including (but not limited to) system-scale and/or site-specific geologic, climatic, geotechnical, hydrotechnical, environmental, regulatory, land owner, and operational considerations. Operators should be engaged in the selection of the approach, methods, and techniques for mitigation and monitoring and ultimately decide upon the appropriate and acceptable level of mitigated risk. In so doing, Operators may decide to mitigate all or only portions of identified hazards.

The most effective mitigation strategy requires recognition of the multiple factors governing a site and may require long-term performance monitoring before full mitigation can be achieved. Mitigation measures should be tailored to address the site-specific and potentially variable conditions, consider and incorporate the Operator's risk tolerance, consider the costs and benefits of short- versus long-term solutions, incorporate construction considerations into the planning and design efforts, and integrate all these factors with the construction installation process.

All alternatives require an understanding of the type, nature, magnitude, and rate of movement of hazard and the site geology; i.e., data collected during the Phase Assessments. The phased approach can be utilized for both new pipelines and existing pipelines. Some mitigation approaches are listed below:

- No action, with monitoring and emergency response as needed

- Remove the effects of the hazard through engineered solutions
  - Avoidance (e.g., re-route, HDD, deep burial, above-ground)
  - Hazard stabilization (collect/control surface and groundwater, remove driving forces, increase resisting forces, improve slope geometry)

- Stay in place and mitigate (remove/reduce/delay) the effects through stress relief excavation and engineered solutions (drainage and deformation improvements) in

the pipe trench and drainage improvements on the slope.
- Performance monitoring of landslide and pipe
- Periodic, as needed, stress relief of pipeline and repair of mitigation measures to maintain integrity
- Favorable pipe trench orientation/geometry and select backfill

FIGURE 10 – Strain gauge attached to a pipeline for monitoring stress/strain due to slope movement.

DATA MANAGEMENT

Data management is critical for the long-term management of geohazards, in order to properly inventory potential hazards, and track them through time (e.g., including changing conditions or hazards, and assessments and/or remediation that may be completed through time). Data can generally be managed in a GIS Geodatabase which is designed to inventory and track geohazards through the phased approach and the life of the hazard. For example, a database may hold the following data:

- Inventory and characteristics of geohazards
- Hazard classifications
- Status of each site (e.g., mitigated, monitored, etc.)
- Observations from multiple events (e.g., aerial reconnaissance, ground visits, monitoring events, etc.), which track the site history

The database may ultimately be used by the Operator to:
- Maintain an inventory of identified hazards
- Track the status of individual sites
- Prioritize responses
- Maintain records to document the history of a site

A data management system should be developed specific to the hazard types prevalent in an area as well as the desired approach to geohazard management of the Operator.

GEOHAZARD APPROACH – CASE HISTORY

Phase I, II, and III Assessments were completed for a major pipeline in the Appalachian Basin region that traversed the states of Pennsylvania, Ohio, and West Virginia. The pipeline segment included in the assessments was approximately 400 miles (approx. 650 km) in length.

The assessments were completed over approximately a four-year period, and work is currently ongoing (at the time this paper was written). The assessments included landslide, mine subsidence (both related to underground mines and surface mines), karst subsidence, and seismic hazards. To emphasize how the phased approach works to identify features and then "zero-in" on hazards of most concern, in the following discussion, we will quantify landslide hazards (see Table 2).

During the Phase I Assessment, data were collected and analyzed along the pipeline. A remote sensing review of high quality, project-specific LiDAR data and aerial photography was completed, and an aerial reconnaissance was conducted. The use of LiDAR data proved critical for landslide identification, as only about 20 percent of the landslides were visible in other data sources (e.g., project-specific aerial photographs and Google Earth imagery). During the desk-top portion of the Phase I Assessment, 217 landslides were identified and classified. Upon completing the aerial reconnaissance, an additional 4 landslides were identified, and some classifications were adjusted (Table 2).

Phase	Hazard Classification			Total
	Low	Moderate	High	
	Number of Landslides			
Phase I (Desktop Only)	130	47	40	217
Phase I (Aerial Reconnaissance)	131	50	40	221
Phase II	14	24	15	53
Phase III	1	6	7	15 (1 unknown hazard)

TABLE 2 – Count of landslide hazards through each phase of assessment.

The Phase II Assessment included site-specific ground characterization of 53 landslides and 29 reclaimed surface mine areas, as well as detailed research and interpretation of underground mining footprints and mining methods for underground mines crossed by the pipeline. The landslide assessment included all the high hazard sites identified during the Phase I Assessment, and some of the moderate hazard sites. As can be seen in Table 2, at the end of the Phase II Assessment, only 15 high hazard sites remained (i.e., the remainder were downgraded to moderate or low hazard sites based on the field observations).

The Phase III Assessment included site-specific sub-surface characterization through excavation of test pits at the 15 high hazard sites identified during the Phase II Assessment. The test pits were aimed at confirming the lateral limits and depth of each landslide relative to the pipe, and also at identifying possible sources of surface and subsurface water. Based on the results of the Phase III Assessment, 7 of the landslides were identified to pose current or near-term integrity threats to the pipe, 6 sites were determined to pose potential future integrity threats to the pipe, 1 site was determined to not pose a current or future integrity threat, and 1 site was inconclusive.

Following the Phase III Assessment, mitigation and monitoring plans have been designed for each of the 7 landslides identified during the Phase III Assessment to pose current or near-term integrity threats.

In addition to the Phase I, II, and III Assessments, aerial reconnaissance's are completed annually for this pipeline, to monitor movement of existing hazards, and to identify possible new hazards that may develop each year. Also, inline inspection (ILI) inertial measurement unit (IMU) bending strain data were used throughout the phased assessment, to aid in identifying sites where the pipe may already be impacted by geohazards, and to help prioritize sites for further assessment and mitigation. Throughout the four years of work completed to date, one landslide site underwent rapid response mitigation, based on landslide characteristics observed during the Phase II Assessment along with the presence of detected IMU bending strain.

The geohazard data that were collected throughout all phases of work were compiled into a GIS Geodatabase, where data were continually entered and updated throughout the assessments.

CONCLUSIONS

The recent, rapid expansion of pipeline construction and operation in the Appalachian Basin region, along with natural geologic and geographic conditions which are conducive to landsliding and ground subsidence, have resulted in a recent increase in geohazard-related incidences both during and post-construction of pipelines. As such, there is an increasing need to recognize, understand, and closely manage geohazards in this region, prior to, during, and post-construction of pipelines.

The phased approach to geohazard assessment provides a cost-effective method to systematically identify, characterize, evaluate, and if necessary, mitigate and monitor hazards that may have the potential to affect a pipeline. The approach starts off with a regional-scale assessment and "zeros-in" on hazards of most concern in subsequent phases of work, allowing for mitigation and/or monitoring to be focused on only sites where necessary and as-needed, while the remainder of identified sites remain part of the overall geohazard inventory, which can be used for reference if conditions change through time.

REFERENCES

[1] Hengesh, J.V., et. al. 2004. A Systematic Approach for Mitigating Geohazards in Pipeline Design and Construction, ASME, Proceedings of the IPC 2004.

[2] King, Hobart. 2019. Marcellus Shale – Appalachian Basin Natural Gas Play, Geology.com.

[3] Penn State – College of Education. 2019. Marcellus Shale Natural Gas Development, Website: https://ed.psu.edu/crec/research/marcellus-shale-natural-gas-development.

[4] Cruden, D.M. 1991. A simple definition of a landslide: Bulletin of the International Association of Engineering Geology, No. 43, p.27-29.

[5] Cruden, D.M., and Varnes, D.J. 1996. Landslides Types and Processes. In Landslides: Investigation and Mitigation. Transportation Research Board, National Academy of Science, Special Report 247, Washington, D.C.

[6] Whyatt, J. and Varley, F. 2008. Catastrophic Failures of Underground Evaporite Mines, Proceedings of the 27th International Conference on Ground Control in Mining, July 29 – July 31, 2008, Morgantown, West Virginia. West Virginia University, 2008. NIOSH – Spokane Research Laboratory, Spokane, WA.

[7] Derby, M.P., Saunders, M.D., and Zand, B. 2016. Geotechnical Instrumentation: Monitoring Longitudinal Stress of a High Pressure Pipeline During a Long Wall Mining Operations – A Case Study in West Virginia, ASME, Proceedings of the IPC 2016.

[8] Theriault, B., O'Leary, D., West, D., and Nixon, M. 2018. Terrain Analysis and Geologic Hazards Assessment: A comparison of the Objectives and Methods of Each, and the Benefits of Completing Both in Parallel, ASME, Proceedings of the IPC 2018.

This page left blank intentionally.

IPG2019-5339

FINITE ELEMENT MODELLING OF A SERIES OF GROUND DISPLACEMENT EPISODES AND STRESS RELIEF PROCEDURES

Hamid Karimian
BGC Engineering Inc.
Vancouver, BC, Canada

Pete Barlow
BGC Engineering Inc.
Edmonton, AB, Canada

Chris Blackwell
Enbridge Pipelines Inc.
Calgary, AB, Canada

Chris Campbell
BGC Engineering Inc.
Vancouver, BC, Canada

ABSTRACT

The Wapiti River South Slope (the Slope) near Grand Prairie, Alberta, Canada, is 500 m long and consists of a steep lower slope and a shallower upper slope. Both the upper and the lower slopes are located within a landslide complex with ground movements of varying magnitudes and depths. The Alliance Pipeline (Alliance) NPS 42 Mainline (the pipeline) was installed in the winter of 2000 using conventional trenching techniques at an angle of approximately 8° to the slope fall line. Evidence of slope instability was observed in the slope since 2007. The surficial geology of the slope comprises a colluvium layer draped over bedrock formation in the lower slope, and glacial deposits in the upper slope. Available data indicated two different slide mechanisms. In the lower slope, there is a shallow translational slide within a colluvium layer, and in the upper slope there is a deep-seated translational slide within the glacial deposits. Both the upper and lower slope landslides have been confirmed to be active in the past decade.

Gradual ground displacements in the order of several centimeters per year were observed in both the upper and lower slopes between 2007 and 2012. Large ground displacements in the order of several meters were observed between 2012 and 2014 in the lower slope that led to the first stress relief and subsequent slope mitigation measures in the spring and summer of 2014. Monitoring of the slope after mitigations indicated significant reduction in the rate of ground movement in the lower slope. Surveying of the pipeline before and after stress relief indicated an increase in lateral pipeline deformation in the direction of ground movement, following the stress relief. This observation raised questions regarding the effectiveness of partial stress relief to reduce stresses and strains associated with ground movements. Finite element analysis (FEA) was conducted in 2016 to aid in assessing the condition of the pipeline after being subject to ground displacements prior to 2014, stress relief in 2014, and subsequent ground displacement from July 2014 to December 2016. The results and findings of the FEA reasonably matched the observed pipeline behaviour before and after stress relief in the lower slope. The FEA results demonstrated that while the lateral displacement of the pipeline, originally caused by ground movement, increased following the removal of the soil loading during the stress relief, the maximum pipeline strain was reduced within the excavated portion.

The FEA was also employed to assess the pipeline response to potential ground displacement scenarios following December 2016. For this assessment, three ground displacement scenarios that comprise different lengths of the pipeline were analyzed. An increased rate of ground displacement, with a pattern that matched one of the analyzed scenarios, was observed in the upper slope in the spring of 2017. The results of FEA were used to assess the pipeline response to the increased rate of displacement in the upper slope. Subsequently a decision was made to stress-relieve the pipeline. The second stress-relief was conducted in the summer of 2017. This stress relief was conducted locally at the toe and head of the active slide in the upper slope, where the FEA showed the greatest stress concentrations in the pipeline.

INTRODUCTION

The Wapiti River South Slope is approximately 500 m long, 130 m high, and with an average incline of 20° and 11° at the lower and upper sections of the slope, respectively. A 3D LiDAR® view of the slope and the pipeline route is shown in Figure 1. The upper and lower slopes are marked in this figure. At this site, Alliance's NPS 42 pipeline (the pipeline) runs parallel and approximately 24 m to the west of a third-party NPS 12 Crude/NGL pipeline both of which are oriented approximately 8° to the slope fall line. The pipeline was installed in the winter of 2000 and hydrotested in the spring of 2000.

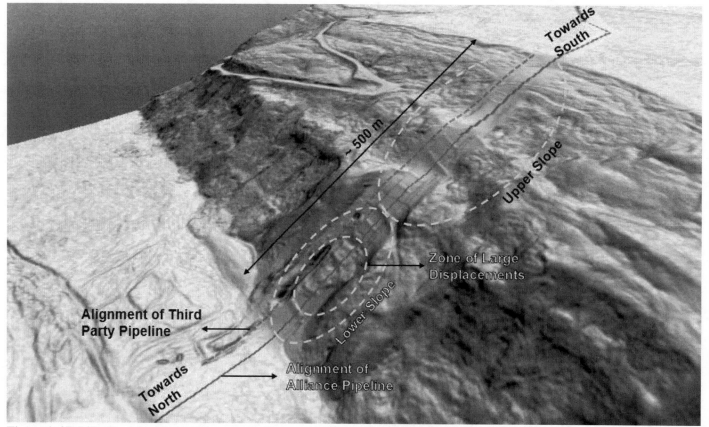

Figure 1. 3D LiDAR of the Wapiti River South Slope and Alliance's 42" Mainline

Regular inspections of the slope conducted between 2007 and 2014, including slope surveys since 2009, indicated a zone of active slope movement in the lower part of the slope. The active zone included the entire lower slope and extended approximately 80 m into the upper slope. The displacement was limited to several centimeters prior to 2012. A zone of large ground movement formed between 2012 and 2014. The zone intersected approximately 40 to 50 m of the pipeline at the toe of the slope, with tension cracks, head scarps and several meters of measured ground movement.

In 2014 the third-party NPS 12 pipeline, located adjacent and approximately 24 m to the east of the Alliance pipeline, was investigated and repaired. The activities associated with this repair caused an acceleration of landslide movement in the lower slope, observed visually, which raised additional concerns regarding the integrity of the pipeline. As a result, Alliance completed a partial stress relief over an 80 m section of their pipeline, extending approximately 20 m upslope and downslope of the visible slide margins. In early 2017, finite element analysis (FEA) was conducted to:
- better understand the stress and strain state of the pipe following the landslide movement in the lower slope and subsequent stress relief,
- estimate the most recent stress and strain state of the pipe in the lower and upper slopes at the time of modeling (until December 2016), and

- assess the pipeline response to potential ground displacement scenarios following December 2016.

In spring of 2017, an increase in the rate of ground displacement in the upper slope was observed, most likely associated with heavy precipitations. The increased rate of ground movement in the upper slope prompted a second stress relief that was conducted in June 2017. The extent and location of this stress relief was decided based on the results of FEA.

This paper presents the results of the FEA, with specific focus on the behavior of the pipeline subject to the large ground movement in the lower slope, and the effect of the first stress relief on the pipe stresses and strains. The results of the FEA are then compared with the survey data, and field observations during and after stress relief.

GEOLOGICAL SETTING

A geological model of the slope was established after a detailed assessment of the historical borehole data, instrumentation, and regional geology. The geological model indicated two distinct slide mechanisms governing the ground displacement, as shown schematically in Figure 2:
- In the lower slope (below elevation 611 m) where the valley is incised into the bedrock, there is a shallow translational slide (i.e. failure surface sub-parallel to the slope) within the colluvium layer that is draped over a stable bedrock formation.

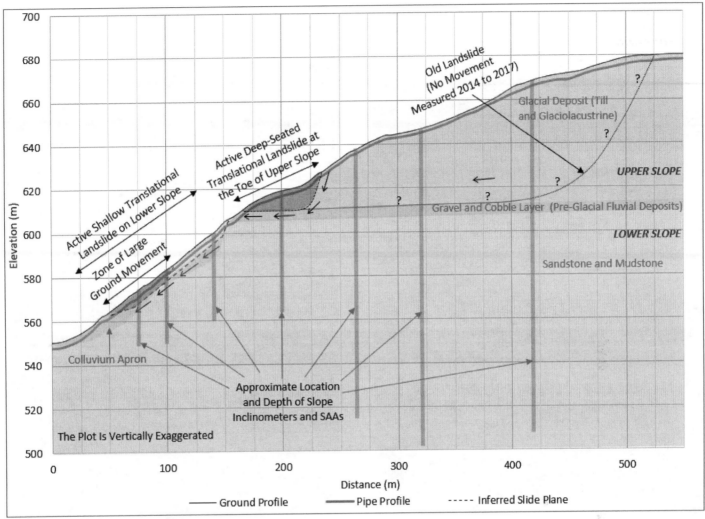

Figure 2. Schematic Configuration of Slope and Slide Zones

This slide moves towards the northeast and is orientated approximately 10° to 15° to the pipeline axis. This slide feature intersects approximately 90 m of the pipeline between elevations 565 m and 605 m and is referred to as "the lower slide" in this paper. The zone of large ground movement is located within the lower portion of the lower slide and is referred to as "the zone of large displacements" in this paper. Slope inclinometer (SI) and ShapeAccelArray (SAA) measurements confirmed that the shallow slide extends below the pipeline level.

- In the upper slope (above elevation 611 m), there is a separate slide feature that is characterized as an active deep-seated translational slide within glaciolacustrine and glacial till deposits. This slide intersects approximately 80 m of the pipeline between elevations 611 m and 628 m. The failure surface of this deep-seated slide is immediately above a pre-glacial fluvial (sand and gravel) unit. This slide is oriented towards the Northeast, approximately 30° to 35° to the pipeline axis. This slide is referred to as "the upper slide" in this

paper. Review of the overall topography shows a historical slide that extends to the top of the slope at elevation 680 m. Slope inclinometers and survey monitoring suggest that the slide above elevation 628 m is likely dormant at this time.

2014 STRESS RELIEF AND OBSERVATIONS

Conventional slope monitoring surveys were ongoing since 2009. The 2014 survey indicated that the total surface movement between 2009 and 2014 on the lower slope below elevation 590 m (within the zone of large displacements) was 2 to 3 m. The ground movement in the same period, immediately upslope of the zone of large displacements, between elevation 590 m and 611 m, was 0.1 to 0.2 m. Movements increased each year after 2010, with the highest magnitudes measured in the zone of large displacements between 2013 and 2014. Additional ground movement was measured following the 2014 survey during the ground disturbance and pipeline repair on the adjacent third-party RoW in 2014.

The pipeline is located on the (west) margin of the zone of large ground displacements where soil was observed to drop down and move away from the pipeline. Figure 3 provides an aerial view of the slope immediately prior to the stress relief.

Figure 3. Overview of the Slope Prior to Stress Relief - Looking South from Downslope, The Pipeline Alignment is shown in Red (Image Date: May 20, 2014)

The adjacent third-party pipeline is to the left in this photo. There was little observational evidence at the time to confirm whether the Alliance pipeline was displaced by the ground movement leading up to June 2014. Nevertheless, an 80 m length of the pipeline was stress relieved in June 2014.

No detailed monitoring was conducted during the stress relief to document pipeline movement as the soil restraint was removed. Visual observations did not show noticeable pipeline movement during stress relief, or evidence of damage to the fusion bonded epoxy coating, which could be indicative of large plastic strain accumulation due to ground movement.

Review of site photos and surveys of the pipeline centerline following the stress relief showed a lateral bend with a magnitude of approximately 0.5 m to the east, over a length of approximately 80 m. Figure 4 illustrates the pipeline lateral bend following the stress relief. The original pipeline alignment in the vertical plane included several field bends; hence small variation

in vertical alignment following stress relief could not be detected in visual observations or survey data. Construction records show that the pipeline at the time of installation was straight in the horizontal plane at this location.

Figure 4. Overview of the Exposed Pipeline – Looking South from Downslope. The Yellow Line Indicates the Assumed Original Straight-Line Position of the Pipeline (Image Date: June 14, 2014)

The shape, direction, and pattern of the lateral misalignment, observed in site photos and survey data matches the extent and orientation of ground displacement within the zone of large ground displacement, which supports the pipeline deformation being caused by soil loading. The fact that the misalignment was recorded following the stress relief, suggests that a pipeline rebound to pre-loading conditions did not occur, and raised questions regarding the effectiveness of the stress relief.

The pipeline was instrumented with strain gauges after stress relief and before backfilling. A total of 42 vibrating wire coaxial strain gauges were installed at seven locations along the excavated section of the pipeline. At each location, strain gauge pairs were installed at 0°, 90°, and 270°. The strain gauges were installed on laterally deformed pipe as explained above.

Monitoring of the strain gauges indicated some minor strain accumulation during pipeline backfilling in June 2014. There has been little to no evidence of ground movements impacting the pipeline since the pipeline backfilling in June 2014.

Alliance completed construction of several subsurface drains on the lower slope during and after stress relief. Ground survey and monitoring of slope inclinometers after mitigative works on the slope in the summer of 2014 until December 2016 indicated a significant decrease in the rate of movement in the lower slope. Ground movement in the lower slope following the stress relief was approximately 50 mm over a period of two years, compared to approximately 2 m of displacement over the one-year period prior to stress relief. The orientation of ground movement in the lower slope was similar to that prior to stress relief.

2017 STRESS RELIEF AND OBSERVATIONS

An acceleration in ground movement was observed in the spring of 2017 at an SAA installed in the lower part of the upper slope. This accelerated movement prompted a series of ground inspections which identified active slope movement between approximate elevations of 611 m and 628 m. The zone of active movement is located at the toe of a larger, deep-seated historical landslide on the upper slope. More than 300 mm of cumulative movement occurred between April 20 and June 6, 2017 which is greater than the displacement over the 30 month period prior to April 20, 2017. Based on the observed surface expression and a horizontal failure plane near elevation of 611 m, the active landslide is estimated to be about 70 m long, 70 m wide and up to 8 m deep (See Figure 2).

As a result of the increased ground movement rate, Alliance initiated a pipeline stress relief to reduce localized strain on the pipeline. The stress relief was conducted across two sections of the pipeline coincident with the crest and the toe of the visibly active landslide. The first excavation was conducted at the crest between elevations 617 m and 628 m with a total exposed length of 42 m. The excavation at the toe was conducted next, between elevations 600 and 611 m, with a total exposed length of 35 m.

The pipeline was surveyed during and after completion of stress relief. At the crest excavation, a sag bend in the alignment with a vertical downward magnitude of approximately 2 m was observed. The change in the pipeline position at the crest during the excavation process was negligible (less than 1 cm). The sag bend at the crest is a field bend, unrelated to ground movement.

At the toe, a gentle overbend was observed, with a total post-excavation magnitude of approximately 0.4 m. During the excavation, an upward movement of up to 0.1 m was recorded. Additionally, a gap of up to 0.3 m was observed below the pipeline in the middle of the toe excavation. The gap and lifting of the pipeline, and the gentle overbend at the toe were likely associated with the bending on the pipeline induced by the horizontal shear plane at approximate elevation of 611 m, the compressional load on the pipeline at the toe of the landslide induced by downward movement of the slide, and the removal of the soil restraint during the excavation. Visual observations did not show evidence of damage to the fusion bonded epoxy coating, which could be indicative of large plastic strain accumulation due to ground movement. Figure 5 shows the

pipeline condition at the toe following completion of the excavation.

Prior to backfilling, the pipeline was instrumented with 18 strain gauges at three discrete locations, including one location within the crest excavation and two locations within the toe excavation. Each location comprises a pair of gauges on top of the pipeline (0°) and a pair of gauges on each side (90° and 270°). Monitoring of the strain gauges in 2017 indicated some minor strain accumulation during pipeline backfilling, with little to no evidence of ground movements impacting the pipeline since installation.

Figure 5.   Overview of the Exposed Pipeline – Looking Northwest from Upslope (Image Date: June 16, 2014)

PIPE STRESS ANALYSIS

Model Specifications and Input Parameters

The finite element analysis (FEA) was conducted in early 2017, prior to accelerated ground movement in the upper slope and subsequent stress relief. The intention of the modelling was to assess the response of the pipeline to known ground displacements at the time of modeling and predict the response of the pipeline to potential subsequent displacements. Although the modelling was conducted following large ground displacement in the lower slope and stress relief procedure in 2014, no adjustment in the model input parameters was done to "match" the results to observations, making the modelling a Class B prediction of the pipeline response to ground displacements and stress relief before December 2016, and Class A prediction of response of pipeline to ground displacements after December 2016.

The FEA was conducted using ANSYS [1]. The pipe stress analysis accounted for inelastic pipeline behavior, the nonlinear behavior of the surrounding soil mass, and large displacement effects. Specifically:

- Bilinear (elastic - fully plastic) spring elements were used to simulate soil restraints (COMBIN39 elements). Hyperbolic soil springs were first calculated using estimated soil properties along the slope and surveyed depth of cover over the pipeline as per Audibert et al. [2] and C-Core et al. [3]. The equivalent bilinear springs were then developed as per recommendations by Thomas [4].
- Plastic pipe elements were used to represent the pipeline behaviour (PIPE20 elements). In absence of a product-specific stress-strain curve, a generic Ramberg-Osgood curve that represents the lower limit of the specified steel was used in the analysis. The pipe diameter, wall thickness, and steel grade at this slope are 1067 mm, 11.43 mm, and X70, respectively.
- The large displacement analysis option of ANSYS was used to account for the geometric changes in stiffness due to large transverse movements of the pipe, if required.

In the analyses, each soil spring set comprises three spring elements representing axial, horizontal, and vertical soil restraint. Each spring element has one node attached to the pipe element and the other attached to a rigid beam. The use of a rigid beam facilitates the input of ground displacement patterns in the global coordinate system instead of the local pipe element coordinate system.

The spring parameters were developed for flat ground. At this site, the ground slope and ground deformation are sub-parallel to the pipeline alignment, resulting in minimal effect of ground slope on spring parameters. However, it should be noted that the effect of ground slope on spring parameters was not explicitly assessed in this study.

The 3D finite element model includes approximately 1200 m of the pipeline, extending 300 m downslope and 500 m upslope of the zone of potential ground movement. The extent of the modelled pipeline route is shown in Figure 1. The end conditions were "fixed" at the model boundaries. The sharp horizontal bend upslope and the vertical bend downslope act as anchors for the pipeline section within the slope, minimizing the effect of boundary conditions on pipeline response. Reaction loads at the boundaries were checked after each stage of loading and did not show any appreciable change, confirming negligible effect of the boundary conditions on pipeline response.

The 3D geometry of the pipeline was modelled using the results of pipe and ground surveys. The survey results include both grade elevation and the depth of cover measurement using a pipeline locator. The depth of cover over the zone of ground movement varies between 1.0 and 1.5 m.

The soil at the pipe level in both the upper and lower slopes is best described as low plasticity clay (CL) in the Unified Soil Classification System (USCS), based on grain size analysis and Atterberg limits from soil index testing.

The rate of ground movement is generally considered slow, which allows dissipation of shear-induced pore water pressure in the soil; hence, the loading can be considered drained. For drained loading conditions, effective stress parameters should be used to calculate soil strength and associated soil spring parameters. Considering the magnitude of ground movement, the normal stress at the pipe level, and the soil properties from limited laboratory testing, an effective secant friction angle, φ', of $28°$ (with zero cohesion) and a wet unit weight, γ', of 18 kN/m^3 were assumed for drained analysis.

Modelling Approach and Loading Stages

To properly assess the condition of the pipeline at the time of modeling and to incorporate potential ground displacements in the future, the analysis was conducted in five stages:
- Stage 1 included application of operational loads. A differential temperature of +25°C between installation and operation (considering winter installation) and an internal operating pressure of 8,275 kPa were applied.
- In Stage 2, known ground displacement activity up to May 2014 was applied to the pipeline. The applied displacement is based on survey measurements since 2009. The displacement profile included 2 m of ground displacement between elevations 565 m and 590 m (zone of large ground movement), and 0.1 m of ground displacement between elevations 590 m and 630 m (the upper part of the lower slope and the active portion of the upper slide). Ground displacement vectors were considered parallel to the ground surface, and oriented 10° and 30° to the east of the pipeline alignment in the lower and the upper slopes, respectively.
- Stage 3 modeled the stress relief in the lower part of the lower slope in June 2014. This is considered a "partial" stress relief, as it only offsets the soil loads within the zone of large ground displacements at the bottom of the slope. The stress relief comprised a length of approximately 80 m of the pipeline between elevations of 560 m and 590 m. To replicate stress relief and excavation procedure in the FEA model, the first set of soil springs (including axial, horizontal, and vertical spring elements) at the top of the slope was detached (using EKILL command) and the model was analyzed to reach equilibrium, before removing the next set of springs. This procedure was repeated until all soil spring sets within the zone of stress relief were detached from the pipeline.

  After the stress relief procedure, the pipeline was partially in contact with the soil beneath. In order to assess the effect of vertical bearing, the analysis of this stage was repeated without gravity. The results show slightly less vertical downward deformation (less than 0.1 m along the exposed length) and negligible change in strain profile.
- Stage 4 modeled backfilling of the excavated pipeline and application of ground movement from June 2014 to December 2016. The backfilling procedure was modeled by attaching new sets of soil springs to the partial stress relief zone (using EALIVE command).
- Stage 5 modeled potential scenarios of ground displacement in the upper slope after December 2016.

Survey results following slope remediation in 2014 indicated that ground movement in the lower slope was minimal, likely due to the slope mitigation conducted following the first stress relief, hence no ground displacement was applied in the lower slope for the potential future scenarios. Three scenarios were considered for this stage. Scenario 1 assumes that the ground displacement in the upper slope follows the same pattern as Stage 4 loading, extending to elevation 628 m and with a total length of approximately 70 m. Scenarios 2 and 3 assume progression of the upper slope slide up to the flat bench at elevation 647 m, and up to the top of the slope at elevation 680 m, respectively. The length of the pipeline subject to the upper slope slide in these scenarios was approximately 150 m and 350 m, respectively. The extent of the potential slide zone in Scenarios 2 and 3 was assumed based on the interpreted extent of previously active slides as suggested by the topography (i.e. flat bench at elevation 647 m, and top of the historical slide at 680 m). In all three scenarios the slide movement is assumed to be 35° oblique to the pipeline, have a dip angle of 45° at the headscarp, and extend to the sub-horizontal cobble and gravel layer at elevation 611 m. In all scenarios, ground displacement was gradually increased following the assumed pattern until a maximum displacement of 2 m is reached.

Model Results

The applied ground displacement during Stage 2 results in lateral and vertical deformation along the pipeline is shown in Figure 6. The profile of the ground displacement component transverse to the pipeline alignment is also overlain in this figure. Maximum lateral and vertical displacements along the pipeline are 0.35 m (Point A in Figure 6) and 0.23 m (Point B Figure 6). The lateral deformation of the pipeline follows the same pattern as the lateral component of the ground displacement.

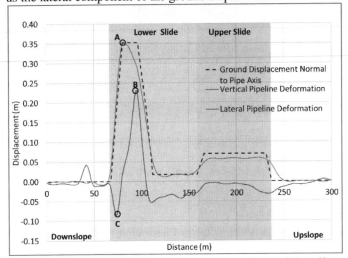

Figure 6. Pipeline Deformation Profile after Stage 2 Loading

Ground displacement in the lower slide is applied parallel to the ground surface and does not have a perpendicular component to the pipeline axis in the vertical plane. Despite loading that is parallel to the slope, noticeable vertical deformation in the pipeline is observed at the lower section of the slope (Points B and C). This vertical deformation is associated with the compression in the pipeline at the bottom of the loading zone. The applied ground displacement profile has an angle of 10° to 35° relative to the pipeline axis and includes a large component that is parallel to the pipeline axis (which is not shown in Figure 6). This longitudinal component of ground displacement generates axial tensile and compressive forces at the head and at the toe of the slide, respectively. The compressive force at the toe can result in lateral or vertical buckling.

Compressive buckling typically occurs in the vertical plane, as observed here in the FEA model, due to lower vertical soil restraints and preexisting vertical misalignments along the pipeline. The location of the maximum vertical deformation within the compression zone is generally at the point of maximum preexisting vertical misalignment in the pipeline. The preexisting misalignment also affects the shape and magnitude of vertical deformation in the initial stages of loading. The presence of a preexisting misalignment results in a gradual formation and increase of vertical deformation as ground displacement increases; whereas in a straighter pipeline, vertical deformation may occur suddenly in the form of a snap-through upheaval buckling.

The maximum tensile and compressive strains along the pipeline, associated with the operational loads and ground movement between 2009 and 2014, are shown in Figure 7.

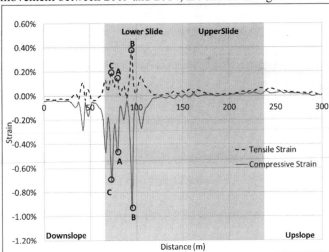

Figure 7. Strain Profile after Stage 2 Loading

The two highest strain peaks in Figure 7 are associated with the vertical bends (Points B and C) and the third peak is associated with the lateral bend (Point A). Considering 0.2% to 0.5% as the threshold for onset of plastic deformation, the results indicate that several points along the pipeline experienced plastic deformation. Relatively large strains (0.2% to 0.9%) along the pipeline at the end of Stage 2 are due to a combination of the following:

- large lateral soil loads (up to 200 kN/m) over a section of approximately 40 m at the bottom of the lower slide movement zone,
- longitudinal soil loads over a length of approximately 170 m along the pipeline, and
- initial vertical misalignment along the pipeline which triggered vertical deformations.

The lateral and vertical pipeline deformation profiles after the stress relief process (Stage 3) are presented in Figure 8. The zone of stress relief (in dashed blue line) and profile of the transverse component of applied ground displacement prior to stress relief are also overlain in this figure. The maximum lateral and vertical deformations after Stage 3 loading are 0.6 m (Point A) and 0.2 m (Point C), respectively. The lateral deformation of 0.6 m in the FEA model matched observed lateral displacement in post stress relief photos as shown in Figure 4 and pipeline survey as shown in Figure 9.

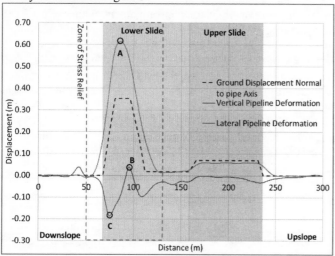

Figure 8. Pipeline deformation Profile after Stage 3 Loading

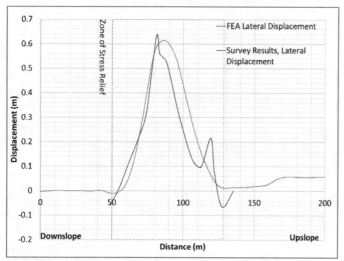

Figure 9. Comparison of Survey Results and FEA Results

Despite detaching all spring elements, including vertical spring elements, no global upheaval (or vertical downward) buckling was observed in the model, which matches field observations. As noted above, the model may generally predict vertical deformations greater than those in the field, due to removal of partial bearing soil restraints. However the shape and the pattern of vertical deformation, including magnitude of differential deformation between Points B and C are properly captured in this model, and confirmed by a second model without gravity.

Of note, the maximum lateral displacement actually increased with stress relief, whereas the maximum vertical displacement decreased compared to the end of Stage 2 loading. The overall shape of the vertical and lateral deformation profiles is similar to that prior to the stress relief; however, the profile after removing lateral and vertical soil restraints is smoother at the location of high deformation gradients (e.g. points A, B, and C). The smoother profile is due to a combination of removing soil restraints, response of the free-span section of the pipeline to gravity and operational loading (i.e. internal pressure and thermal differential), and compression loading from ground displacement upslope of the stress relief zone.

Maximum tensile and compressive strains along the pipeline are shown in Figure 10. Maximum strain at points A, B, and C decreased by approximately 0.15% to 0.2%, which is associated with the rebound of the elastic portion of strain following the pipeline exposure and removal of soil restraints. However, a substantial portion of the strain at these locations, which is mostly plastic strain, remains in the pipeline after stress relief.

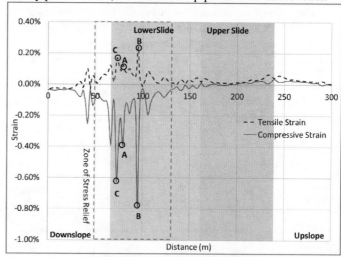

Figure 10. Strain Profile after Stage 3 Loading

Following the pipeline stress relief and backfilling, ground displacement continued upslope of the zone of stress relief. Small displacements were also measured within the zone of the stress relief. The total lateral and vertical pipeline deformations at the end of Stage 4 loading are shown in Figure 11. Transverse ground displacement profiles from Stage 2 (prior to stress relief) and Stage 4 (after stress relief until December 2016) are overlain in this figure. The pipe deformation in the lower slope and within the zone of the previous stress relief is similar to that of Stage 3. However, upslope of the zone of the first stress relief, the pipe in the upper slide deforms further laterally and vertically, conforming with the pattern of the applied ground displacement.

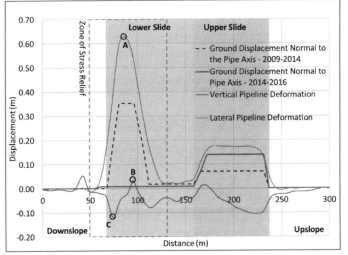

Figure 11. Pipeline deformation Profile after Stage 4 Loading

Maximum tensile and compressive strains along the pipeline at the end of Stage 4 (associated with loading on the pipe from 2009 to December 2016) are shown in Figure 12. The strain profile along the lower slope and within the zone of the first stress relief is similar to that of Stage 3. A zone of elevated strain is noticeable at a distance of 230 m to 240 m, which is associated with the bending at the top of the upper slide. The displacement profile of Stage 4 forms an abrupt boundary at the top of the upper slide and has a component that is perpendicular to the pipe.

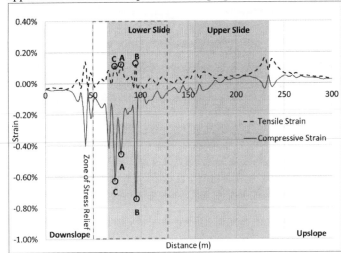

Figure 12. Strain Profile after Stage 4 Loading

The minor change of strain profile in the lower slope indicates that the ground movement in the upper slope has negligible effect on pipeline strains in the lower slope. This finding is in agreement with the strain gauge data, which indicated less than 200 micro-strain (or 0.02%) variation after installation and backfilling in June 2014 until December 2016.

As expected, minor accumulation of strain up to 0.03% was observed in strain gauges immediately after backfilling.

The assumptions and rationale regarding loading scenarios in Stage 5 were discussed in the previous section. Applied maximum ground displacement profiles for the three assumed scenarios are shown in Figure 13. The displacements in each scenario were increased gradually, following the pattern shown in this figure, until maximum displacement values were reached. Strain profiles at the end of the loading indicated that the maximum stresses and strains on the pipe in all three scenarios occurred at the top and at the toe of the slide zones, where the bending moment associated with the differential transverse and vertical ground movements (i.e. transition between stable and moving ground) are highest. As an example, the strain profile at the end of loading in Scenario 1 is shown in Figure 14. The ground displacement in the upper slope had negligible effect on the strains in the lower slope.

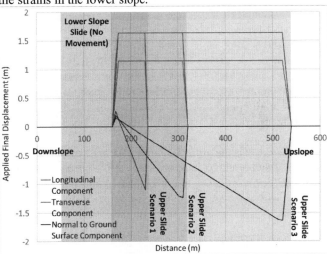

Figure 13. Ground Displacement Profiles of Stage 5

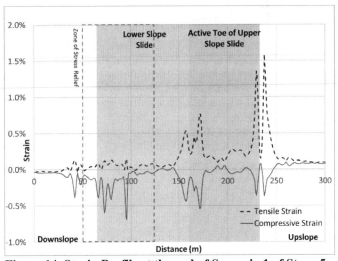

Figure 14. Strain Profile at the end of Scenario 1 of Stage 5

Variation of maximum tensile and compressive strains with ground displacement magnitude for each scenario are shown in

Figures 15 to 17. Compressive and tensile strains at the top of the slide in Scenario 2 are similar to those of Scenario 1, which indicates that the strains at the top of the slide are mainly governed by bending associated with the transverse and vertical components of ground movement. However, strains at the toe of the slide are greater in Scenario 2 due to the effect of the longitudinal component of ground movement and compression at the bottom of the slide, which results in reduction of bending capacity of the pipe and induces lateral and vertical buckling and associated bending strains.

In Scenario 3, the longitudinal component of ground movement significantly affects strains. Due to the axial tensile loads associated with the longitudinal component of ground movement, the entire cross section of the pipe at the top of the slide is in tension. At the bottom of the slide, large compression loads associated with the longitudinal component of ground movement result in significant loss of bending capacity of the pipe and subsequently large lateral and vertical displacement and associated bending strains. As such, maximum compression strain at the bottom of the slide, even after 0.4 m of ground displacements, is greater than that observed at the end of Scenarios 1 and 2 loading with 2 m of ground displacement.

The pattern of the accelerated ground displacement observed in the spring of 2017 matched the analyzed Scenario 1 loading in Stage 5. Measured maximum ground displacement between December 2016 and June 2017, just before the second stress relief, was in the order 300 mm. Although the strains were considered to be within the acceptable range for the measured displacements, the decision to conduct a stress relief was made considering the increased rate of ground displacement and pre-existing strains associated with potential unmeasured displacements.

SUMMARY AND CONCLUSION

Site investigations and ground monitoring since 2007 indicate different slide mechanisms in the lower slope and the upper slope governing the ground displacement:

- In the lower slope, a shallow translational slide is occurring within a colluvium layer. Approximately 80 m of the pipeline within the lower slope, which includes a zone of large displacements (up to several meters) was stress relieved in May 2014. Slope stabilization measures following the stress relief significantly reduced the rate of movement in the lower slope.
- In the upper slope, there is a deep-seated translational slide occurring within glacial deposits. The lower section of the upper slope is actively moving, with a rate that is much lower than that observed in the zone of large displacements in the lower slope between 2012 and 2014. The rate of displacement in the active section of the upper slope significantly increased in the spring of 2017, which resulted in a second stress relief at this site.

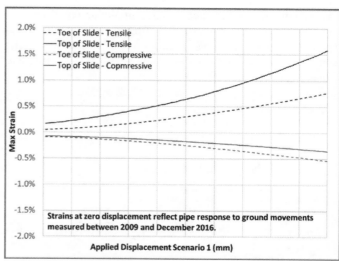

Figure 15. Strain versus Displacement – Scenario 1, Stage 5

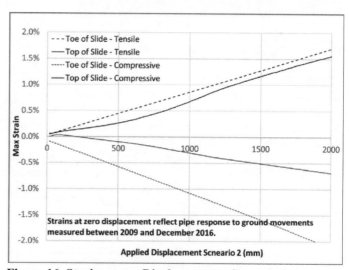

Figure 16. Strain versus Displacement – Scenario 2, Stage 5

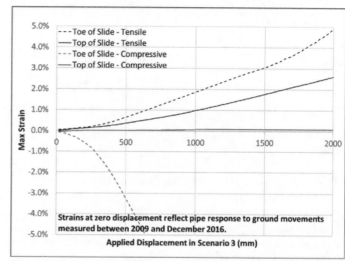

Figure 17. Strain versus Displacement – Scenario 3, Stage 5

Following the first stress relief in the lower slope, the exposed pipeline exhibited a lateral deformation of approximately 0.5 m over a length of approximately 80 m. The direction and pattern of lateral pipeline deformation matches the pattern and direction of ground movement, demonstrating that it was caused by soil loads on the pipeline. In addition, the observed pipeline deformation following stress relief suggests that the pipeline did not rebound to its original position.

The second stress relief was conducted further upslope over a 42 m length of pipeline at the head and a 35 m length of pipeline at the toe of the active slide. Little deformation was recorded during the excavation at the head of the landslide. At the toe, an overbend with a vertical magnitude of approximately 0.4 m was recorded at the end of excavation process, most of which (approximately 0.3 m) occurred during the excavation. The upward displacement at the toe, which occurring during the excavation, is an expected behaviour, associated with the compression and bending in vertical plane, and removal of soil restraint during the pipeline exposure.

FEA was conducted in early 2017 to assess the effect of ground movement and subsequent stress relief on the pipe at the lower slope. Ground displacements measured using surveys and instrumentation between 2009 and December 2016 were applied in the FEA model. Results of the FEA were in agreement with the survey results and field observations, and showed that:

- The slide movement in the lower slope produced a lateral deflection of approximately 0.35 m over an 80 m length, in the direction of ground movement.
- The stress relief in the lower slope caused the deflection to increase from 0.35 m to 0.6 m.
- Despite the increase in lateral deformation, the maximum strain in the pipe decreased from 0.9% to 0.7%. The strain reduction is associated with the rebound of the elastic component of the pipeline deformations, while the residual strain after the stress relief is associated with the non-reversible plastic deformations.
- The maximum strain was not at the point of maximum lateral deformation but occurred instead at the point of maximum vertical deformation, which was smaller in magnitude, but over a shorter length and with a greater curvature.
- A comparison of the pipeline profile before and after the first stress relief indicated that the lateral and vertical deformation profiles became smoother after removing soil restraints, despite the greater maximum pipe deformation. This behaviour is due to a combination of the residual plastic strains in the pipe, and the response of the free-span section of the pipeline to operational loading (i.e. internal pressure and thermal differential) and the compression loading from ground displacement upslope of the stress relief zone.
- Results of the FEA after the 2014 stress relief until December 2016 (Stage 4) indicated minimal change in pipeline strain in the lower slope which aligns with the strain gauge data where less than 0.02% strain variation was measured since installation and backfilling in June 2014 to December 2016.

The FEA was extended to predict the response of the pipeline to potential future ground displacements. Three ground displacement scenarios in the upper slope with different slide lengths were considered for analysis. The results of the analysis indicated that:

- The largest strains occur at the head and toe of the slide zone where the differential transverse and vertical ground movements are maximum (i.e. transition between stable and moving ground)
- The strains at the head of the slide zone increase gradually with the magnitude of ground movement. Regardless of the length of the slide zone, after 2 m of ground movement, the tensile and compressive strains at the head of the slide zone remain below 2.5% and 1%, respectively.
- Unlike the strains at the head, the length of the slide zone has a significant impact on the strains at the toe. As the slide zone increases in length, the larger compression loads associated with the longitudinal component of ground movement results in significant loss of bending capacity of the pipe and subsequently large lateral and vertical displacement and associated bending strains at the toe.
- The pattern and extent of the ground movement observed in the spring of 2017 matched one of the analyzed scenarios. The results of the FEA guided the decision on timing and location of the second stress relief in the upper slope.

ACKNOWLEDGMENTS

The authors would like to thank Mr. Doug Honegger of D.G.Honegger Consulting for performing the numerical analysis and providing valuable feedback during this project. The authors would also like to thank Alliance for permission to use the information in this paper.

REFERENCES

[1] ANSYS Inc. 2010. www.ansys.com.

[2] Audibert, J.M.E. Nyman, D.J. O'Rourke, T.D. "Differential Ground Movement Effects on Buried Pipelines". *Guidelines for the Seismic Design of Oil and Gas Pipeline Systems*. American Society of Civil Engineers - Committee on Gas and Liquid Fuel Lifelines. NY (1984) pp 150-228.

[3] C-Core. D.G.Honegger Consulting. SSD Inc. *Guidelines for Constructing Natural Gas and Liquid Hydrocarbon Pipelines Through Areas Prone to Landslide and Subsidence Hazards*. Pipeline Research Council International. (2009).

[4] Thomas, H.O. "Discussion of Soil Restraint against Horizontal Motion of Pipes by M.E. Audibert and K.J. Nyman", *Journal of the Geotechnical Engineering Division*. ASCE. Vol. 104, No. GT9 (1978): pp. 1214-1216.

This page left blank intentionally.

IPG2019-5342

NATECH RISK MANAGEMENT ON PIPELINES OF CENIT

Jaime Aristizabal Ceballos[1], Julian Fernando Chaves Agudelo,
Carlos Eduardo Motta Tierradentro, Maria Isabel Montoya Rodríguez[2]
Cenit Transporte y Logística de Hidrocarburos
Bogotá D.C. Colombia

ABSTRACT

In recent years, the Colombian government has strengthened its legislation moving towards a disaster risk management system (Law 1523 in 2012) and has established guidelines on the role of public and private entities (decree 2157 in 2017) when defining the structure of disaster risk management plans. This paper presents the advancements on Natech risk management implementation in Cenit (major Colombian pipeline operator of hydrocarbons transport), to identify areas of potential disaster based on the application of its geohazards assessment model that considers prevention specific elements and consequence analysis.

Keywords: Natech, Geohazards Management.

INTRODUCTION

Natechs are chemical accidents triggered by natural hazards (geohazards for us). Petroleum industry, risk management and assessment plans consider separately both (chemical accidents and geohazards). In the risk equation where consequences and failure probability are products, about each component of the equation there is an extensive bibliography in technical literature that can be consulted. These allows to identify emergency response or integrity mitigation plans to reduce risk. So, recently models had been developed to consider the impact of geohazards in the risk. In the last IPG version a paper was presented with a probabilistic approach for geohazard assessment in Cenit pipelines using a Bayesian Belief Network [1]. To apply this model in the construction of a disaster risk management plan was necessary to modify its structure by generating a new node to independently assess the impact of Right of Way (ROW) inspection findings and the pipeline vulnerability on failure probability considered by the risk model.

This paper presents the process to identify areas of potential disaster and the changes in geohazards assessment model of Cenit required to obtain a supported result that allows the definition of risk-based pipeline intervention actions.

1. BACKGROUND

1.1 Natech Considerations

Statistics indicates that between 1998 and 2017 climate-related and geophysical disasters around the world killed 1.3 million people and left a further 4.4 billion injured, homeless, displaced or in need of emergency assistance. While most fatalities were due to geophysical events (mostly earthquakes and tsunamis) extreme weather events (i.e. floods, storms, droughts, heatwaves) corresponds to 91% of all disasters [2].

Recently, although statistics [3] [4] shows a reduction in the number of disasters triggered by natural hazards and deaths caused by natural disasters, the estimates of natural disaster economic damages had become higher in the last two years like a suggestion of an emerging trend in natural disaster events demonstrating lower mortality but higher cost (see Table 1).

TABLE 1: Statistics of Natural Disasters (adapted from [3] and [4])

	2006-2015 Annual Average	2016	2017
Natural Disasters	376.4	342	335
People killed	69,827	8,733	9,697
Costs (US billion)	137.6	153.9	333,9

---

[1] Contact author: jaime.aristizabal@cenit-transporte.com
[2] Contact author: maria.montoya@cenit-transporte.com

The relationship between Natural disasters and Technological disasters in the American Continent (1900-2018) was presented by [5] (see Figure 1) considering data available on The International Disaster Database (EM-DAT) launched by the Centre for Research on the Epidemiology of Disasters (CRED), part of the Institute for Health and Society of University of Louvain in Brussels (Belgium).

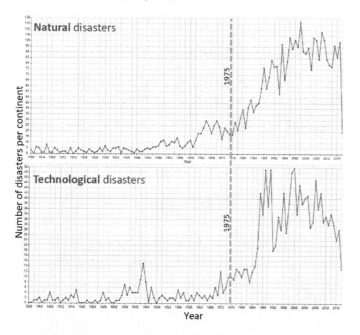

FIGURE 1: Natural and Technological Disasters Relationship Source: [5] and Presentation downloaded in https://natech-workshop.de/session-8-natech-risk-management-the-public-sector-natech-risk-governance-regulation-enforcement on 01/07/2019

This graphical relationship establishes the need to define disaster risk management strategies to consider natural hazard effects on industrial installations (pipelines infrastructure for example). Events like the fire of all Liquefied Petroleum Gas (LPG) tanks in Cosmo Oil Refinery in Japan after the Great East Earthquake (2011) and the flooding in Refinery at Port Arthur after Hurricane Harvey (2017), are some examples that point out this relationship.

Regulatory context of major accident and disasters risk management in Colombia started with a reactive approach, but gradually has become more preventive in order to define policies to minimize and reduce the number of accidents and their possible consequences through risk management [6] (Figure 2).

The creation of a national disaster risk management system in Colombia established the mandatory requirement for all facilities involved in industrial activities, to carry out specific risk analysis (Law 1523 in 2012) considering possible impacts of natural hazards and their consequences on the surrounding areas [5]. Recently with Decree 2157 (2017) a guideline on the role of public and private entities was set to define their disaster risk management plans.

Petroleum industry engagement is necessary not only in the final stage of revision and implementation of the laws and decrees, but from the initial stages where can add value based on its experience on risk management and can support a balanced construction of sharing good practices to be directed towards consolidating a Natech risk management system, and take advantage of increased awareness among governmental organizations on the importance to assessing and managing this kind of risks.

FIGURE 2: Steps to Create a Colombian disaster Risk Management System. [6]

1.2 Cenit Geohazards Assessment Model

This model presented in IPG 2017 [1] is based on structured expert judgment methods integrated with complementary existent models using Bayesian Belief Networks. The sequence of activities shown in Figure 3 were carried out for the conceptualization and construction of the model.

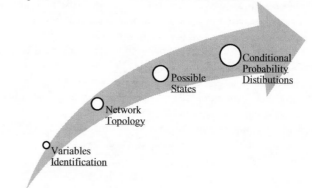

FIGURE 3: Sequence of activities in geohazards model construction

The initial developed model network topology (see Figure 4) for hazard modelling, included four fundamental groups of variables: triggering events, susceptibility, geotechnical events and vulnerability.

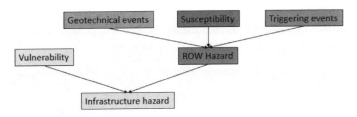

FIGURE 4: Initial Developed Model Network Topology [1]

The variables included on the model are described based on a probabilistic perspective, which includes the uncertainty associated with instability processes, information gathering and analysis and ultimately with risk perception, among others. The results showed that this model has greater sensitivity to the hazard level while being consistent with stability condition of the (ROW) and pipeline exposure.

1.3 Cenit Consequence Analysis

A major part of the hydrocarbons transport infrastructure in Colombia crosses 230 municipalities (representing nearly a quarter of all cities). Infrastructure runs through the Andean Mountains, which form the most populated region of Colombia, including the most important cities e.g. Bogota and Medellin, where delivery of refined products occurs as an economic priority.

In order to complete risk assessment, it is necessary to combine probability of failure obtained from Geohazards Assessment Model with consequence analysis results. This analysis follows the steps indicated in Figure 5 and considers direct or indirect consequences due to effects on people, environment and economy (see Figure 6).

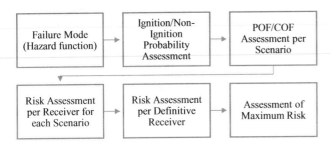

FIGURE 5: Steps in Cenit Risk Assessment

The identification of potential receivers and areas affected due to a loss of containment is the result of quantitative consequence analysis. Several risk scenarios from 1 to 4 (see Figure 7) are considered in order to differentiate the effects on receiver due to failure mode (see Table 2).

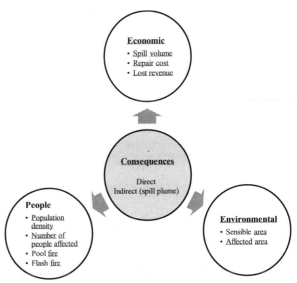

FIGURE 6: Consequence Analysis Overview

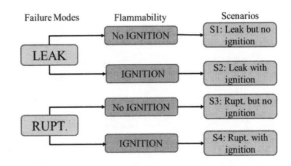

FIGURE 7: Calculation of Risk per Scenario

TABLE 2: Failure Mode and Receiver Considerations

		Rupture	Leakage
Receiver	People	S4	S2
	Environment	S3	S1
	Economic	S3	S1

The above is along with spill volume and spill route are the main elements considered in the estimation of exposure of vulnerable elements. The results obtained guides the preparedness and the definition of prevention strategies in the emergency plans.

2. ANALYSIS OF POTENTIAL MAJOR ACCIDENT AREAS IN CENIT

In order to asses and manage the risk of a pipeline rupture with high consequences either directly or indirectly in the spill route, it is necessary to identify the potential major accident areas, that by definition are the most susceptible segments to geohazards events that would lead to a rupture or leakage impacting a populated area or a high environmentally sensitive area, following the simplified process shown in Figure 8.

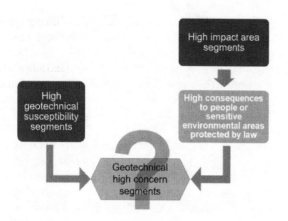

FIGURE 8: Simplified Process Carried out to define major accident potential areas [7].

To apply this simplified process was necessary to adjust the geohazards model structure initially implemented evolving from the showed in Figure 4 to the shown in Figure 9.

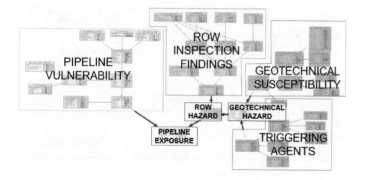

FIGURE 9: Cenit Geohazards Model Structure Adjustment [7]

The Geotechnical Hazard node was included in the model in order to estimate the probability of occurrence of an instability event considering only ROW susceptibility (e.g morphometry, lithology, structural geology, land cover) and its interaction with triggering agents (rainfall, earthquake and man-made). This represents a measure of a potentially damaging processes of a given magnitude in a determined segment of ROW.

The ROW Hazard node now focuses on actual instability processes identifying in ROW inspections. This node is a measure of the geotechnical probability of failure, involving the ROW, of a given damaging process.

The Pipeline Exposure node (former "Infrastructure Hazard" in the first version of the model), represents the probability of a pipeline to fail.

Note that every node like all variables corresponds to a probability distribution in which the results may report the complete distribution with a probability value for each one of the possible states, the most probable state and the expected value.

For decision-making purposes, the most probable state and the mean of each variable are compared. When analysis is highly uncertain, these values might differ and allows to identify zones that needs further assessment.

Based on this model structure a hazard sensibility analysis of the model was completed, through several scenarios that provides the highest and lowest hazards level compared with current condition.

Figure 10 represents the relationship between the Expected Value (E) of Geotechnical Hazard and ROW Hazard nodes useful to identify ROW segments with high potential of instability processes or active geotechnical events.

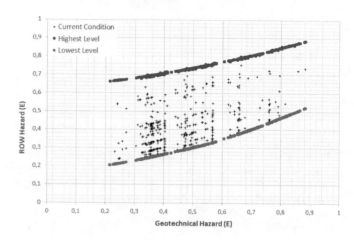

FIGURE 10: Geotechnical Hazard vs ROW Hazard [7]

The lowest dots in this graph represents the output of the Geotechnical Hazard node in which there is no influence of geotechnical findings and the highest dots represents the existence of active events with high severity. This should be considered like lower and upper limits of the model, respectively. Current condition is represented by crosses.

Figure 11 shows the relationship between the Expected Value (E) of ROW Hazard and Pipeline Exposure nodes, useful to identify ROW segments with a high probability of pipeline failure.

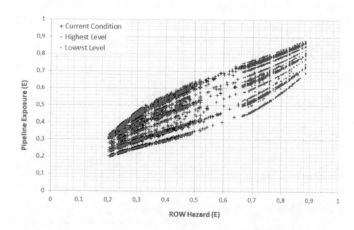

FIGURE 11: ROW Hazard vs Pipeline Exposure [7]

To identify all segments where there is a high probability of pipeline failure due to its interaction with instability processes were considered a combination of ROW Hazard and Pipeline

Exposure expected values (E) and Pipeline Exposure most probable state.

Finally, to define Potential Major Accident Areas obtained segments were crossed with consequences levels equal or greater than 6 in People and Environmental receivers, based on Cenit Risk Matrix. This is a result of combine Probability of Failure (PoF) and Consequences (CoF) as shown if Figure 12.

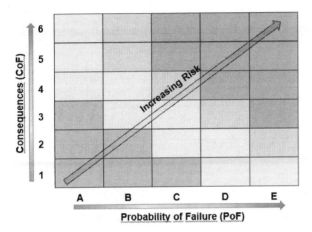

FIGURE 12: Risk Matrix (RAM)

DISCUSSION

As has shown in sections above, geotechnical high concern segments obtained through the simplified process shown in Figure 8 are an effort to carry out risk analysis considering the possible effects of geohazards and its consequences on the surrounding areas of a pipeline infrastructure.

This changes on traditional approaches trough Bayesian belief networks allows the probabilistic modeling of the hazard with an explicit relationship between variables and clarity in the management of the uncertainty associated with instability processes, information gathering and analysis, and hazard perception. Given that the methodology used for the combination of the Conditional Probability Tables is satisfactory to summarize the judgement of the experts consistently is possible to have a differentiated strategy over each pipeline segments as a component of a disaster management plan.

CONCLUSIONS

For the decision-making process supported by the model, it is important to consider the complete behavior of the probability distribution of each node. The greater the dispersion between sites that coincide in their most probable state, further analysis are required since the change in the state of any variable will cause large changes in the hazard levels.

The independent analysis of each node and the understanding of their relationship allows to differentiate existing geotechnical hazard conditions from potential ones.

This assessment supports the decision-making process regarding immediate mitigation actions, short- and long-term remediation plans, and Further Studies.

An advantage of adjusted model is its flexibility and it allows changes in the database. In addition, for continuous improvement is possible to modify the conditional probability tables in order to apply changes in the relationship between variables.

Petroleum industry engagement is necessary not only in the final stage of revision and implementation of the laws and decrees, but from the initial stages where can add value based on its experience on risk management and can support a balanced construction of sharing good practices to be directed towards consolidating a Natech risk management system, and take advantage of increased awareness among governmental organizations on the importance to assessing and managing this kind of risks.

ACKNOWLEDGEMENTS
To Cenit for allowing us to participate in training events, in which knowledge management and share experiences are the key of continuous improvement.

REFERENCES
[1] Chaves et al (2017). *Probabilistic Approach for Assessing the Weather and External Forces Hazard Using Bayesian Belief Networks.* Proceedings of the ASME 2017 International Pipeline Geotechnical Conference. Lima, Perú. July 24-26, 2017

[2] CRED[3] (2018). *Economic Losses, Poverty and Disasters 1998-2017.* Downloaded on https://www.emdat.be/publications or https://cred.be/sites/default/files/CredCrunch52.pdf

[3] CRED[3] (2017). *Annual Disaster Statistical Review 2016 – The numbers and trends.* Downloaded on https://www.emdat.be/sites/default/files/adsr_2016.pdf

[4] CRED[3] (2018). *Natural Disasters 2017- lower mortality, higher cost.* Downloaded on https://www.emdat.be/publications or in http://cred.be/sites/default/files/CredCrunch50.pdf

[5] Suárez, M. et al (2018). *Current Natech Risk Management Status in the Colombian Context: An Overview.* Proceedings of the UN/OECD Workshop Natech Risk Management. Potsdam, Germany. September 5 - 7 2018.

[6] Montoya, M. et al (2018). *Perspectiva de la regulación de accidente mayor en Colombia y el rol de la industria en la gestión de riesgos.* Prepared for Presentation at American Institute of Chemical Engineers 8th Latin American Conference on Process Safety. Buenos Aires, Argentina. September 11-13, 2018.

[7] Aristizábal, J et al (2018). *Decision making methodology for geohazards management and its impact on pipeline integrity.* Proceedings of the UN/OECD Workshop Natech Risk Management. Potsdam, Germany. September 5 - 7 2018.

---

[3] Centre for Research on the Epidemiology of Disasters, Institute for Health and Society, University of Louvain, Brussels, Belgium

This page left blank intentionally.

IPG2019-5346

ENHANCING GEOHAZARD MANAGEMENT PRACTICE FOR SOUTH AMERICAN PIPELINES

Michael Porter[1,2], Elisa Scordo[2], Pete Barlow[3], Daniela Welkner[4], Miguel Leach[5]

[2]BGC Engineering Inc., Vancouver, BC, Canada
[3]BGC Engineering Inc., Edmonton, AB, Canada
[4]BGC Engineering Inc, Santiago, Chile
[4]BGC Engineering Inc, Mendoza, Argentina

ABSTRACT

Pipeline geohazard management practices and technologies have evolved rapidly over the past 15 years in step with industry's drive towards zero failures. This paper describes the evolution in geohazard management for pipelines since the early 2000's and describes how technology and management practices are currently being adapted to accommodate South American site conditions and data sources. It ends by outlining a possible framework for industry, regulatory and academic collaboration within South America that offers the potential for another step-function improvement in pipeline safety.

Keywords: Geohazards, Risk Management, Data Management, Innovation.

INTRODUCTION

Most pipeline systems in South America were constructed during or prior to the early 2000's when geohazard management was just beginning a transition from a reactive to a proactive approach (e.g., [1]). During this transition, pipeline operators began developing systematic geohazard inventories using topographic maps, aerial photographs and maintenance records. However, inventory data were often stored in multiple spreadsheets and desktop databases and geohazards were prioritized based on simple indexing methods capable of generating relative estimates of hazard [1, 2]. Soil-pipe interaction analyses and assessment of in-line inspection (ILI) data were often carried out by personnel who were unfamiliar with landslide mechanisms and other site-specific details contained within the geohazard inventory. Technology for gathering and interpreting large volumes of real-time precipitation, streamflow and other geotechnical instrumentation data to associate with specific geohazard sites was lacking.

Despite these limitations, geohazard management programs implemented in the early 2000's resulted in a reduction of pipeline failure rates by a factor of 2 to 10 on some South American pipeline systems [3, 4].

Geohazard management practices and technologies have evolved rapidly over the past 15 years in step with industry's drive towards zero failures. Some of these advancements include: enhanced inventory and characterization of geotechnical (landslide) and hydrotechnical (watercourse) geohazards using LiDAR (Light Detection and Ranging) and ILI data; creation of intelligent digital stream networks to facilitate calculations of upstream catchment area, stream gradient, process type (i.e. flood, debris flood and debris flow), flood frequency, and bed scour; and data management and predictive quantitative geohazard algorithms using secure web-accessible geospatial databases. Software functionality and tools to allow for near-real time monitoring of streamflow, precipitation, and seismicity have been developed. These tools are currently used to house data and help manage geohazards on several hundred thousand kilometers of pipeline in North America and are starting to be used in South America. Furthermore, improvements in collaboration between personnel conducting geohazard assessments, assessments of ILI data, and pipe stress analysis are resulting in better understanding of pipeline integrity issues and more effective mitigation programs.

This paper describes the evolution in geohazard management for pipelines since the early 2000's and describes how technology and management practices are currently being adapted to accommodate South American site conditions and data sources. It ends by outlining a possible framework for industry, regulatory and academic collaboration within South America that offers the potential for another step-function improvement in pipeline safety.

---

[1] Contact author: mporter@bgcengineering.ca

GEOHAZARD INVENTORIES

Geohazard inventory creation is the starting point for all proactive geohazard management programs. In the absence of rigorous, terrain-based approaches, geohazard inventories would often comprise a list of sites with known past problems and more visually obvious hazard locations, such as the larger rivers and slopes. In order to shift from reactive to proactive geohazard management, it is critical to identify sites where elements are present that have the potential to cause a future threat to the pipeline. A comprehensive inventory and characterization of geohazards allows for a rational prioritization of geohazard sites for assessment, monitoring and mitigation, with the objectives of preventing pipeline exposures, impacts and failures in a cost-effective manner.

In the early 2000's geohazard inventories were largely developed using topographic and geologic maps and stereo aerial photographs. Map scale typically ranged from 1:50,000 to 1:250,000 and aerial photographs were typically 1:20,000 to 1:50,000 scale.

Working at these scales, a typical geohazard inventory for a pipeline constructed through mountainous terrain would usually capture most watercourse crossings with the potential to cause pipeline failure, although small steep streams prone to debris floods and flows would sometimes be missed. As a result, small, headwater streams with the potential to cause pipeline exposure were often not included in the office-based geohazard inventory.

Landslide inventories in mountainous terrain, particularly in areas containing densely tree-covered slopes, would often be incomplete. The spatial extents of some landslides would be underrepresented, and other landslides would be missed entirely.

Two significant advances over the past 15 years are yielding much more robust geohazard inventories: (1) higher-resolution digital stream networks, and (2) digital elevation models (DEMs) created from LiDAR imagery [5].

Regional digital stream networks have been created by many government agencies at a variety of scales and are becoming increasingly accessible (e.g., National Hydrography Dataset). Software tools are being developed to assemble these stream networks over large regions and to extract valuable data from them, including upstream catchment areas, stream gradient, stream segment, Strahler order [6], and morphometrics that provide insight to the potential for debris flow and debris flood hazards [7]. In areas of interest, such as near to pipeline infrastructure, the accuracy of the stream networks can be improved using LiDAR and satellite imagery to correct alignment errors and digitize lower order stream segments. BGC Engineering's (BGC's) River Network Tools™ (RNT) is an example of one of these solutions (Figure 1). RNT is a web-based platform used to generate hydrotechnical information at watercourse crossings throughout North America and parts of South America. A website 'point and click' interface provides visual access to large spatial datasets that include 10 million kilometers of streams and rivers across Canada, USA and Mexico, and 36,000 Water Survey of Canada (WSC) and US Geological Survey (USGS) hydrometric gauging stations. A suite of tools is used to perform analyses such as extraction of channel characteristics, flood frequency analysis, and flood monitoring. These tools allow for the rapid development of hydrotechnical hazard inventories, and quick extraction of relevant watercourse crossing data that can be used to help prioritize each site for follow-up office and field assessment.

Figure 1: DIGITAL STREAM NETWORK IN RIVER NETWORK TOOLS

LiDAR is a laser scanning technique that is capable of producing very high resolution DEMs from airborne or terrestrial platforms. Processing techniques to remove vegetation can yield bare-earth models for morphological mapping (Figure 2). Provided minimum specifications for data acquisition and processing are met these models enable much more reliable landslide identification and characterization than could be achieved with aerial photography, particularly in areas of dense vegetation cover. In the authors' experience, use of LiDAR imagery for enhancing landslide inventories that were originally developed using aerial photographs will often double the number of identified landslide features, and will enable much more precise characterization of the extents, mechanisms and degree of activity of previously-identified landslides. Furthermore, the bare earth models are much easier for laypersons to understand and allow for much more effective communication between landslide specialists and other practitioners working in pipeline integrity. In North America it is now standard practice to build landslide inventories using LiDAR.

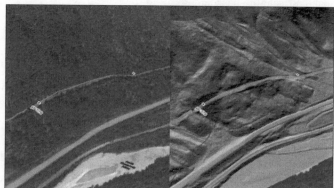

FIGURE 2: SATELLITE IMAGE VERSUS BARE-EARTH LIDAR IMAGE

In addition to the above advances, the availability of recent and historical satellite imagery through Google Earth™ and other providers has become another useful resource to improve geohazard inventory creation. Aerial photographs are still used, where available, to gain insight to historical changes in land use, landslide activity, and river channel migration.

NEAR REAL-TIME MONITORING

Enhanced geohazard inventories will often yield a large number of geohazard sites crossed by pipeline infrastructure. Monitoring techniques can support the management of those hazards in a number of ways, including determining the depths, spatial extents and movement rates of landslides, monitoring streamflow discharge at watercourse crossings, monitoring precipitation for conditions likely to trigger or accelerate landslides, floods and debris flows, and supporting rapid response to seismic events.

For monitoring to be effective a site-specific characterization of the geohazard and expected pipeline response to impact from the geohazard is carried out in advance so that appropriate monitoring thresholds and action-response plans can be established. For a watercourse crossing, this would involve determination of the flood discharge expected to cause pipeline exposure and sufficient span length that failure by vortex-induced vibration or impact loads could occur. An action-response plan might include procedures to shut-in or purge the pipeline if predetermined flood flow thresholds were exceeded, in addition to procedures to verify pipeline integrity and re-start operation after the flood subsided. While these activities might not prevent a pipeline failure, they could dramatically reduce the consequences of failure.

For landslide hazards, sufficient characterization of the landslide and pipeline should be carried out to determine the length of pipeline being impacted, and the strain history and remaining strain capacity of the pipeline. Exceedance of pre-determined movement thresholds usually triggers the planning and execution of pipeline stress relief, or other mitigation measures, with the objective of reducing the probability of pipeline failure.

Improvements in telemetry, geotechnical instrumentation, radar and satellite-based monitoring, combined with software solutions, are enabling near real-time monitoring of streamflows, precipitation, seismicity, and instrumentation data over wide regions, and the ability to relate those monitoring observations to specific geohazard sites. These methods are supplementing, and in many cases, replacing, the manual reading of instrumentation that was commonly carried out at 3 to 12-month intervals in the early 2000's.

Software such as RNT is now able to query every available hydrometric station linked to the stream network and uses these data to estimate streamflow at thousands of pipeline watercourse crossings every hour. Where pre-set monitoring thresholds have been established, automated email alerts are issued to pipeline operators when those thresholds are exceeded so that site-specific trigger action response plans can be put into action.

For smaller watersheds, and for regions where few hydrometric stations are present, regional precipitation models can be used in a similar fashion for flood monitoring. These models are available from several government agencies and research institutes. They usually combine satellite observation and real-time rain gauge data to produce gridded models of predicted precipitation at 4 to 8-hour intervals. Software and analysis is required to associate gridded precipitation model data to specific geohazard sites and, in the case of watercourse crossings, to convert rainfall intensity/duration/frequency (IDF) estimates within a catchment area to estimates of flood return period.

These same tools can associate modelled precipitation estimates to landslide hazard locations. Pre-determined precipitation thresholds can be used to trigger alerts and follow-up ground inspections or manual instrumentation monitoring if those thresholds are exceeded. Precipitation thresholds are generally not well-established for landslides, particularly for deep-seated landslides, because appropriate historical data for threshold calibration have generally not been available. Association of gridded regional precipitation model predictions with site-specific hazard observations following rainfall events will enable the development of more rational precipitation thresholds for different landslide mechanisms and specific landslide sites.

Earthquakes can trigger landslides, and liquefaction and lateral spreading. When an earthquake occurs, it is useful to know if the earthquake was large enough and close enough to potentially cause permanent ground displacement at a geohazard site so that follow-up pipeline inspection efforts can be prioritized appropriately. Correlations between earthquake magnitude, distance and occurrence of different landslide types have been developed (e.g. [8]). Again, for this type of monitoring to be carried out efficiently, software is required to relate earthquake magnitude and epicenter location (provided by government agencies) to specific pipeline assets and geohazard sites, to send automated alerts to pipeline operators if ground displacement may have occurred in response to an earthquake. Several pipeline operators in western Canada have begun to implement these types of earthquake monitoring systems.

Other monitoring technologies continue to evolve, including use of fibre-optic cables and satellite-based InSAR for ground movement monitoring. These technologies have not been widely-adopted by industry yet, but likely will be once more case histories emerge of their successful application in challenging environments, such as on slopes with dense vegetation cover.

DATA INTEGRATION AND MANAGEMENT

The past 15 years have seen significant change in how data for geohazard management are integrated, organized and shared. Early spreadsheet models quickly gave way to desktop-based tabular databases to store geohazard and pipeline attributes, assess multiple overlapping and changing model variables using dynamic segmentation, and to calculate numerical ratings of geohazard exposure and vulnerability for each pipeline segment.

Over time, the pipeline geohazard databases were made accessible online so that geohazard inventories, inspection and detailed investigation results, and recommended management actions and action timings could be centralized and communicated more effectively to the various integrity management stakeholders. Their sophistication continued to grow so that they could pull in results from several of the near real-time monitoring tools described above, as those tools became available. The results of detailed geohazard assessments were also uploaded directly into the data management system, with key recommendations and action timings captured in a way that they were less likely to be forgotten than if they were buried in the hard copy of a large engineering or geoscience report.

BGC's Cambio™ geohazard data management software provides an example of the current state-of-practice for geohazard data management (Figure 3). The latest version of Cambio was developed by software developers working alongside geoscientists and engineers and was released in July 2018. The Cambio web application consists of an ESRI ArcGIS database and map, risk calculation algorithms as well as real-time flood, seismic and rainfall monitoring. Monitoring components integrate site-specific geohazard and pipeline data with streamflow, precipitation and earthquake data available from the United States Geological Survey, Water Survey of Canada, Environment and Climate Change Canada, and National Resources Canada. The system is cloud-hosted on Microsoft Azure to maximize reliability, availability and data security. The web application has a modern user interface that utilizes the interactive ESRI ArcGIS map, which shows the locations of the pipelines, geohazard sites, satellite imagery, LiDAR and other datasets in 2D and 3D views. A companion mobile application was developed to collect data in the field during pipeline geohazard inspections. The mobile app synchronizes with the web app, so that inspection results can be reviewed the same day in the office, providing rapid delivery of inspection results to pipeline operators.

FIGURE 3: SCREEN CAPTURE SHOWING CAMBIO MAP, TABLE AND FORM

One of the important benefits of having the combination of a comprehensive geohazard inventory and a good geospatial geohazard data management program, is that it then allows the opportunity to identify the co-location of features or events with geohazard sites. A range of information from ILI runs (crack colonies, bending strains or other pipeline anomalies), past dig sites, and other relevant historical information can be critical to reveal the role that geohazard processes may be playing that may not have been recognized.

The other area of significant progress over the past decade has involved closer collaboration between parties conducting landslide hazard assessment and monitoring, assessment of ILI data, and soil-pipe interaction analysis. Integration of more realistic landslide loading mechanisms based on integration of LiDAR and other available datasets is resulting in better quality stress analyses, improved landslide and pipeline monitoring programs, and more effective stress relief programs. This is allowing for much safer operation of pipelines through slow-moving landslides.

BIG DATA FOR IMPROVED GEOHAZARD ALGORITHMS

Fortunately, pipeline failures caused by geohazards occur relatively infrequently. The downside, however, is that there are fewer data to calibrate algorithms for predicting geohazard occurrence, pipeline vulnerability, and failure compared to other pipeline threats such as corrosion and third-party damage. The monitoring tools and pipeline and geohazard data integration and management efforts described above are quickly changing this.

For example, Cambio currently hosts geohazard inventory, inspection and monitoring data for approximately 300,000 kilometres of pipeline in North and South America, including data for approximately 145,000 individual geohazard sites. Precipitation and flood monitoring data are being gathered for each of these sites at 1 to 6-hour intervals, and higher-priority sites are being inspected by geotechnical and hydrotechnical specialists on at least an annual basis. The end result is the assembly of a very large, very rich dataset that allows for the development of powerful statistical correlations between geohazard site features and triggering processes to improve predictions of geohazard probability, and pipeline characteristics and performance data to improve predictions of pipeline vulnerability to different geohazard loading conditions. This dataset grows every hour. Machine learning trials are underway to improve our ability to forecast floods and landslides in small catchment areas, to improve estimates of pipeline vulnerability, to better understand and communicate the significance of data and model uncertainty, and to improve our ability to automatically detect anomalous and erroneous monitoring and inspection data.

Improved geohazard algorithms are important because they help prioritize management effort at the sites that need it the most, and they provide better insight to the costs and benefits of different risk management options. A transition from the risk indexing geohazard algorithms that were common in the early 2000's to algorithms that generate quantitative estimates of geohazard impact and pipeline failure is also improving pipeline integrity managers' ability to compare the likelihood and consequence of geohazard threats to risks from other hazard types.

SOUTH AMERICAN CHALLENGES AND OPPORTUNITIES

South American pipelines encounter the same types of geohazards that are common in North America (e.g., [9]), but several factors increase the difficulty of geohazard management in South America. Because of topography, climate, and weathering processes, average geohazard exposure tends to be higher on a per-kilometre basis for many Andean pipelines compared to their North American counterparts. Historical pipeline construction practices may have differed, and in some parts of South America a higher percentage of operating pipelines appear to have been constructed with less consideration to mitigating geohazard threats. Pipeline infrastructure in some parts of South America is much more remote and difficult to access for inspection, maintenance and emergency response activities, and key datasets for geohazard inventory, assessment and management are sometimes not available or are more difficult to access. Consequently, the frequency of pipeline failures caused by geohazards on a per-kilometre basis is as much as 10 to 50 times higher on some Andean pipelines than it is on most North American pipelines that are operated through mountainous terrain [4].

In light of the above we outline three potential opportunities for industry, regulatory and academic collaboration within South America that could help achieve a large improvement in pipeline safety.

In North America, geohazard inventories now benefit from the availability of free or low-cost LiDAR. Often this LiDAR has been acquired by federal or state/provincial agencies; in other instances, it has been jointly acquired by owners who have assets that share adjacent or common rights-of-ways. In some cases the point cloud data are available for free; in others only lower-resolution shaded-relief imagery is free and point cloud data must be purchased from the LiDAR vendor. Not only does access to LiDAR significantly improve geohazard inventory and characterization, the availability of historical LiDAR creates opportunity for topographic change detection analysis to better understand erosion and landslide activity by comparing multiple LiDAR datasets in time. The data are also used to supplement survey data for engineering design and support many areas of academic research. *Are there opportunities within South America for industry, government and academia to pool resources to increase the availability of historical LiDAR, and to reduce costs of acquisition of new LiDAR?*

In North America, many government agencies collect hourly or more frequent precipitation and hydrometric data and make these freely-accessible for consumption by tools like the RNT. The myriad ways rapid access to these data benefit pipeline geohazard management have been outlined above. In addition, the data are used by many other stakeholders including transportation, mining, forestry, agriculture, and local governments. Where hydrometric gauges are lacking in areas with a high concentration of pipeline assets, pipeline operators have begun collaborating with the government agencies responsible for management of the hydrometric monitoring network to help offset the cost of installing and maintaining new stations. The merging of regional hydrometric and precipitation datasets, combined with systematic collection of monitoring and inspection data from specific geohazard sites is opening up incredible opportunities for industry and academia to advance technologies to forecast rainfall-triggered landslides and floods. *Are there similar opportunities in South America to increase the spatial coverage, quality and accessibility of precipitation and hydrometric data?*

In North America, most pipeline regulators require pipeline operators to report the location, cause, and contributing factors associated with all pipeline failures. Furthermore, these failure reports are increasingly made public in recognition that each failure represents a valuable learning opportunity, and in recognizing that improved transparency will help build trust amongst stakeholders. The pipeline industry recognizes that improvements in safety and pipeline reliability benefit everyone, and that failures have a negative impact on the social license for the entire industry. In their drive towards zero failures, industry organizations such as the Canadian Energy Pipeline Association (CEPA) and BGC's Cambio Users' Group share information on pipeline incidents, near misses, and management practices, and collaborate on research and other initiatives to improve pipeline safety. BGC maintains a global database of pipeline failures caused by geohazards, and this database provides valuable information for improving geohazard risk algorithms and management practices. *Would there be appetite amongst South American industry and regulators to move towards more open collection and sharing of information about pipeline failures?*

CONCLUSION

Significant improvements have occurred since the early 2000's in how geohazards are assessed and managed by the pipeline industry, and pipeline failure rates are dropping as a result. Some of these improvements are simply the result of greater awareness and recognition by industry and regulators that geohazards are an important cause of failures, particularly in certain environments, and that methods are available to manage geohazards in a proactive manner. Other improvements are being made possible by technological advancements in the areas of topographic survey (LiDAR), monitoring of streamflow, precipitation, and geotechnical instrumentation, information management systems, and data analytics. Collaboration amongst industry, regulators and academia is accelerating the pace of technological advancement by reducing costs to acquire and access key data, and by pooling pipeline performance data to help improve the predictive capabilities of geohazard algorithms and the effectiveness of management practices.

REFERENCES

[1] Savigny, K.W., Porter, M., Chen, J., Yaremko, E., Reed, M., and Urquhart, G. 2002. *Natural Hazard and Risk Management for Pipelines*. Proceedings of the 4th International Pipeline Conference, Calgary, Alberta. September 29 - October 3, 2002.

[2] Savigny, K.W., Esford, F., Porter, M., Muhlbauer, K., and Dunlop, C. 2004. *A risk assessment model for pipelines exposed to geohazards*. 5th International Pipeline Conference, Calgary, Alberta. October 4 - 8, 2004.

[3] Porter, M., Reale, R., Marcuz, G., and Savigny, K.W. 2006. *Geohazard Risk Management for the Nor Andino Gas Pipeline*. 6th International Pipeline Conference, Calgary, Alberta. September 24 - 29, 2006.

[4] Porter, M., Leir, M., Ferris, G., Leach, M., and Haderspock, M. 2016. *Updated estimates of frequencies of pipeline failures caused by geohazards*. 11th International Pipeline Conference, Calgary, Alberta. September 26 – 30, 2016.

[5] Porter, M., Leir, M., Baumgard, A., and Ferris, G. 2014. *Integrating Terrain and Geohazard Knowledge into the Pipeline Lifecycle*. Proceedings of the 6th Canadian GeoHazards Conference - GeoHazards 6, Kingston, Canada. June 15-18, 2014.

[6] Strahler, A.N. 1952. *Hypsometric (area-altitude) analysis of erosional topography*. Bulletin Geological Society of America. 63:1117-1142.

[7] Holm, K, Jakob, M., and Scordo, E. 2016. *An inventory and risk-based prioritization of steep-creek fans in Alberta, Canada*. FLOODrisk 2016, 3rd European Conference on Flood Risk Management, E3S Web of Conferences 7, 01009. E3S Web of Conferences.

[8] Keefer, D.K. 1984. *Landslides caused by earthquakes*. Geological Society of America Bulletin, v. 95, p. 406-421, April 1984.

[9] Porter, M., Savigny, K.W., and Esford, F. 2004. *Andean pipelines – a challenge for natural hazard and risk managers*. Terrain and Geohazard Challenges facing Onshore Oil and Gas Pipelines, London. June 2-4, 2004.

IPG2019-5303

Oil Pipeline Geohazard Risk Mitigation via On-Line Optical Fiber Strain Monitoring

Alexis Méndez[1]
Micron Optics Inc.
Alameda, CA, USA

Andrés Salazar Ferro
Salazar Ferro Ingenieros S.A.
Bogotá, Colombia

ABSTRACT

Pipelines are naturally vulnerable to operational, environmental and man-made effects such as internal erosion and corrosion; mechanical deformation due to geophysical risks and ground movements. This paper describes the on-line monitoring of multiple critical sections of buried oil pipelines, part of Ecopetrol's transportation network across the country, which were experiencing mechanical deformations due to local soil and geohazard effects using fiber optic strain sensors. Over 1,000 individual fiber optic Bragg grating (FBG) strain sensors were installed across 72 different sectors dispersed across the Colombian pipeline network. The system has been in service since 2013 and has helped provide early warning on several severe pipeline accumulated strain deformations and imminent ruptures, as well as to understand the mechanical behavior on buried pipelines under diverse soil geohazard conditions.

Keywords: Inspection technologies, fiber optic sensors, FBG sensors, pipeline monitoring, leak detection, intrusion detection.

NOMENCLATURE

Place nomenclature section, if needed, here. Nomenclature should be given in a column, like this:

FBG	fiber optic Bragg gratings
$\mu\varepsilon$	micro-strain
nm	nano-meter

INTRODUCTION

Pipelines are naturally vulnerable to operational, environmental and man-made effects such as internal erosion and corrosion; mechanical deformation due to geophysical risks and ground movements; leaks from neglect and vandalism; as well as encroachments from nearby excavations or illegal intrusions [1]. The actual detection and localization of incipient and advanced faults in pipelines is a very difficult, expensive and inexact task [2]. Anything that operators can do to mitigate the effects of these faults will provide increased reliability, reduced downtime and maintenance costs, as well as increased revenues.

Historically, monitoring of pipelines has relied on the use of conventional electronic strain gauge sensors based on resistive foil or vibrating wire sensors [3]. Unfortunately, such devices are prone to failure due to exposure to rainwater or moisture, as well as induced electrical shorts caused by lightning and thunderstorms. Other pipe monitoring systems have relied on the use of periodic scans made by motorized so-called "pigs" fitted with mechanical measuring calipers and/or magnetic sensors to detect any pipe deformations or irregularities, as well as reduction in wall thickness brought about by gradual erosion, corrosion or external geotechnical earth movements. Such scans are time-consuming, expensive and infrequent and do not provide a direct, incipient and early warning of an imminent defect or sudden hazard.

In contrast, optical fiber based sensors; offer the possibility to perform localized as well as truly distributed sensing over multi-kilometer distances, with immunity to EM interference,

---

[1] Contact author: amendez@micronoptics.com

water effects or electrical shorts. Over the last decade, optical fiber sensors have seen an increased acceptance and more widespread use for structural sensing and monitoring in civil engineering, aerospace, marine, oil & gas, electrical power, composites and smart structure applications. Given their immunity to electromagnetic effects and compatibility with outdoor use, fiber optic sensors have proven themselves to be rugged and long-lasting for installation along pipelines.

1. BACKGROUND: Optical Fiber Sensors

The field of fiber optics has undergone a tremendous growth and advancement over the last 50 years. Initially conceived as a medium to carry light and images for medical endoscopic applications, optical fibers were later proposed in the mid 1960's as an adequate information-carrying medium for telecommunication applications. Optical fibers are also used for other applications such as in sensing, control and instrumentation. In its simplest form, an optical fiber sensor is composed of a light source, optical fiber; sensing element and a light detector (see Fig. 1). The principle of operation of a fiber sensor is that the sensing elements modulates some parameter of the optical system (intensity, wavelength, polarization, phase, etc.) which gives rise to a change in the characteristics of the optical signal received at the detector.

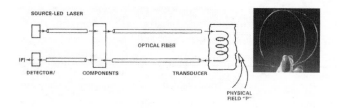

FIGURE 1: Generic building blocks of an optical fiber sensor.

To date, several different types of fiber sensors are commercially available to measure parameters such as pressure, temperature, refractive index, displacement, gas concentration, and several others [4].

1.1 Fiber Bragg Grating Sensors

A fiber Bragg grating (FBG) is wavelength-dependent filter/reflector formed by introducing a periodic refractive index structure, with spacing on the order of a wavelength of light, within the core of an optical fiber. Whenever a broad-spectrum light beam impinges on the grating, will have a portion of its energy transmitted through, and another reflected off as depicted in Fig. 2 The reflected light signal will be very narrow (few nm) and will be centered at the Bragg wavelength which corresponds to twice the periodic unit spacing Λ. Any change in the modal index or grating pitch of the fiber caused by strain, temperature of polarization changes, will result in a Bragg wavelength shift.

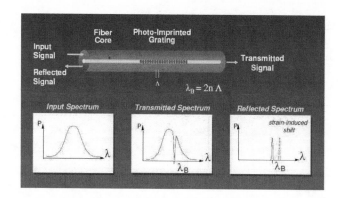

FIGURE 2: Operating principle of a FBG.

The value of Λ needed to induce constructive resonance in the grating and produced a reflected light signal is known as the Bragg condition, hence the name "Bragg grating":

$$\lambda_b = \Lambda\, 2n$$

(1)

Where n is the refractive index of the optical fiber's core, and λ_b is the peak wavelength value at which the resonance occurs, and this is the optical frequency that is monitored and tracked as a means to perform sensor measurements of physical variables. FBGs are attractive for sensing applications due to the dependence of their spectral shift as a function of grating separation change with external effects. They are commonly used in harsh environment applications as a replacement to standard resistance electrical strain gauges. This is especially helpful in environments such as high-temperature or highly corrosive. It is also possible to use fiber Bragg gratings to sense other environmental parameters such as pressure chemical reaction by using an additional transducer instead of using Fiber Bragg grating itself.

Mechanical stresses can be measured using FBG by properly mounting them on or embedding into the substrate of interest. One of the advantages of this technique is the fact that the detected signal is spectrally encoded, so that transmission losses in the fiber are of no concern. Mechanical strain shifts the Bragg wavelength by physically increasing or decreasing the grating spacing by mechanical strain and by changes in the refractive index due to the strain optic effect. For axial loads, the fractional wavelength change is ~1.2 pm/με at an operating wavelength of 1550nm.

Figure 3 illustrates the aspect of a FBG strain sensor. The device is rugged and designed for use in diverse field applications. The FBG sensing element is pre-stretched and mounted on a protective metallic carrier flexure. The strain sensor can be surface mounted to test specimens of interest using epoxy bonding or spot welding techniques. This, in practice, becomes the optical fiber equivalent of a conventional foil strain gage sensor. Similar FBG strain sensors were used in the monitoring of the oil pipelines instrumented in this project.

FIGURE 3: Aspect of FBG strain sensors.

FBGs have been studied for a wide variety of civil and geotechnical mechanical sensing applications [5-9] including monitoring of civil structures (highways, bridges, buildings, dams, etc.), smart manufacturing and non-destructive testing (composites, laminates, etc.), remote sensing (oil wells, power cables, pipelines, space stations, etc.), smart structures (airplane wings, ship hulls, buildings, sports equipment, etc.), as well as traditional strain, pressure and temperature sensing. The main advantage of FBGs for mechanical sensing is that these devices perform a direct transformation of the sensed parameter to optical wavelength, independent of light levels, connector or fiber losses, or other FBGs at different wavelengths. The advantages of FBGs over resistive foil strain gauges include:

- Totally passive (no need for electric power)
- Small size
- Non-conductive (immune to EM interference)
- Non-corrosive
- Remote, long distance sensing

2. Ecopetrol Oil Pipeline Network

Ecopetrol S.A. has an 8,500-kilometer network of pipelines that go from the production centers to the refineries and ports in the Atlantic and Pacific oceans. Of these, there are approximately 5,269 kilometers of main crude oil pipeline networks connecting various fields to the Barrancabermeja refinery and Reficar, as well as to export facilities. Pipelines range in outside diameter from 10" to 48" inches.

Given Colombia's geography and tropical climate, there is continuous propensity for pipelines to suffer deterioration and damage due to geohazards caused by heavy rain storms, flooding, landslides and overall soil settlement and movement. Buried pipelines are susceptible to accumulated strain, bending and possible rupture from these effects (Fig. 4). As part of their maintenance efforts, Ecopetrol desired to have a means for real-time, on-line monitoring of critical sectors of their extensive pipeline network and get advance warning of over-stressed, bent or ruptured oil pipelines. The project demanded a solution that is intrinsically safe to avoid any possible explosions, immune to lightning effects and electric shorts, resistant to humidity and contact with water, as well as capable of remote

interrogation. The chosen solution was based on fiber-optic FBG temperature-compensated strain sensors mounted around the perimeter of the pipeline in critical locations. The original motivation, pipeline integrity strategy and the criteria used to select the monitoring sites and the thresholds stress/strain that led to the adoption of the FBG sensor solution are described in reference [10]. In this paper, by contrast, we describe in detail the FBG operating principles, the installation methodology, as well as the overall monitoring system configuration and the results and progress made to-date from the original inception of the project. The work was performed by Salazar-Ferro Ingenieros S.A. with support from Micron Optics Inc. under Ecopetrol contract MA 0015048.

FIGURE 4: Example of pipeline bending from soil movement.

2.1 Pipeline Geohazard Monitoring System

As described above, the goal of this project was to provide an early warning system to Ecopetrol pipeline operators about possible pipeline mechanical bending or rupture from soil movements in critical locations of the oil pipeline network. An integral part to a pipeline monitoring system should include the following elements:

- Identifying the specific hazard
- Evaluating the hazard risks
- Designing a monitoring program (with mitigation actions that define expected strain level thresholds and associated correction and contingency plans), and
- Review of acquired data

Hence, as an initial project step, Ecopetrol conducted a country-wide survey to identify the locations with the highest level of geohazard risk and locate specific points where critical geohazard risk is known to have happened in the past or of being suspected to happen in the future that would merit continuous monitoring.

The pipeline monitoring system consisted of three, temperature-compensated FBG strain sensors installed on the outside perimeter of the pipeline at points corresponding to clock positions at 8, 12 and 4, as depicted on Fig. 5, and designated as sensors A, B and C, respectively (with the direction of flow from left to right of the pipe).

Whenever a pipeline crosses a landslide, it is subjected to shearing forces at the lateral edges of the slide, causing bending and both tensile and compressive strains on opposite faces of the pipe. This can result in bending and subsequent rupture of the pipe. When the axis of the pipeline is in alignment with the direction of a landslide, it will be subjected to compressive and tensile stresses only, caused by the moving soil. Compressive stresses cause buckling and rupture. Having the permanently mounted triad of strain sensors, allows for the measurement of any accumulated strain on the pipe. Furthermore, induced bending is determined by the difference in slope and relative behavior among the 3 individual strain readings. For instance, when only axial stress is present, all 3 traces move in unison; hover, under bending, portions of the pipe will be under tension, and others in compression resulting in opposing readings of strain by one or two of the individual strain sensors compared to the third one.

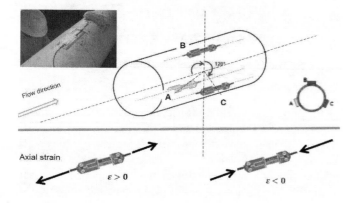

FIGURE 5: FBG strain sensor arrangement used to monitor pipeline strains caused by soil movements.

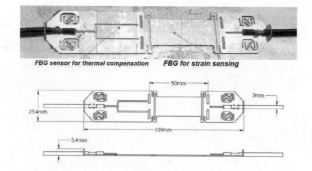

FIGURE 6: FBG fiber optic strain sensor used.

The FBG strain sensors used were Micron Optics model os3155 (see Fig. 6). These sensors have 2 individual FBGs. One element used for measuring the strain, while the second FBG is mechanically isolated and measures only the temperature effects so that the strain reading can be corrected for any temperature-induced apparent strain effects. This sensor is installed on steel metal surfaces by spot-welding, and later covered with an impermeable patch to protect against humidity and the elements. The optical fiber is protected inside a 3mm OD metal armored fiber optic cable. The end of the cable is terminated in a FC/APC type optical fiber connector.

2.2 Installation Process

Once specific locations to be monitored along a given pipeline route were identified, the pipeline portion of interest was previously dug (if buried) and exposed so that the strain sensors could be mounted on its surface. The installation process begins by cleaning the area around the pipe where the sensors will be mounted and removing with an electric sander, any rust and/or protective coating or paint from the pipe's surface. This is done in order to ensure good physical contact between the sensor and the pipe's outer surface. In any given monitoring sector, anywhere from 1 to 10 sensor rings (triad of strain sensors) were mounted. This was done so in order to ensure that the full pipeline segment under potential geohazard risk was properly monitored. Once the set of 3 strain sensors were installed via spot welding, they were covered with Polyurethane, water-impermeable, protective patches to ensure that neither the sensor nor the pipe's surface would get corroded by water or moisture ingress. All the sensor installation steps are depicted in Fig. 7.

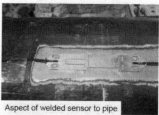

FIGURE 7: Strain sensor installation process.

Each sensor is provided with a 10m long, armored fiber-optic cable. The cables' ends are protected inside a PVC pipe mounted next to the pipe, this prevented damage from wild animals or vandalism. A protective rubber mat is wrapped around the perimeter where the sensors are mounted to ensure that no soil, rocks and gravel debris damage the mounted sensors or their cable terminations. The exposed pipeline is then re-buried and initial strain readings taken to verify the operation of the sensors as shown in Fig. 8.

Over 300 strain sensors "belts" (triads) were installed with only 3 sensors damaged during installation procedures. Each sensor installation required 2-3 days of installation (not counting excavation and re-burial operations).

Sensor wrapping protection   Pipeline re-burial   FO cable junction terminal

FIGURE 8: Sensor protection and pipeline re-buring.

RESULTS

71 different critical geohazard sectors along Ecopetrol's oil transportation pipeline network were instrumented with anywhere from 1 to 10 (triad) FBG strain sensing belts. Each geo-hazard location along the pipeline network has a set of 1 to 10 separate strain-sensing FBG sensor belt. Each "sensor belt" had its strain readings manually recorded bi-weekly, by connecting the sensor's connectorized end to a Micron Optics sm125 optical interrogator instrument as illustrated in Fig. 9.

FIGURE 9: Taking strain sensor readings in the field.

Once strain data has been collected for a few weeks, it is possible to start detecting possible geotechnical effects on the pipeline integrity and the onset of sever axial deformation or bending. For example, Fig. 10 shows the accumulated strain readings on a sector experiencing purely axial tension over a period of two years. It can clearly be observed that each of the

three individual strain readings is increasing gradually with time and with positive slope (tension). After 18 months of monitoring, the accumulated strain has reached the warning threshold imposed of 1,000 micro-strains. Afterwards, the pipeline was dug and strain relieved, producing a sharp decrease in the strain readings and even resulting in a slight compression. This clearly illustrates the value of knowing the mechanical stress condition of a pipe as function of time and under steady and unforeseen geotechnical or weather conditions, thus providing early warning of imminent damage.

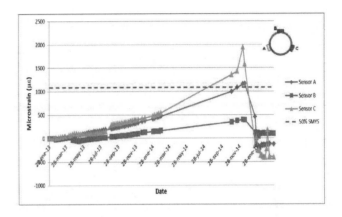

FIGURE 10: Accumulated strain readings over a two year period. Notice pipe is under uniform axial tension. Pipe was stress-relieved.

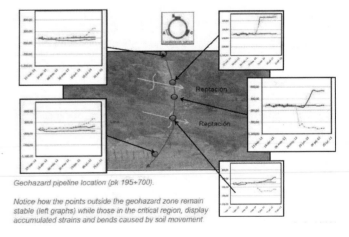

Geohazard pipeline location (pk 195+700).

Notice how the points outside the geohazard zone remain stable (left graphs) while those in the critical region, display accumulated strains and bends caused by soil movement.

FIGURE 11: Time-accumulated strain readings for a pipe zone experiencing severe axial and transverse soil loading. Each inset figure represents the accumulated pipeline strain for each of its 3 FBG strain sensors, depicted with different colors according to their position on the pipe. Strain scale is in micro-strains. It can be seen that the insets on the left show uniform axial strain over several months, while each of the 3 pipe locations in the middle eventually experience bending effects from transverse soil movement with respect to the pipe, as shown by the split in the individual strain traces for their respective curves.

In contrast, Fig. 11 shows the accumulated strain vs. time for a sector undergoing both axial and transverse tension causing pipe bending. The sector uses 5 separate strain "belts" to monitor discrete points along the geohazard zone. We can see that both the entry and exit zones are stable and produce uniform, low-value pipe strains. However, the three middle locations, report instances of pipe bending, indicated by the split in the individual strain sensor reading with opposite polarities (tension vs. compression, depending on the side of the pipe and the direction of the soil movement).

CONCLUSIONS

The monitoring system has been in operation since spring of 2013. Data is taken manually every fortnight by a field crew that visits each sector and records strain data. Valuable behavior of critical pipeline sections has been obtained, quantifying accumulated axial strains, pipeline bending and potential sites for incipient pipe rupture or leaks. To date, 3 serious pipeline failures have been averted. In addition, multiple individual locations with accumulated strains have been identified and appropriate stress-relieving pipeline activities carried out. The fiber-optic FBG strain sensors provided valuable advantages to conventional electronic strain sensors, such as:

- *Fast and easy installation*
- *Accurate data*
- *Immunity to electric interferences (storms or electric motors near to the pipeline)*
- *No need for re-calibration with each measurement (as compared to resistive and vibrating string based sensors).*

Periodic monitoring of accumulated pipe strains and bendings were made successfully on critical locations where geohazard risks were identified or anticipated. Measured data also provided a valuable operations tool for:

- *Stress relieving of severe pipeline stresses*
- *Early warning of potential pipe ruptures*
- *Better understanding of time evolution of mechanical effects on pipeline network*

- *Help define new maintenance protocols and set safety strain thresholds*

The system helped save Ecopetrol millions of dollars in prevented pipeline ruptures and associated environmental remediation costs.

ACKNOWLEDGEMENTS
The authors would like to acknowledge the support of Ecopetrol S.A. in the funding and execution of this project as well as in authorizing publication of this article. In particular, we appreciate the contributions made by Juan David Betancur Rios, Jaime Hernán Aristizábal, Camilo Torres, Alexander Guevara, Karlo González, Adriana Galvis, Henry Osorio, Ronald Diaz and Diego Trespalacios.

REFERENCES

[1] Nyman, D. J. et al., Mitigating Geohazards for International Pipeline Projects: Challenges and Lessons Learned. IPC2008-64405.
[2] Datta, S. and Sarkar, S., A review on different pipeline fault detection methods. Journal of Loss Prevention in the Process Industries, Vol. 41, pp97-106.
[3] Bucovansky, M. and Major, G., Twenty years of monitoring pipelines in landslides, proceedings of the first European conference on landslides; 2002.
[4] Krohn, D, MacDougal, T., and Méndez, A., *Fiber Optic Sensors: Fundamentals and Applications, Fourth Edition*, SPIE Publishing, 2015.
[5] Raymond M. Measures, Structural Monitoring with Fiber Optic Technology, Academic Press, 2001.
[6] Eric Udd, Fiber Optic Smart Structures, John Wiley & Sons Inc., 1995.
[7] Farhad Ansari, Applications of Fiber Optic Sensors in Engineering Mechanics, American Society of Civil Engineers, 1993.
[8] Brain Culshaw, Smart Structures and Materials, Artech House, 1996.
[9] A. Méndez, T. F. Morse and F. Méndez, "Applications of Embedded Optical Fiber Sensors in Reinforced Concrete Buildings and Structures", Proc. SPIE, Vol. 1170, pp. 60-69. September 1989.
[10] Betancur, J.D. et al., Monitoring Stress/Strain in Buried Pipelines Through the Use of Fiber Bragg Grating Sensors, IPG2015-8540

Proceedings of the ASME-ARPEL 2019
International Pipeline Geotechnical Conference
IPG2019
June 25-27, 2019, Buenos Aires, Argentina

IPG2019-5304

FIELD DATA COLLECTION USING GIS TECHNOLOGY FOR THE MANAGEMENT OF GEOHAZARDS AND THIRD-PARTY DAMAGE THREATS IN THE PIPELINE TRANSPORTATION SYSTEM OF NATURAL GAS (NG) AND NATURAL GAS LIQUIDS (NGL)

Karin Oviedo[1]
John Erick Malpartida Moya
Compañía Operadora de Gas del Amazonas
Gerencia de Ingeniería & Proyectos
Distrito de Lurín, Lima 16, Perú
Contact Author[1]

KEY WORDS

GIS, Geohazards, Damages by third parties, Integrity, Right of way, geodatabase.

ABSTRACT

The Camisea Pipelines Transportation System (STD) owned by Transportadora de Gas del Peru (TGP) is operated and maintained by Compañia Operadora de Gas del Amazonas (COGA). The system consists of two pipelines: a 730-kilometer long Natural Gas (NG) pipeline, which runs from the Upstream facilities in the Malvinas to the Receptor Station in Lurín (south of Lima), which has a loop in the area of Coast of 135 km in length and the Natural Gas Liquids pipeline (NGL) of 557 kilometers, which transports the condensed liquids from Malvinas to Pisco, on the coast of Peru.

In the first 210 km, it crosses a complicated zone of the Peruvian Amazon, between the kilometric poste (KP) 210 and KP 420, the sector of the mountain range is defined and between the KP 420 and KP 730, the coastal sector is located.

Due to the influence area and the project magnitude, solutions for many problems frequently require access to various types of information that can only be geographically related or by their spatial distribution. In this sense the Geographic Information Systems (GIS), provides the necessary tools to store and manage information using these references, thus allowing to analyze patterns of behavior, relationships and trends in information, all with the interest of contributing to the taking of better decisions.

Likewise, given the complicated geography on which the project is developed, as well as the populations dynamic, the threats of geohazards and damages by third parties respectively, require evaluations and field data collection on a permanent basis, this also because it is about threats that are independent of time and that represent the highest percentage of failures for the South American pipelines. In this sense, data collection using GIS technology allows users, through the use of previously established forms, to capture field information, as well as the corresponding photographic record. Also, during the data collection, users have at their disposal on their mobile devices relevant information that allows a more objective spatial and temporal analysis of a specific place. This information is synchronized with the GIS database of the organization and used in the evaluation of risks to the integrity of the pipelines.

This article describes the methodology for field data collection, using GIS technology, as well as the process of validation and publication of the data in the Geodatabase of the company and the benefits associated with having updated and available information to guarantee the best decision making.

INTRODUCTION

The Camisea Pipeline Transportation System (STD) in Peru, owned by Transportadora de Gas del Peru (TGP) and operated by Compañía Operadora de Gas del Amazonas (COGA), starts in the Amazon jungle, crosses the Andes mountain range (4850 masl) and finally descends towards the coast. The STD has more than 14 years of operation and has transportation pipelines of Natural Gas (NG) and Natural Gas Liquids (NGL). The NG pipeline is 865 km long and includes a 135 km loop. The NGL pipeline has a length of 557 km.

Figure 1 shows the location of the project in the context of Peruvian geography.

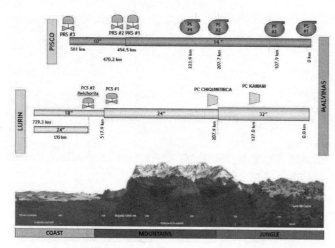

FIGURE 1 – Components and project location

Due to the complexity of the influence area and the project magnitude, solutions for many problems frequently require access to various types of information that can only be geographically related or by their spatial distribution. In this sense the Geographic Information Systems (GIS), allow storing and manipulating information using these geographical references, thus achieving analysis of patterns of behavior, relationships and information trends, all with the interest of contributing to making better decisions.

Without well-structured data the information that can be extracted from them can be very small, in turn it can take a long time to obtain results.

The implementation of Geographic Information System (GIS) TGP was given in response to the need for a technology that allows to manage and analyze the information obtained from construction activities, operation and maintenance of the Pipeline Transportation (STD). Likewise, the GIS of TGP - COGA, allows users to perform data queries that are only spatially related through the pipelines, offering a global view of the entire STD and its area of influence.

The field data collection, developed as part of the monitoring and surveillance activities of the STD, is one of the main sources of information stored in the GIS. However, due to the complexity of keeping a manual record of the data collected, in many cases the registry of valuable information is lost or not taken properly. In this sense, geographic information systems (GIS) allow the collection of data through the development of previously established forms, including the spatial location of the event, as well as the photographic record of them, synchronizing the information with the Geodatabase of the organization, even allowing the operator to compare the data with information from previous periods and / or technical information from other areas and / or sources, in order to achieve a more accurate, reliable and available data collection almost immediately.

Based on what was previously established, the tools and methodology used to collect data in the field are presented below, mainly oriented to the management of Geohazards and Damages by third parties.

GEOGRAPHIC INFORMATION SYSTEM

The data model used in the implementation of the Geographic Information System of our organization is based on the ArcGIS Pipeline Data Model (APDM), adopted in various operations of hydrocarbon transport systems in the world. The use of this model facilitates the risk assessment of the transport system because it is a relational data model,

allowing the evaluation of cascade data. In turn it ensures data integrity and facilitates storage and administration thereof.

At the same time, the company has implemented an Integrity Management System for its pipelines - PIMS (Pipeline Integrity Management System), which aims to operate and reliably maintain the pipeline transportation system, minimizing damage to people, environment and facilities. The main tasks of the PIMS are to identify and analyze current and potential events that may result in incidents, examine risks and possible activities for their reduction, design and implement risk reduction activities and the corresponding monitoring of their performance.

The basis of the integrity management system are the risk assessments, which analyze the probability and consequence of the different threats to which the pipelines are subject (corrosion, damage by third parties, external forces or geohazards, etc.).

In addition to the standard models for the evaluation of Geohazards it has been considered especially the development of algorithms adapted to the geological and geotechnical reality of the right of way of Camisea, for which it developed a database of "Geopeligros" with all the relevant information, allowing risk assessment of this threat more effectively.

A. DATA MODEL

As already mentioned, the Data Model used in the GIS, allows to manage the information related to the STD, storing it in a Geodatabase or geographic database, with specific characteristics according to the standards of the Relational Database Management System – RDBMS.

In this sense, the Model establishes as a main element within the database, a linear reference system composed by the pipes (station series) and control points composed by each one of the welds. All other events or information that is part of the database are related to these two main elements, either along the pipeline, taking the progressive (stationing) as a reference, or at a certain distance from it, taking as reference a measure (length) or geographical coordinate.

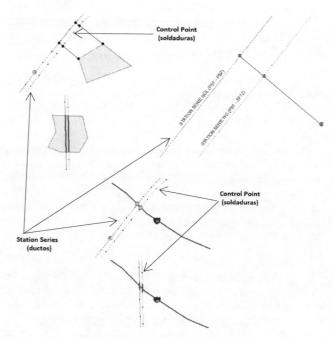

FIGURE 2 - Data Model - Main elements of the BD
B. Management of the information of Geohazard and Damages by

Third Parties.

Geohazards can be classified in different ways, depending on the specific nature of the threat to be assessed. Figure 3 shows the different types of geohazards identified for the Camisea STD.

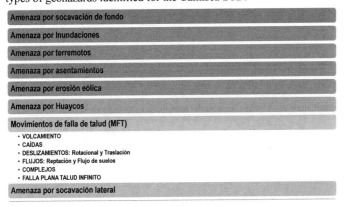

FIGURE 3 – Types of Geohazard

The information corresponding to the different Geohazards is stored in the geodatabase of the organization, taking as reference its geographical location and its spatial relationship to the pipelines and welds.

Not only the characteristics of the land and its geological condition are taken into account, but also the detonating factors such as: seismic activity, precipitation (intense, accumulated, etc), wind action (currents, tornadoes, hurricanes, etc) and the action of man (deforestation, land use change, etc).

The variables and attributes have been defined for each geohazard, as well as the corresponding domains (attribute rules) for each field. Figure 4 presents the different types of geohazards stored in the geodatabase.

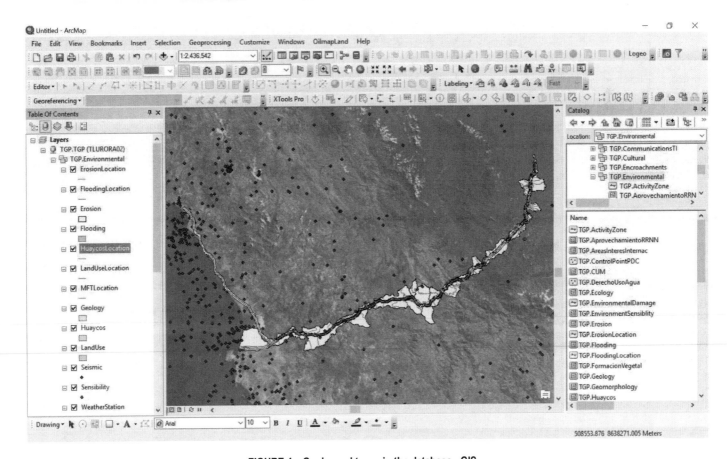

FIGURE 4 – Geohazard types in the database - GIS

Similarly, in the case of the threat of damage by third parties, the corresponding information has been collected and stored in the geodatabase, taking as a reference its geographical location and its spatial relationship with the pipelines and welds. The attributes corresponding to each table and their corresponding domains (attribute rules) have also been defined. Figure 5 shows the different types of third-party affectations identified and stored in the geodatabase.

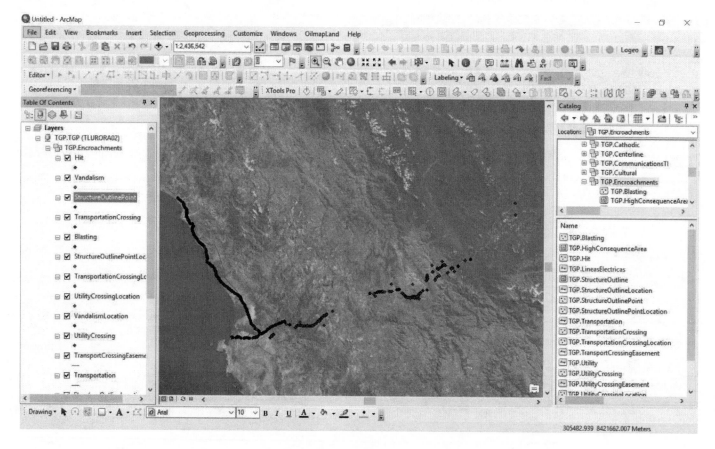

FIGURE 5 - Types of third parties damages in the BD - GIS

DATA COLLECTION USING MOBILE DEVICES AND GEOGRAPHICAL INFORMATION SYSTEMS

Due to the complexity of the geography that the Camisea STD goes through, as well as the large number of variables to be considered, the data field collection in a manual way has some disadvantages. For example, the loss of information due to adverse weather conditions and the characteristics of the land, loss of the photographic record and its relation to the information collected, time spent in the transfer of data to digital formats, reports, forms, etc. and its subsequent publication and / or sending to the operating personnel responsible for the analysis of the data collected. In contrast, the collection of data using mobile devices linked to geographic information systems, using previously established forms, favors the collection of more accurate information, in addition to providing additional information that is often not visible in the field or can be passed through by the operator (geographical location, altitude data, location of pipelines or other facilities of interest), ensures the photographic record linked to each of the points surveyed, also reduces the time for the transfer of information and the normalization of data in the geodatabase, managing to have the information available for the analysis in a more effective and efficient way.

Next, we present the methodology and tools used for field data collection applied to Geoamenazas (Monitoring of River Crossings) and third parties damages (Affectation of the layout class due to the appearance of new structures).

A. Variables Definition / Domains and Forms.

As a first step, the "feature class" (data layers) to be used for data collection were identified in the geodatabase.

In coordination with the user areas, the variables and attributes that should be completed with field information were selected. For each variable, a domain or rule of attributes was defined, this allows defining the values corresponding to each attribute, by means of a drop-down list in order to help the operator fill the form and ensure the integrity of the collected data.

As an example, we will take the case of the river crossings that are evaluated within the Geohazard. A layer was created in the GIS (feature Class) with point type geometry, creating a point for each of the 67 main rivers identified. Likewise, a table related to the layer of river crossings was created by the "EVENTID" field, unique identifier of each river crossing. In this way each reading taken in the field is related to the corresponding river crossing.

Ensuring in this way that the historical information of each river crossing is maintained in the database and can be consulted both by the operator in the field, and by the analyst in the cabinet.

A map was also created with the corresponding layers, which allow the operator in the field to verify relevant information of the river crossing to be inspected. The main layers of information considered were: location of the pipelines, welds, kilometer posts, anomalies, soil type, etc.

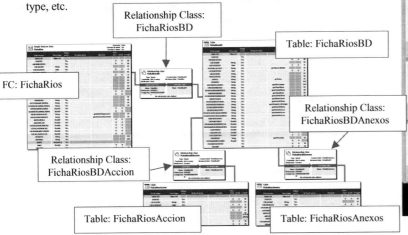

FIGURE 6 – Data Model – River Crossing

FIGURE 8 - Collector For ArcGIS - Map third parties damage"

The layers selected for data update in the field are hosted as a cloud service, using an ArcGIS Online account. In addition, a map was created and published in the same ArcGIS Online account, so that it can be consulted by the operator in the field with reference information through mobile devices through ArcGIS Explorer or Collector for ArcGIS. Both applications allow you to download the complete map or part of it (work area) to be consulted in offline mode, in areas where there is no internet connection.

B. Preparation and publication of Surveys

The field data capture forms were prepared, by way of surveys, using the Survey 123 for ArcGIS application.

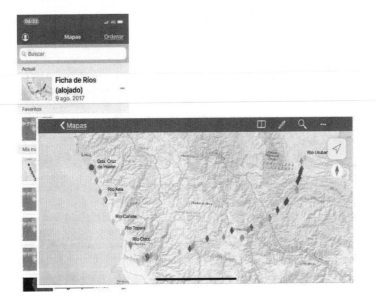

FIGURA 7 - ArcGIS Explorer - Map published "River Crossing"

FIGURE 9 - Publication of surveys Survey123 for ArcGIS

The domains previously defined for each attribute were loaded in the surveys as a "selection list", thus facilitating field data collection and ensuring the integrity of the data.

FIGURE 10 - Definition of Forms

Likewise, the application uses the geographic location provided by the equipment (Easting - North - Altitude). The operator can adjust the location on the map, approaching or moving away from the point to be pointed out, which may not be the exact location where the operator is standing, for example, the bank in front of a river, the head or end of a landslide, location of houses or structures, etc.

FIGURE 11 - Geographical location of the intake point

C. Publication of information in index cards and the geodatabase.

The information collected in the field is synchronized, as long as there is an internet connection, with the service hosted in the cloud (ArcGIS Online), which in turn is published in the WebGIS on the intranet of the organization.

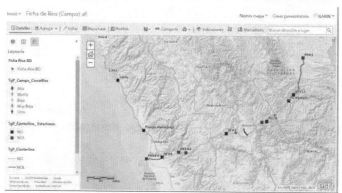

FIGURE 12 - Service publication Rios Crossign - Arcgis Online

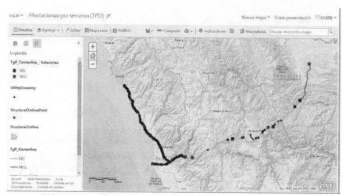

FIGURE 13 - Publication Service Third Parties damage - Arcgis Online

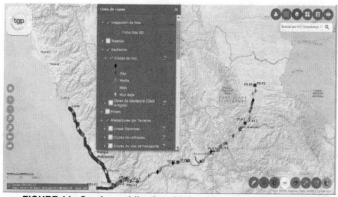

FIGURE 14 - Service publication third parties damage - river crossing - Web GIS Intranet of the organization

The data is reviewed by the field operator, the responsible analyst or supervisor and, once validated, they are synchronized by means of an update geoprocess in the organization's geodatabase.

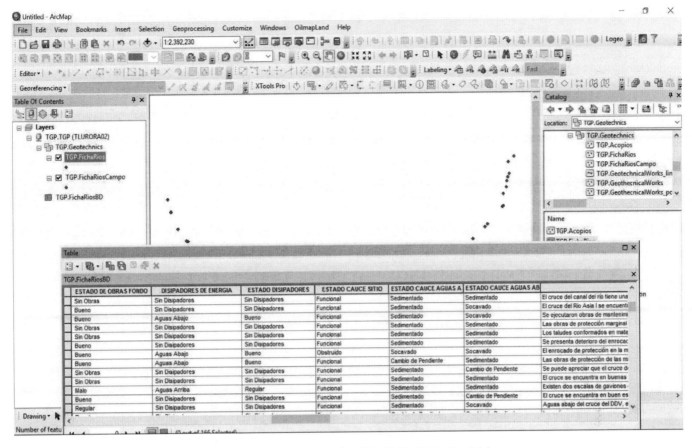

Figure 15 - Data synchronization "Rios Tab" with the Geodatabase

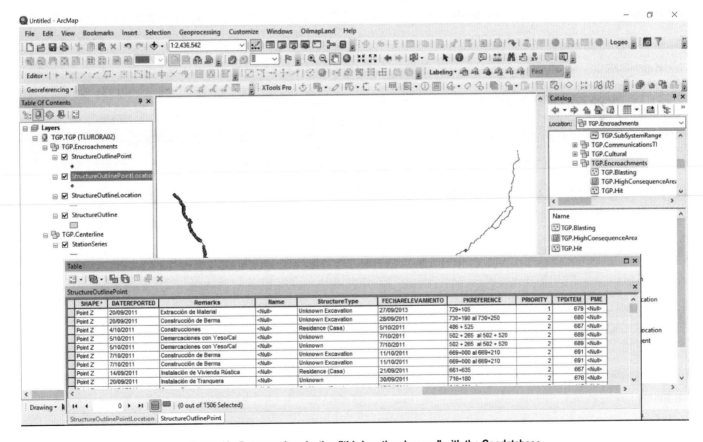

Figure 16 - Data synchronization "third parties damage" with the Geodatabase

CONCLUSIONS

The Geographic Information System (GIS) implemented by our organization, is used permanently by users, because it has updated information and very well organized, achieving access almost immediately to various types of information from different areas. Due to the complexity of our reality, we have a great variety of information that in many cases can only be spatially related, the GIS facilitates in this way the access of the users to information of diverse areas and diverse types of information facilitating the decision making in a successful and fast way.

The use of a Geodatabase using the tools and functionalities of a Geographic Information System allows visualizing the spatial location of high-risk areas, allowing an integral analysis, identifying populated centers, hydrographic network, communities within the area of influence of the system, location of facilities, road network, power lines, geohazards, etc. that are related to the management of the integrity of the pipelines.

The use of a Geodatabase based on the relational data model can be applicable to any Pipelines Transportation System facilitating the administration of data and ensuring that risk assessments and integrity management are carried out on reliable and efficient information.

The field data collection , using GIS technology, through the use of mobile devices, allows the field operator to perform a much more precise work, ensuring the integrity of the data, as well as the accuracy of these, both with respect to their location geographic, as to its spatial relationship with other components of the STD that many times are not visible to the naked eye in the field. It also allows us to share information between field and cabinet staff, accessing the data collected in the field in the shortest possible time, which greatly facilitates the analysis of information, the updating of the database and the reliability of the data obtained.

RECONOCIMIENTO

The development of this document is based on the team work carried out by the different user areas of the COGA GIS.

REFERENCES

IPG2015-8518 Oliveros F., 2015, "Errores no forzados en actividades de monitoreo geotécnico de un DDV".

VII INGEPET 2011 (GAS-3-KO-17-N) Oviedo K., 2011, "Administración y manejo de geodatabase para la gestión de integridad y evaluación de riesgo de un sistema de transporte de hidrocarburos"

Compañía Operadora De Gas Del Amazonas - COGA (2014), Oficina técnica áreas: Geotecnia, GIS e Integridad.

IPG2019-5312

RISK CONTROL THROUGH EVALUATION OF CATASTROPHIC SCENARIOS

José Vicente Amórtegui Gil

Escuela Colombiana de Ingeniería, Bogotá D.C, Colombia
Ingeniería y Geotecnia SAS, Bogotá D.C, Colombia

ABSTRACT

In sectors where pipelines cross areas exposed to severe hazards or where the consequences are serious, traditional analyses based on the Risk Analysis Matrix (RAM) do not reflect the effect of the works and actions taken for risk control. That condition induces the idea of ineffectiveness or uselessness of the works and actions taken for protection and reinforcement. In this paper, for those situations it is proposed the analysis of hypothetical scenarios to determine which of them can become catastrophic, in order to assess which situations can trigger a catastrophe, and in consequence to take actions regarding them and thus to avoid the catastrophic situation.

The suggested method consists in proposing scenarios of damages, corresponding an event of loss of product containment of a hydrocarbon transport system. In those scenarios, the following consequences of the oil spill are determined: the behaviour of the product, its route, the site of rupture, the possible threats that affect it, and the triggers of the threatening processes.

Critical or catastrophic scenarios are selected and the chain of events regarding them is determined as detailed as possible. When analysing that chain, it is possible to find actions that may modify it, such as the control of the route so that it does not reach the sensitive elements, the strengthening of the pipeline to bear the hazards, the reinforcement of the ground to prevent the action of the hazards and to avoid that the hazard takes place.

It must be determined how to protect the exposed elements and how to handle the spilled product to avoid the affectation of the elements mentioned above. For this point, it is important to know the infrastructure of the Contingency Plan and therefore to evaluate the possibility of strengthening it.

Keywords: Risk

1. INTRODUCTION

Within the techniques of the Strategic Planning DOFA, we have the strategic scenario approach, an original technique from the military strategy, that has been used successfully in the Planning of the Oil Industry, which later in 1990 was adopted in disciplines of Social Policy, with the purpose of approaching the future.

The strategic scenario is a systematic way of thinking to improve the understanding of the current operating environment and the various plausible futures.

In Actuarial Science the Concept of Catastrophic Risk has been developed as the one that has its origin in extraordinary events, whose own abnormal nature (low frequency) and the high intensity and quantity of the damages that may derive from them (high severity) prevent that their coverage from being covered in an ordinary insurance policy. Due to its nature, the occurrence of a catastrophe can endanger the solvency of the insurance sector and cause a significant impact on the economy of a country. It is defined under this concept when it is necessary to reassure.

The analysis of catastrophic scenarios arises from those concepts, for which it is possible to use techniques such as HAZOP, which enables the evaluation of the incidence of variables in the behaviour of parts of the whole or the system. HAZOP is a common procedure in the oil industry, which may facilitate its adoption.

The modelling of future scenarios is a global prediction technique. For example, at the University of Denver, Colorado, the headquarters of the Josef Korbel School of International Studies together with the Frederick S. Pardee International Futures Center are located. At this school the Model of International Futures (IF) has been created for the long-term integrated analysis of the problems of development, security and sustainability, enable the production of forecasting for 186 countries until the year 2100.

2. CHARACTERISTICS OF HIDROCARBON TRANSPORTATION SYSTEMS

In the hydrocarbon transport systems there are flow lines that transport the products extracted from the wells to the initial treatment centres by means of steel pipes. The product is generally a mixture of liquid and gaseous hydrocarbon, with solid waste (three-phase), almost always at elevated temperature. Those pipelines are usually developed in the oil fields forming a closed system.

In the initial treatment facilities, the separation of the products takes place, which are stored separately in the liquid state. Those products can be crude oil or condensed hydrocarbon, or in a gaseous state, natural gas. The products are generally combustible, flammable and sometimes explosive. Crude oil may have various characteristics that define its behaviour: there are heavy (high viscosity) crudes that often require additional treatments for transport, including the increase of its temperature and the addition of diluents and viscosity reducers; and there are medium and light crudes, which are usually more flammable and explosive.

From the industrial facilities, hydrocarbons are transported by pipelines made of steel mainly. The crude oil and the condensated are shipped to refineries or ports, and gases are sent to consumption centres or ports. For transporting, pumping or compression facilities are required to put pressure on products, which can modify some of their properties and make them more dangerous. Those pipes are usually laid on rural land, preferably far from urban centres.

In refinery facilities the oil is refined and petroleum derivatives are obtained, such as asphalts, fuels of different types (fuel oils, gasoline, naphtha and gas) and assets for the petrochemical industry. Those refined products are transported in general by steel pipes and require pumping facilities, to take them to the centres of consumption or transformation, which are generally urban centres, thus they are installed neighbouring or within the urban areas.

Gas pipelines reach the vicinity of urban centres, from which distribution networks, principal and residential, appear. In the latter the pressures are low and the pipes can be made, besides from steel, from polymers.

The transport system is constituted by, besides the pipeline and the pumping or compression facilities, measuring elements, blocking or control valves, scraper stations, drains, vents and others mechanisms for protection or control.

For the design and installation of the transport systems, rigorous standards are followed regarding the operational efforts and the control of hazards to the integrity of the pipelines, mainly corrosion; for this purpose, corrosion resistant covers are installed and quality control tests are carried out. In addition, it is sought to occupy the most stable ground and works of ground reinforcement are carried out. During the operation, there are monitoring and maintenance programs, procedures and actions for the hydrocarbon transport systems.

There are contingency plans, during the construction and operation stages, in which risk analyses are carried out, the necessary adjustments are made and measures are taken to control any unforeseen situation that may arise.

3. ANALYSIS OF CATASTROPHIC SCENARIOS

For the analysis of catastrophic scenarios, some techniques have been proposed, for example, Peter Schwartz, in 1991 proposed a five-step method to generate future scenarios, namely:
1. Make a model, trying to identify the relevant variables of the system.
2. Plot a graph with two axes, which represent the most uncertain variables that have been identified.
3. Imagine possible futures. Sometimes defining scenarios is very cold task, so it is proposed to transform each scenario into a future story.
4. Think about implications and actions that can be developed in each scenario.
5. Define monitoring indicators, scenarios and actions, in order to modulate the actions.

The HAZOP is an inductive risk identification technique based on the premise that risks, accidents or operability problems occur as a consequence of a deviation of the process variables with respect to the normal parameters of operation, in a given system and at a certain stage. Therefore, whether they are applied in the design stage, or in the operation stage, the method consists in evaluating, for all lines and for all the systems, the consequences of possible deviations in all the process units, whether it is continuous or discontinuous. The technique consists of analysing systematically the causes and the consequences of deviations of the process variables, found through some "guide words". The method arose in 1963 from Imperial Chemical Industries, ICI, which used critical analysis techniques in other areas. Subsequently, it was generalized and formalized, and it is currently one of the most widely used tools internationally for the identification of risks in the industrial facilities.

The method of analysis of catastrophic scenarios has its advantages and disadvantages. Among the advantages there are the following:
a. Powerful risk management and management tool, since it allows determining the probability of ruination.
b. Allows estimating loss scenarios, including all possibilities.
c. The analysis is sensitive to the risk variables, it is possible to model different combinations.
d. It determines the capital and reserve requirements, as a function of subscribed risk, which allows maximizing the use of the invested capital.

Among the disadvantages there are the following:
a. It is based on theoretical assumptions that require validation tests.
b. Complexity of its use that requires training, information, infrastructure and operating costs.
c. The use of different models leads to different results. If the most sensitive variables and the modelling logic are not understood, the method can stay as a black box analysis.
d. Some risk factors are beyond the scope of the models.

In the case of hydrocarbon transport systems, exposed to natural hazards, the following procedure is proposed:
1. Determine the possible hazards to which the transportation system may be exposed.

2. Identify the characteristics of the conduction system, such as the type of pipe, quality, state of operational stress, coating, construction conditions, and operation conditions, as a result of the mechanical inspections.

3. Determine the characteristics of the transported hydrocarbon and its behaviour in the event of a loss of containment.

4. Identify in the environment the elements that may be exposed to a loss of containment of the transported hydrocarbon.

5. Analyse the changes in the stress state that can be induced by natural hazards.

6. Identify and characterize the events triggering the hazards that can induce changes in the stress state of the transportation system.

7. Evaluate the operation of the contingency plan of the transportation system.

8. Determine the dynamics of ground usage around the hydrocarbon transport system.

9. Determine and qualify the sectors of the system where hazards to its integrity are expected.

10. Determine and qualify the mechanical state of the system and its ability to withstand hazards.

11. Determine and qualify the sectors adjacent to the transportation system where adverse consequences could be generated if an event of loss of containment takes place.

12. In the sectors of medium and high hazards, of medium and high vulnerability, or of medium and high consequence, perform detailed analyses of all the risk variables that may happen.

13. Propose containment loss scenarios and determine their possibility, determine the chain of events that could lead to the failure, the route of the spilled product and the effects of the oil spill.

14. Analyse each scenario and determine which could be catastrophic.

15. Analyse in detail the chain of events that would lead to the catastrophe and propose actions for its control.

16. Analyse the scenarios with the control measures and determine the actions to follow.

The following diagram (Fig 1) shows the sequence of activities proposed for the evaluation of catastrophic scenarios in hydrocarbon transport systems.

4. APPLICATION EXAMPLE

There is an oil pipeline that runs through an area of a mountain range piedmont. The pipeline transports oil of various characteristics, according to the fields of origin. One of the best price crude oils, which is transported in a third of the operation is a light, very volatile, highly flammable and potentially explosive crude oil. The pipeline was installed partially buried for the most part and it has aerial sections mounted on H frames, in sectors of marginal stability, which were defined during the tracing, and the crossing of bodies of water are made by means of hanging bridges. The installation of this system was completed in 1987 and it lasted 18 months.

The occupied terrain varies from flat to undulated ground with some steep sectors. The climate is warm, humid, with precipitations that exceed 5000 mm/year and with sporadic high intensity rains, of the order of 200 mm/hour.

BASIC INFORMATION:
- About the hazards.
- State of Transportation Systems.
- Behavior of product.
- Exposed elements.

ANALYSIS OF THE INFORMATION:
- Effects of the hazard on the transport system.
- Triggers of the hazard.
- Consequences.
- Contingency plan

EVOLUTION OF THE SET:
- Mechanical state.
- Environment dynamics.

RISK ANALYSIS:
- Probability of breakage (Hazard and state of the System).
- Consequences (Behavior of the product and exposed elements).

If they qualify as Medium or High

CATASTROPHIC SCENARIOS:
- Propose possible scenarios.
- Analyze each scenario.
- Identify the catastrophic scenarios.
- Determine the chain of events.
- Determine the control possibilities.
- Propose scenarios with control.

ACTION PLAN:
- Works or control actions.
- Continue with the System.

FIGURE 1: PROPOSED SEQUENCE OF ACTIVITIES. (SOURCE: OWN)

As the pipeline is located in a piedmont area, there is a major geological fault parallel to the pipeline. That fault is classified as a seismic source and with proven neotectonic activity. The fault is partially covered by deposits of colluvial and alluvial origin.

The route crosses the Rio Grande river, crossing its basin in about 15 km, in which other intermediate and minor streams are crossed as well. Besides, close to the riverside there was an urban centre of smaller size at the time of construction. This urban centre which, as a consequence of oil developments in the region, has had an important growth, to the point that in some sectors the urban area has approached the pipeline and some roads have been built occupying the pipeline right of way. The local basin starts 6 km from the pumping station.

In those fifteen kilometres of the Rio Grande basin, multiple ground instability processes have occurred, one of which, back in the 1990s, generated a loss of containment in the pipeline. Those situations of instability have required important interventions, such as reinforcement of the ground with containment structures, intensification of the elements of drainage, subsurface and deep, construction of protections on the margins of the water currents and rearrangement of the pipe in the H frames. In a sector it was necessary to uncover the pipeline and leave it aerial, supported on skids that would isolate it from the ground movements. All those works have required permanent maintenance and some have had to be rebuilt several times.

When carrying out the threat analysis along the pipeline section, within the Rio Grande basin, it was found the following:

At the K8 + 500, that corresponds to a pipeline section on skids, there is the possibility of a rapid land flow if heavy rains take place.

At the K9 the thrust of a tank against the pipe in a stretch of 20m is observed.

At the K10, in the passage of a ravine, there is the possibility of an avalanche due to instability in the upper part of the slope.

A t the section between K11 and K14, where the pipe is laid on H frames, the trace of relative displacements between the tube and the H frames is observed, due to the creep of the colluvial deposits and the activity of the geological fault.

At K14, in the transition from aerial to buried pipeline, a concentration of deformations is observed.

At K14 + 500, corresponding to the aerial passage over the Rio Grande 150 m long, the right bank is affected by the river flow.

At the K15 + 300, there is pressure on a 150 m pipeline sector by movements of the colluvial deposit.

In the section between K15 and K17 there is influence of the Geological Fault and in the sector from K16 to K17 a road was built next to the pipeline.

In the sector from K17 + 100 to the K17 + 400, there is a movement of the ground in the axial direction of pipeline due to a landslide of a soil deposit.

At the K21 an urbanization was built next to the pipeline, where the access road is on both sides of the pipe, with a 2 m wide median strip along a pipeline length of 300 m.

The activity of the geological fault is estimated to be about 5 cm/year with jumps of up to 25 cm and periods of stillness from

3 to 7 years. In addition, an earthquake of magnitude higher than 7 on the Richter scale could be generated by this fault.

The soil deposits susceptible to movement are activated mainly by the effect of rains and may be associated with El Niño Southern Oscillation (ENSO) periods. In general it has been seen that the reactivation of the landslides is every two cycles (13 to 16 years).

When considering the presence of exposed elements, it is found that the following scenarios can be configured:

At the K8 + 500 a rapid flow of land can be induced, due to the intense rains, which could drag the pipeline and produce a loss of containment; the product would descend by a ravine that arrives near a national highway and flows parallel to it in a section of 300 m. In this sector, between the highway and the ravine there is a recreational centre where barbeques and picnics are common, the ground is flat and the stream can overflow due to its low slope. In consequence if an event of loss of contention occurs on a Saturday or a holiday past noon (in the region the heaviest downpours occur around noon), there could be an agglomeration of people and the presence of fire from the barbeque could generate an hydrocarbon fire, especially if a hydrocarbon of the highest volatility is being transported at that moment. To control this process, it is proposed to install the pipeline on a flyover pass that will allow a potential landslide to flow without affecting the pipeline. At the K14, in addition to the concentration of deformations, the ILI tool found a point with a decreased pipe thickness. If the loss of containment occurs, the hydrocarbon would generate a "geyser"-like jet, impregnating with oil about five houses that are located around the pipeline and then the hydrocarbon would flow towards the national highway and the Rio Grande river. To control this situation, the pipe could be repaired in order to replace the thinner pipe point, to relieve the concentration of deformations and to allow the pipe to be rearranged.

At the K14 + 500, in the crossing of the Rio Grande, it is recommended to reinforce and maintain the margins, to avoid that the effect of the current affects the foundation of the bridge.

At the K15 + 300 there is pressure on the pipe from the sliding of a soil deposit and the activity of the geological fault. In case of a loss of containment, spilled oil could pass next to three houses, before reaching the national highway and then entering the Rio Grande channel. It is proposed to improve the situation of the pipeline by uncovering it so that it releases deformations and complementing the drainage works. Also in the spill route a pond can be formed with a floating retention structure, API type, to retain the largest amount of hydrocarbon in the vicinity of the loss of containment.

In the section between K15 and K17, the pipeline is exposed to the activity of the geological fault, and the ILI tool detected bending anomalies in the crossing sites of the faults associated with the main fault. In case of loss of containment, the product could reach a channel parallel to the national highway, already in the urban area of the city, where it could run along a route of about 3 km and with a high possibility of fire that could affect more than 2000 people. In the sector where the road parallel to the pipe was built, which is paved with rigid concrete and has platforms on both sides, in case of loss of containment the product would go down the road, that has a channel shape and could reach the neighborhood of the Regional Hospital, and if at that time the light crude was being transported any spark could generate a fire, disabling access to the hospital, even affecting it, as well as neighbouring buildings, most of them housing buildings. It is proposed to excavate the pipeline to release the deformations and build channels that intercept the flow, before reaching the urban area and lead it to a dock, equipped with a floating control structure at the exit, before its arrival to the stream, in order to retain the hydrocarbon at that point. On the road, it is suggested to build speed reducers, as a flow cutter that divert the flow to the edge, where an API-type concrete box would be built to collect the hydrocarbon. In this manner the affectation of the urban area is avoided.

5. CONCLUSION

The analysis of scenarios allows to identify the critical sectors and the places where to carry out actions that interrupt the chain of events that may lead to a catastrophe.

It is also a decision tool in a risk management assessment to determine if the organization is able to assume that risk.

ACKNOWLEDGEMENTS

The author is indebted to Ivan Javier Amortegui who kindly help with the translation of this paper from Spanish into English and Engineer Edgard R. Barbosa Cruz for having read this paper and made helpful comments.

REFERENCES

[1] Amórtegui, José V. 2017. "Risk assessment of hydrocarbon pipelines facing natural hazards", Proceedings of the ASME 2017 International Pipeline Geotechnical Conference IPG2017, Lima, Perú.

[2] Danihelka, Pavel. 2018. "Natech, Education and Capacity Building", Faculty of Safety Engineering VSD _ Technical University Ostrava, Czech Republic, UN/OECD Work Shop, Potsdam, Germany,.

[3] Gómez, Alfredo, Swiss Re, 2010. "Riesgos Catastróficos – Bases Conceptuales de los Modelos Catastróficos", Seminario Técnico de Reaseguro SVS, Chile.

[4] Goodman, Richard E. and Gen-hua Shi, 1985. "Block Theory and Its Application to Rock Engineering", Prentece Hall Inc., New Jersey.

[5] Taleb, Nassim Nicholas. 2008. "El Cisne Negro – El Impacto de lo Altamente Improbable", Ediciones Paidós Ibérica S.A., Barcelona.

This page left blank intentionally.

Proceedings of the ASME-ARPEL 2019
International Pipeline Geotechnical Conference
IPG2019
June 25-27, 2019, Buenos Aires, Argentina

IPG2019-5313

INTERFERENCES BY THIRD PARTIES: THE CHALLENGE OF THE CONSTRUCTION OF HIGHWAYS ON THE RIGHT OF WAY OF OIL PIPELINES — CASE OF AUTOPISTAS DEL NORDESTE-OCENSA

Julian Javier Corrales Cobos[1]
Geotechnical Engineer, Ocensa
Puerto Berrio, Colombia

ABSTRACT

The development of third world countries is surrounded by a thousand challenges, one of them is to increase and modernize the transport infrastructure to improve competitiveness in an increasingly interconnected world. Colombia in recent years has undertaken a titanic task of construction of highways to meet this purpose, have hired more than 8170 km of roads, however, this task generates a major challenge for the oil industry since the construction of these roads generates an unplanned interference with the hydrocarbon transport infrastructure that, if not handled correctly, can cause ruptures or damage in the pipelines and the consequent economic and environmental losses.

In 2015 the design of the highway that interconnects the municipalities of Remedios and Caucasia in the department of Antioquia began. This project was called Autopistas del Nordeste. The road was designed to pass through the Pocuné river valley, however, the environmental licensing of this type of project requires the revision of the interference with other networks. It was found that the new road crossed the Ocensa pipeline at 26 points. The geographical conditions require the use of this small corridor by many lines, 2 pipelines (Ocensa and ODC), a 500 KV power line and, of course, the current tertiary route and the projected highway that connects these municipalities. The challenge is huge, in this article the project is described, the negotiation stages that have been necessary to carry out with the way to make compatible the projects and the threats that have been overcome in the constructive stage.

Keywords: Pipeline, interferences, third parties.

INTRODUCTION

The development of a country is linked to its ability to compete with others for goods and services, that depends on the balance of tcommerce to tilt in their favor. This competition is governed by market laws and one of the most important variables is cost. Colombia has many areas where it is possible to set up many productive projects, however, due to the difficult topography of the country and the climatic conditions, although important steps have been taken to fulfill this task, there is still a lot to do.

According to the world economic forum [1] the country is in the 66th place of the Global Competitiveness Index, however in the 2nd pillar (infrastructure) it is in the 87th place.

The Colombian authorities are aware that until the competitiveness in infrastructure is increased, the country will not develop at the desired speed. For this reason the country made the decision to invest in this sector and launched a very ambitious road construction program.

But this decision puts the roads to compete with the other means of transport by the most profitable corridors and better topographic conditions.

In 2015, the construction of a road that interconnects the valleys of the Magdalena and Cauca rivers (the two most important river arteries in the country) was presented and approved, this road was designed crossing the foothills of the central mountain range, avoiding the flood zones to the north of the country with very soft soils. The designers of Ocensa and ODC made the same decision twenty years ago. The two means of transport compete for the same space.

---

[1] Contact author: julian.corrales@ocensa.com.co

DEVELOPMENT OF THE ROAD

1. Design Stage

During the design stage of the road, the presence of the Ocensa and ODC pipelines was noticed, and the discussion of the best way to coexist the three projects began. However, in the valley of the Pocuné river, although many discussions were set in place, it was not possible that the projects interfere with each other, the first design started with 26 crossings of each pipeline with the road and finally after many considerations they were reduced to 19 crosses with Ocensa.

The road project is composed of two functional units, functional unit 1 (UF1) starts from the municipality of Remedios to the municipality of Zaragoza with a total of 58 km corresponding to the construction of new road. The functional unit 2 (UF2) starts from the municipality of Zaragoza to the municipality of Caucasia with a total of 82 km that corresponds to the improvement of existing road, this improvement consists of increasing the design speed of the road which implies changes in the alignment and increase in track width.

UF2 being an existing road in which there are 6 crossings of the Ocensa pipeline and the road. In this functional unit, design discussions were limited to defining whether the same number of crosses were maintained.

In UF1 the discussion was more complex since the natural corridor to travel from Remedios to Zaragoza takes place in the Pocuné river valley. Geomorphologically the valley of the Pocuné river runs parallel to the Otu fault [2], at the north of the valley cross the fault and towards the South is necessary to climb the mountains. Therefore, the road decided to use this corridor for its layout. Along this narrow corridor run two pipelines, a 500 KV electric line and now a road track. Interferences between the 4 transport lines are unavoidable. Initially, 16 typical crossings were planned, defining as typical the crossing in which the pipeline is under the track (Figure 1) and three crossings that were called special because in these the road was under the pipeline (Figure 2), due to the specifications of the road any charge to its layout was undesirable. In the special crossings the pipe was protected by a concrete structure with pre-excavated piles and the road passed under it through a false tunnel.

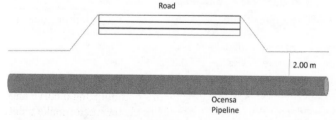

Figure 1. Typical crossing

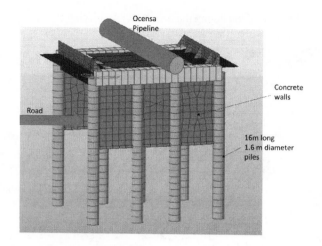

Figures 2. Special crossing

These three special crossings had a very strong discussion due to risk conditions and to date they remain unconstructed waiting for the road concessionaire to deliver the final designs.

2. Construction Stage

Because the road project interferes with an existing one, Law 1682 of 2013 in Colombia establishes that the one that interferes must cover the costs of the protection of the existing network.

Civil works for road construction generally occupy large volumes of excavation and filling, this leads to high yields for the execution of these activities. Cost was the first topic of discussion because in each one of the crossings it was necessary to check the integrity of the pipeline and this way guarantee the coexistence of the two projects, the issue of the yields was the first obstacle that was presented.

For the engineers in charge of the maintenance of the Ocensa 36" Pipeline, it is common knowledge that the pipe excavation yield is less than three linear meters under very soft soil conditions and with a maximum of 12 linear meters in optimum soil conditions (60 -240 m3 per day). Due to the high risk conditions, salaries of the oil industry are also high, in consequence any intervention in the pipeline are expensive.

After a series of negotiations, the concessionaire was in charge of the excavation and capping of the pipe and Ocensa of the mechanical inspection. For this, an agreement was signed between the two companies on June 25, 2017.

In the agreement three unmovable conditions were defined:
- All technical or professional personnel involved in the activities must be evaluated in the Ocensa standards and procedures.
- Throughout the construction phase of the project, they must have staff that will monitor the right-of-way (ROW).
- All road work that approaches 30 meters from the axis of the pipeline must be informed and approved by Ocensa, while its intervention will be subject to monitoring.

The concession began the process of qualifying its personnel to perform the qualified tasks, however, after many attempts they did not achieve the minimum qualifications.

3. Interferences

Due to the delays because the concessionaire cannot intervene the crossings, they requested the realization of provisional crossings to be able to enter their work places. Bearing in mind that the transit of heavy machinery would be constant over each of the crossings, a low resistance concrete plate was necessary for each one of the temporary crossings. This solution corresponds to a concrete plate (fc = 14 MPa), located at a minimum distance of 1.2 m of the pipe.

Crossings is the first concern when reviewing a road interference at the design stage, because they are easy to identify and the effects are direct on the pipeline. However, from experience, these crossings are executed by qualified personnel and are carried out following strictly the protocols and procedures established for these tasks, so in general they don't generate major complications, although the risk of these works is high due to their potential (the threat is high), the possibility of occurrence is very low.

There is another interference that does not have the same focus of attention during the design stage, but during the construction stage it is the one that requires the greatest care, this interference is the parallelism. A parallelism is configured when the two projects pass one path close to the other.

These parallels are those that to date in Ocensa have generated the greatest concerns during the construction of road interferences, the case presented in [3] set the alarms in the company about the controls to this type of interventions, because until now Crosses were the focus of attention and a restriction of 30 meters was considered sufficient to safeguard the integrity of the ROW and the pipeline.

In the case of parallelism, several causes of pipe problems have been detected:

- Destabilization of the ROW, this is the classic interference in which the tracing of the road changes the geometric conditions of the slope and causes a failure of the same, in this case the road passes under the pipeline. Figure 3.

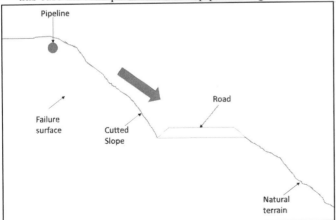

Figure 3. Cutting slope failure mechanism

- Excavation material improperly stored or product of landslides on the ROW, sometimes when making cuts or excavations in the road or in case of landslides in the road slope, the material of the same falls on the ROW, in this case the overweight it may cause failure of the slope of the ROW, scour in the case of flows or changes in water flows due to damming. The path goes upstream of the pipe. Figure 4.

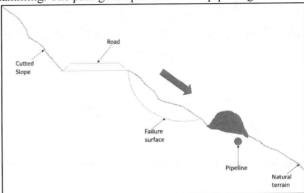

Figure 4. Mechanism of failure due to falling of material

- Water management, the road turns by itself into a water channel, the sites where these waters are discharged become scour spots if they are not treated properly. The failure mechanism is similar to the material that falls on the track.
- Bulging, this is the case treated in [3] is rare but its occurrence in soft soils is due to the shear failure of the soil under the road embankment or landfill in the case of the Management Zones of Debris and Excavation Material (ZODMES). Figure 5.

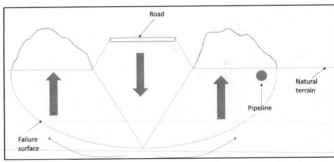

Figure 5. Mechanism of Shear Stress failure due to foundation overload.

3.1. PK 548+100

In April 2018 the first alarm was presented at the site of PK 548+100, the road passes through this point making a curve and to be able to finalize the layout, the road constructor make a cut on the slope where the pipeline is located. As a result of this cut a landslide whose scarp is parallel to the pipeline in a stretch of 12 meters was presented. Photographs 1 and 2.

Photograph 1. The escarpment of the slide parallel to the pipe is observed, the worker of the photograph is standing on the axis of the pipe.

Inspection of the pipeline was carried out and mechanical damage was discarded, the slope was repaired with a geometric design that increased its safety factor to tolerable values for the pipeline.

In the photograph 3 the pipe located in all the escarpment of the landslide is observed, this condition prevented damages in the same because part of the pipe is located in the stable part of the slope.

For the design parameters of the solution it was requested to comply with a factor of safety of 2.0, even thought in case of road slopes the design safety factor is 1.6, this higher safety factor is justified by the consequences in case the failure of the slope affects the pipe.

Photograph 2. Aerial shot of the slide in the Pk 548 + 100

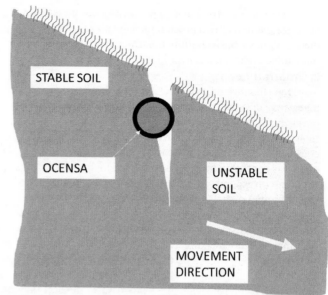

Figure 6. Diagram of ground failure with respect to the position of the pipeline.

Photograph 3. The pipe parallel to the escarpment is observed.

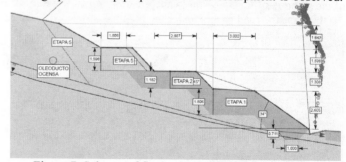

Figure 7. Scheme of final solution on the slope of PK 548 + 100. Stages 3 and 4 are filters and for scales issues are not presented

3.2. PK 548+600

In May 2018 the second action of the concessionaire that required immediate attention was presented at PK 548+600, in this case the old road had a slope of 7.5 meters high, the concessionaire makes a cut and the new slope was more than 20 meters high, a massive failure presented in the slope that requires immediate control measures. Photographs 4, 5 and 6

Photograph 4. The slide area and the route of the pipelines are observed in aerial photography. The Ocensa Pipeline in red is less than 5 meters from the escarpment.

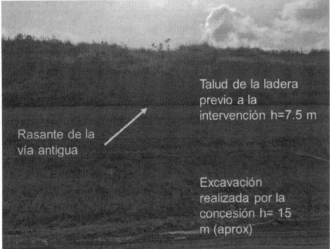

Photograph 5. The intervention on the slope and the initial slope can be observed. This photograph was taken prior to the failure of the slope

Photograph 6. General failure of the slopes on both sides of the road

In view of the risk, immediate intervention was necessary. Plastics were installed on the slope. Three solutions were proposed:
- Piping variant.
- Road variant
- Stabilization of the slope

Due to high costs the first two solutions were discarded, the stabilization of the slope although it was determined as the indicated solution took a long time for its design and construction. To minimize the risk, meanwhile, an interim solution was implemented to support the pipeline. Photograph 7 and Figure 8. Four supports were installed with anchorage dead loads connected to the pipeline by means of steel wires.

Photograph 7. The anchorage sites for temporary support to the pipeline are shown

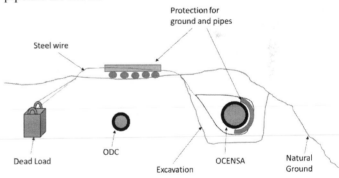

Figure 8. Design of temporary pipe support anchors

The final stabilization solution comprised a combination of active and passive anchors and screens in concrete. Figure 9

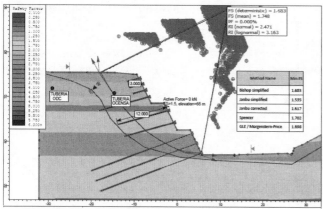

Figure 9. Geotechnical model of stabilization solution in PK 548 + 500

The cost of the two interventions to the Ocensa pipeline (without the final stabilization) reached the USD $ 200,000 that were paid by the concessionaire. After this payment, the concessionaire prior to any intervention presents the stabilization designs and no impacts have been presented on the slopes of the pipeline since then.

LEARNED LESSONS

Based on the events that have occurred to date and the measures taken to correct the course, the following lessons are learned:

1. The need for projects to initiate contacts during the evaluation and structuring stage. This would allow identifying possible interferences and minimizing their consequences avoiding loss of time and money in later stages.

2. In the case of this type of project, the agreements or construction contracts with the incoming project must contemplate not only the obvious interferences in the crossings of the track, the parallelisms should be defined to avoid problems and future cost overruns.

3. Supervision by the affected project must be considered from the very beginning of the project and throughout its construction phase. By focusing on the crosses, the risk in the other work fronts tends to be underestimated.

4. The interference of networks should be the subject of study and definition of future standards and procedures, the lack of this instrument means that when defining what and how, differences of opinions are presented based on the needs of each project.

5. Although in Colombia there is a law (1682 of 2013) that defines the rules of the game for the relationship between the different infrastructure projects, said law is based on the importance of each project that is defined as of national interest. The controversy arises when the two projects have the same importance.

6. The right of way in cases of road interference is not a guarantee of stability, in the article several cases have been shown in which although this distance is respected, it is possible that there may be damages. These distances should be established in the procedures and standards in order to safeguard the process safety in the case of the transport of liquid hazardous substances.

7. Even thought in Ocensa there is a public awareness program, the deadlines of other projects mean that on many occasions risks are taken by these other actors and it is on these occasions when the risks materialize

ACKNOWLEDGEMENTS

The contributions of the work team of the line maintenance superintendence and the support of Ocensa for the presentation of this article are gratefully acknowledged. To my wife and family for the time I dedicate to this publication and consequently I cannot dedicate it to them,

REFERENCES

[1] Wold Economic Forum. The Global Competitiveness Report 2017–2018.

[2] Milton Alvarez, Oswaldo Ordoñez, Mauricio Valencia, Antonio Romero. Geology of the influence zone of the Otu fault in the Segovia-Remedios mining district. Dyna. 2007

[3] Corrales Julian, Garcia Hugo, Marin Alejandro, ereira Mauricio. Ocensa Oil Pipeline damage due to the construction of a highway embankment inf soft soil. IPG2017-2511

IPG2019-5320

RIVER CROSSINGS: DEVELOPING A MOBILE GIS APPROACH TO MONITORING ACTIVITIES

Martin Carnicero, Maureen Vázquez
Transportadora de Gas del Norte
Buenos Aires, Argentina

ABSTRACT

TGN operates a system of 9,000 kilometers of natural gas pipelines with numerous river crossings. According to the mandatory monitoring program, river crossings are visited at least once a year with additional visits for major rivers during the rainy season. Basic data such as depth of cover for each line, photographs and descriptions are surveyed in the field. Later on, this information is manually entered in an electronic form for its use in risk analysis, to evaluate the need of remediation works. This task has two main problems: first, it is very time consuming for surveyors, and second, it is difficult to know the location within the river crossing where data was taken. At the end, monitoring forms came late in the year and its information is difficult to understand. To cope with this problem, a new approach was developed. A GIS mobile application was developed and installed in tablets used in the field, guiding the surveyor through the completion of an electronic form along each pipeline, having a satellite image in the background, as a global reference of where he is standing. All the information is geo-referenced using a built-in GPS. Once it is finished, by means of a simple WIFI/4G connection, information is sent to GIS servers, without the need to be typed at the office. Later on, it is captured and placed into the monitoring form format. Specialists can access and evaluate this information from the database visualizing it in the corporate GIS with minimum delay. This improvement has resulted in a significant decrease in time for the entire data flow process and a better quality of the information gathered, which results in a more realistic risk analysis.
Keywords: river crossings, GIS, monitoring.

INTRODUCTION

During in the past 20 years, the activity of monitoring river crossings has evolved. At the beginning, paper forms where filled and photographs where printed and attached, marking crosses in several yes or no columns. They were sent by internal mail or kept at each of the 34 maintenance bases for later use. Access to monitoring forms was by individual request, becoming a titanic task to have an entire picture of river crossings along the system, each year.

Later on, a database and an electronic form were developed, together with instructions for surveyors regarding how to monitor in the field. Output from this task was materialized in three different formats:

- Form: with relevant information comprising admin aspects, location by means of GPS coordinates, measured values for depth of cover along each pipeline and general comments,
- Hand-made drawing with the space distribution of the information and the approximate location of depth of cover measurements,
- Photographs of the most important changes observed at the crossing such as erosive processes at bed and banks, and uncovered segments of pipelines.

At that time, this was a great improvement in terms of accessibility and quality of the information. By being at the database, forms were easily viewed and analyzed. However, surveyors had to go to the field, capture the information and then go back to the office, type each form and load it to the database. Given the fact that TGN has approximately 650 river crossings, the forms were not always available at the right time or at all. If they came late in the dry season, then there was little time to design, contract and implement remedial works before the next rainy season began. In many cases, the whole monitoring activity was not executed, or the information that appeared in the forms was not updated.

Furthermore, the analysis of the information was also very time-consuming for each crossing, since the specialist had no spatial reference for depth of cover values and photographs. These problems were somehow overcome by knowing the sites or by having telephone conversations with surveyors. Therefore, the entire process needed to be more user-friendly both for surveyors and specialists at the integrity department.

MONITORING RIVER CROSSINGS

Natural hazards affecting crossings are generally listed as follows:
- River bed scour and degradation
- Bank erosion
- Meander migration
- Avulsion and flow through the right of way
- A combination of the above

These hazards occur along the 9,000 kilometers of pipelines operated by TGN, crossing a great variety of natural environments such as pampa plains, mountains, foothills and deserts. Thus the objective of this mandatory activity is to continuously register the interaction between rivers that experience great mobility with time, against a rigid pipeline lay-out resulting from its original design and construction. Early identification of natural hazards to pipeline integrity provides the necessary time to design and build remedial works to avoid pressure reductions that affect natural gas transport and, eventually, line ruptures. Thus, timing is an important issue, since if an uncovered segment of a pipeline is informed late in the dry season there is no time for remedial action before the next rainy season begins. In the following paragraphs a description of monitoring tasks is presented.

Three main tasks are associated to field monitoring:
- Measurements, visual inspection and photographs
- Registration in an electronic form and database
- Data assessment and risk evaluation.

Frequency was established after the following criteria:
- All crossings are surveyed once a year
- Crossings associated with higher risk (greater watershed, history of previous interventions, sites with minimum depth of cover or where changes in river alignment were identified) once a month during the rainy season
- After a major climatic event occurs, such as more than 60 mm of precipitation in a day, interruption of national highways due to flooding, TV news reporting heavy rain, floods and damages.

The monitoring form should include all the information needed for assessing the risk at a particular crossing, in accordance to the methodology described in reference [1]. The following parameters are taken from it:
- Location of the crossing by means of GPS coordinates
- Vertical depth of cover
- Horizontal depth of cover
- River bed material
- River banks materials

- River width
- River banks heights
- Identification of uncovered segments of pipelines and free-span conditions
- Evidence of debris flows
- Status of existing remedial works

Depth of cover takes a predominant role. Simplifying, erosive processes listed above could affect the available depth of cover laterally or vertically, or both. Besides all the measured parameters, photographs help in visualizing the extent of the observed changes and the status of existing remedial works. This later aspect is related to pipeline vulnerability, since their performance adds protection to the lines, decreasing the overall risk. Finally, there is room for comments that are important to surveyors beyond hard data and pictures, which are crucial to a qualitative evaluation.

Electronic forms became a huge improvement from previous paper forms. However, they proved to be quite rigid in terms of fitting to all rivers, from small creeks or canal, to wide rivers. The available room for cover measurements was either too much for little crossings or not enough for large rivers. But the main drawback was the needed time spent for surveyors typing data once they were back at the office. Sometimes, the whole task was put aside or, data was extracted from previous surveys and input in the form as actual one.

At the other end, once the forms and pictures were ready for access, a specialist from the Integrity Department analyzed each of them. All pieces of information needed to be put together in terms of spatial distribution, in order to make a sound analysis. A hand-made drawing coped with this problem, adding extra time for both surveyors and analysts to develop and understand. Then, as the number and size of photographs grew, loading and visualizing each of them also took a considerable amount of time.

SHIFTING TO GIS

TGN began in past years the processes of building a corporate GIS and developing an Integrity Managing System based on risk. The whole GIS architecture, as shown in Figure 1, is designed to integrate our 3 main GIS environments: Mobile apps, Desktop software and GIS on the web; all of them connected to the main GIS data base built on Oracle, using ArcGIS Enterprise.

Following this trend, two issues were selected as a test program: third-party risks and river crossings.

First, focus was placed at developing a mobile field survey application with two main objectives:
- Integrate data obtained from field mobile devices with TGN's corporate GIS and with the existing database, supported by SAP®. At the same time that the information is stored and shown in GIS, it is also saved in the company's data base developed under SAP. TGN´s IT specialists, using a web API (Application

Programming Interface) were able to design a web service to connect and download all data stored in the GIS data base and load it in a custom made monitoring form for river crossings surveys, stored in SAP and that could also be consulted in TGN´s Intranet,

- Provide surveyors the option of collecting data with mobile devices at any work environment, speeding and automating monitoring tasks.

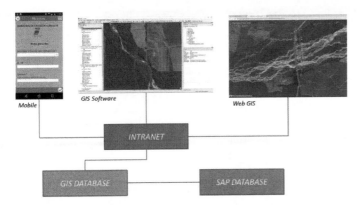

FIGURE 1: GIS ARCHITECTURE

An application was developed using ESRI's Survey123, by means of the company's Portal corporate account, being completely integrated with ArcGIS Enterprise.

Among the application most important characteristics are:

- It is a GIS application that captures data based on XLS forms,
- It allows data compilation in a centralized way by the creation and analysis of surveys,
- Through the company's ArcGIS account, it is possible to download forms that have been shared,
- Once downloaded, data compilation can be started.
- If working without connection, forms are saved locally.

Later on, they will be sent to the GIS database, once connection is reestablished.

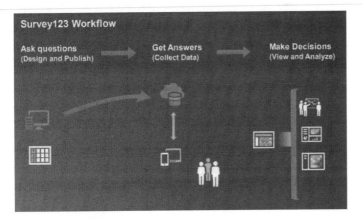

FIGURE 2: SURVEY123 WORKFLOW

The use of this survey application has three basic steps, once it has been designed, created and published in our Portal for ArcGIS (see Figure 2):

- Download the application and the electronic form for river crossings at the office. An internet connection is needed.
- Field survey, no internet connection is needed. This task comprises the survey itself.
- Send the data: usually, once each pipeline is finished, the form is stored to be sent later on, together with other lines and other crossings surveyed on that particular day.

In the following paragraphs, use of the application is explained focusing on its capabilities with a brief description of each feature.

Step 1: Capture information: it starts the whole survey of one pipeline. It also offers the possibility of deleting a survey and to go back to edit previous surveys.

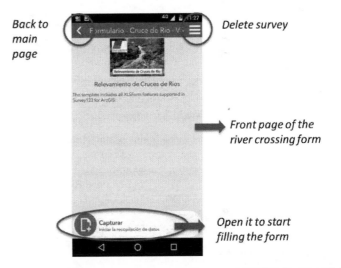

FIGURE 3: STEP 1-CAPTURING INFORMATION

Step 2: Data management: it closes a survey and saves the data. It also offers the possibility of saving information that is common to all lines in a particular river.

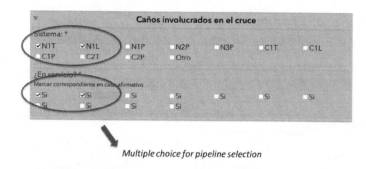

FIGURE 4: STEP 2-DATA MANAGEMENT

Step 3: Choosing the corresponding administrative maintenance base.

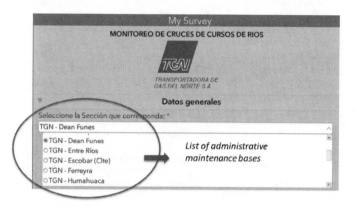

FIGURE 5: STEP 3-ADMINISTRATIVE BASE

Step 4: Capturing GPS coordinates

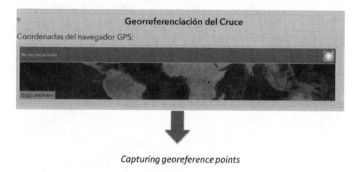

FIGURE 6: STEP 4-CAPTURE OF GPS COORDINATES

Step 5: Line selection

FIGURE 7: STEP 5 – LINE SELECTION

Step 6: State of access roads: access to the sites is one of the most common problems that prevent survey completion. It could be due to flooding, mud or problems with property owners. It gives the possibility of choosing the right or left bank, and documenting the field situation with a picture, stating that they went to the site but could not reach the river.

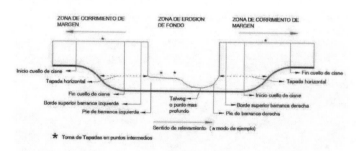

FIGURE 8: STEP 6 – ACCESS ROADS

Step 7: Depth of cover measurements: by means of a sketch it provides and guides the surveyor along the entire process.

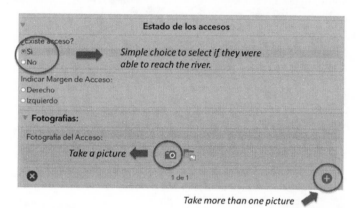

FIGURE 9: STEP 7 – DEPTH OF COVER GUIDING SKETCH

To fulfil this task, surveyors must choose among following options:

- Measurements were taken or not: sometimes high river flows do not allow depth of cover readings. However, pictures still provide valuable information.
- Pipeline diameter
- Bank and direction in which depths are taken
- Specific locations for readings such as (see Figure 9):

  o Initial point
  o Beginning and end of set-back, for each bank
  o Top of each bank
  o Bottom of each bank
  o Deepest point at river bed
  o Intermediate points
  o Final point

Surveyors can visualize where they are at, by looking at a satellite image that is part of the application. At any specific point, GPS coordinates are taken automatically together with an approximate GPS elevation (Figure 11). The value for cover depth is typed into the application. Since this value is given to the center of the pipeline, the real cover depth is obtained by subtracting pipe radius. Then, there is an option for taking a picture of that particular place and to type a comment, if necessary. Finally, by clicking on the plus (+) symbol, a new location can be loaded.

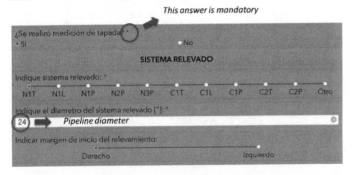

FIGURE 10: STEP 7 – DEPTH OF COVER OPTIONS

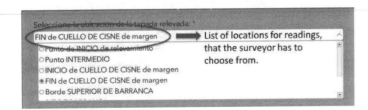

FIGURE 11: STEP 7 – READINGS AT SPECIFIC LOCATIONS

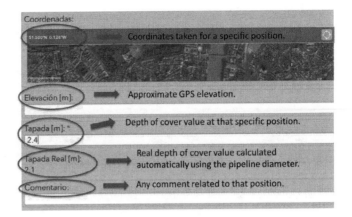

FIGURE 12: STEP 7 – GEO-REFERENCED VALUES

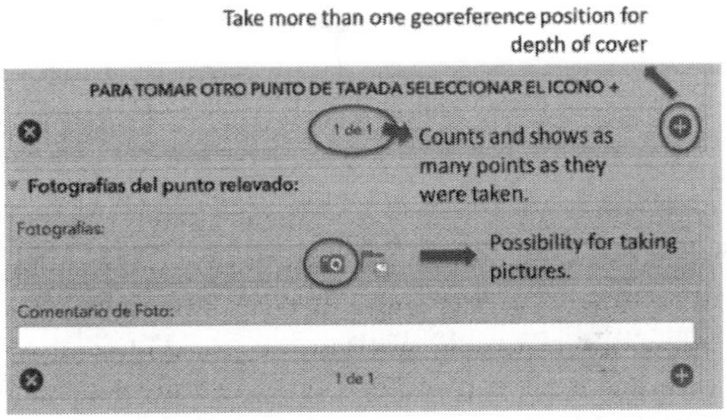

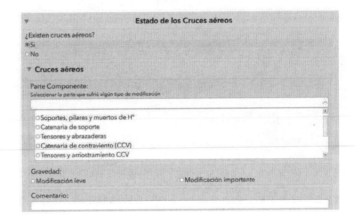

FIGURE 13: STEP 7 – PICTURE AND COMMENTS OPTIONS

Step 8: besides a typical buried crossing, there is an option for aerial crossings, collecting qualitative information of the state of each component (towers, tensors, concrete weights, etc.).

FIGURE 14: STEP 8 – AERIAL CROSSINGS

Step 9: state of prevention signs. Comments and pictures of exiting signs trigger an intervention such as replacement of missing signs or updating its information.

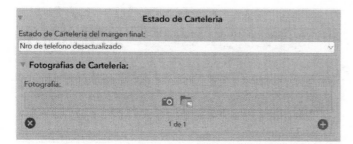

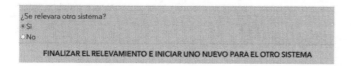

FIGURE 15: STEP 9 – PREVENTION SIGNS

Step 10: Go to next line for the same crossing.

FIGURE 16: STEP 10 – GOTO NEXT LINE

RESULTS

Once the information is loaded into TGN´s GIS, it is easy to visualize and analyze. A Web Map is made to show over a satellite image all measurements made in the field over each line.

An example for the Salí River is presented in a Web GIS. It is located at 26° 16' 35.98"S of latitude south and 65° 14' 31.33"O of longitude west. It has a protection on its left or northern bank consisting in gabion mattresses. It covers two of the three existing pipelines (24" and 16" in diameter). Upstream of them, a new 30" line was built at greater depth and with no erosion control works.

FIGURE 17: VISUALIZATION OF DEPTH OF COVER DATA

All values for the available depth of cover for all lines are between 3 to 4 m for the 30" line, over 1.75 m for the main line, and between 2.7 and 4 m over the 16" line. Furthermore, pictures of north bank protection show that it is in good shape,

covered by vegetation. No signs of erosion were reported. Sediment deposition may change the available river width at the main line crossing, triggering further monitoring to evaluate its evolution. Prevention signs were damaged or removed, needing an immediate replacement. Observing measurements for the 16" line (downstream) it is evident that its route is misplaced in the GIS data base and needs correction.

FIGURE 18: EROSION CONTROL WORKS

FIGURE 19: PREVENTION SIGNS

CONCLUSIONS

River crossing monitoring has been under review given the fact that the previous process based on electronic forms leaded to delays that were not compatible to the right timing needed to develop and construct remedial works once an integrity hazard was identified. Surveyors collected the information in the field and later on typed it at the office to complete the forms. Pictures and hand-made drawings were attached to provide an idea of the spatial distribution of collected data. Analysis performed by integrity specialist was a very time-consuming task since it was necessary to put all relevant data together.

Benefiting from the company's decision of build a corporate GIS, a new approach was implemented. Four main improvements were made:

- Capture information in field in real time, avoiding data entry by hand and impeding the use old data,
- Both depth of cover measurements and pictures have their GPS coordinates incorporated,
- Loading the information is possible by a simple WIFI connection,
- Data access and visualization is possibly right after loading was executed, with all the information from corporate GIS available in the background.

In summary benefits from this tool are:

- Significant time reduction from surveyors,
- Better data quality since it is geo-referenced,
- Access to field data in real time,
- Easiness in the analysis thanks to GIS visualization capabilities

This tool also offers room for future improvements such as:

- Load of geo-referenced remedial works that could be seen in the mobile device by surveyors,
- Use of digital elevation models obtained by drones so as to draw a longitudinal profile of each line.

As it is being used, comments and suggestions from surveyors are updated in an on-going process that will improve its reliability with time.

REFERENCES

[1] IPG2013-1923 Carnicero, M., 2013, "A rating method for assessment risk at river crossings".

This page left blank intentionally.

IPG2019-5324

Monitoring and Screening of Pipelines for Movement
A fast and cost-effective alternative for Pipeline Operators to measure Drift in Pipelines

Michael Schorr[1], Klaas Kole[2], Ferdinand Foessing[1]
[1]Rosen Group, Lingen, Germany
[2]Rosen Group, Oldenzaal, Netherlands

ABSTRACT:

For pipelines in the oil, gas, and mining industry, movement of pipelines is one of the main integrity hazards. This movement in most cases is caused by landslides instigated by heavy rain, earthquakes or volcanic activities. If the pipeline movement remains undetected at an early stage, it can lead to the need for costly repairs to prevent, remove, or repair potential or actual damage. Moreover, if the movements stay undetected for too long, these lines may fail and lead to catastrophic events.

This paper will illustrate what a fast and cost-effective solution to avoid these threats at an early stage looks like and how it works. It will explain the process and demonstrate the full power of this technology on the basis of a case study.

The standard solution for pipelines without a permanent position monitoring system at the time of installation includes the use of intelligent tools that are able to detect even the slightest changes in the trajectory. These inspection tools are quite expensive to run, especially when multiple screening runs are required throughout a year, e.g. before and after the rainy season or after a seismic event. Other monitoring solutions are either limited to only a specific area where the movement has already been detected at an earlier stage or lack the precision required to serve as an early warning system, such as LIDAR or satellite image comparison.

Over the years, ROSEN has developed a technology that can bridge the gap between frequent measurements and cost-effective service. It is based on an electronic gyroscope that is commonly used in Inline Inspection tools but can also be installed in readily available cleaning tools. When first run in a pipeline, it records the whole pipeline trajectory, leaving no segment undocumented. The next step is to compare these recorded pipeline routing measurements with already existing trajectory baseline data, recorded earlier by any ILI tool with an optical gyro or similar. This comparison will reveal any deviation between both trajectories and precisely determine any pipeline movement. A case study will demonstrate how the comparison is achieved.

When performing repetitive inspections, this screening comparison enables the operators to detect the onset of movements and monitor the progress of any known pipeline movement. It allows them to distinguish between stable areas from dynamic ground movements and keeps close track of changes in the pipe course. Through regular repetitions, any further development of the movement is tracked, and appropriate reactive measures can be scheduled in a timely manner. This new service provides a cost-effective and powerful early warning tool for geological pipeline integrity threats that can lead to loss of integrity, the asset, or - worst-case scenario - loss of life or environmental contamination, while at the same time, it reduces the necessity of pipeline intervention that will affect production.

---

[1] Contact author: MSchorr@Rosen-Group.com

1 Effect of Geohazards on Pipelines

In the following, some samples for geohazard effects on the surrounding terrains of pipelines that are causing lines to move from their original location and result in danger of failing.

FIGURE 1: PIPELINE EXPOSED IN ROTATIONAL LANDSLIDE

FIGURE 2: EXPOSURE OF PIPELINE IN RIVERBANK

FIGURE 3: RIVERBANK EROSION CAUSING BANK INSTABILITY AND EXPOSING PIPELINE

2 Identification of Pipeline Movement

As part of any pipeline construction project, a risk analysis is carried out to identify any apparent or underlying risk to pipeline construction and/or operation. These assessments ensure that operational risks are minimized.

	Feasibility					EPC			O&M (Operation and Maintenance)
Description	Conceptual Design	Pre-FEED	FEED			Detailed Engineering	Procurement	Construction	
			Light	Normal	Extended				
Major Deliverable		Process Description · Block Flow Diagram · Cost Estimation							De-bottlenecking & Revamping
			BEDD · PFD · H&MB · Equipment List · Plot Plan						
				P&ID · MSD · Process D/S · Utility Balance · Licensor Selection					
				HAZOP/SIL · EPC ITB					
					3D Model · LLI PO · BOM				
						D/S · Sizing · AFC DWG · Mini-HAZOP/SIL			
							Vendor Print		
								As Built DWG	
Estimate Accuracy (%)	Class 5 -50 ~ +100	Class 4/3 (-15~-30)~ (+20~+50)	Class 3/2 (-10~20)~ (+18~+30)			Class 1 -3 ~ +15	N/A Source: www.theprojectdefinition.com		N/A	N/A

FIGURE 4: TYPICAL PROJECT PLAN WITH FEED PHASE

Executing these measures years before any actual step is taken to actually build the pipeline still does not mean that all risk is eliminated. Climate change and more extreme weather conditions are posing an enormous risk to any asset that lies in the ground or on the seabed.

As a result, even after completion of the pipeline construction, measures must be taken, including maintenance and monitoring for any threats, including corrosion, cracking and also movement that causes extensive strain. The number of different applications and offers on the market are of great variety and differing quality, ranging from purely subjective visual controls to highly accurate terrain scans. In the following, we will cite the, until now, most common solutions and highlight their pros and cons.

2.1 ROW Foot Patrol

Walking the right of way is a very common measure in many regions to eliminate integrity risks caused by constructions on top of the line, illegal vehicle movement across the right of way, or pilfering.

When it comes to ground movements, the assessment is purely subjective, and detection is limited to sudden large movements. Slowly creeping line movement detection is very difficult to assess, even for an experienced surveyor.

Additionally, more often than not, accessibility is limited due to weather or terrain conditions (swamp, desert), or simply due to personal threats such as terrorism, illegal activities, indigenous tribes, etc. This means that large stretches often remain unchecked.

FIGURE 5: RIGHT OF WAY SLOPE STABILIZATION (WEST AFRICA)

2.2 Aerial Surveillance

2.2.1 Visual Surveys

Generally, visual inspections provide a rather nice overview of the local situation. However, geohazards may largely remain unrecognized based on the images, and further monitoring may be difficult.

2.2.2 Satellite imagery

Third party activities, geohazards, and leak detection are some of the possible interpretations that are derived from satellite imagery.

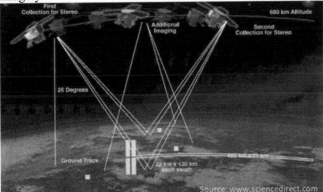

FIGURE 6: COLLECTION OF STEREO SATELLITE IMAGERY

The application for these images ranges from encroachment and pipeline class changes to aerosol-based leak detection and identification of vegetation changes and detection of geohazards caused by changing river crossings or land-slumps/slides.

The images taken and results based on it are calculated from the elevation profile only, not horizontal movement. Resolution of these "eyes in the sky" are given in pixel size. Common pixel size for these images range from 0.41m (GeoEye) to 10m - 15m (Sentinel 2, Landsat) (Source. /1/). Precision is also dependent if the image is taken directly vertical or at an angle. Taking into account an orbit of 700km and pictures taken in a size of about ten to a few hundred kilometers, precision is almost never as required. As an example, an image taken with a Landsat satellite that takes 190km wide images, the angle when looking at the edges is more than 8 degrees, reducing precision significantly. So unless looking straight down, the high resolution of 41cm (some of these satellites theoretically offer even less) is unrealistic in most cases.

Unfortunately, except the operator owns the satellite, access is limited and very costly. Additionally, unless the equipment is geostationary, the flexibility is limited and urgently needed images cannot be retrieved at any time but only when the satellite is in range.

2.2.3 (Un-)manned aircraft surveillance

Similar to the satellite imagery, airborne surveillance is used mainly for monitoring
- illegal access to right of way
- illegal construction on top of pipeline
- suspicious activities around product theft
- sudden pipeline movements caused by mudslides, rock fall, etc.

More often than not local operators offer these kind of surveys all around the world (Source /2/), trying to identify
- Spills or leaks
- Exposed pipe
- Slope stability anomalies
- Ditch settlement
- Erosion anomalies
- Vegetation anomalies
- Third party activity
- Encroachments
- Missing signs & markers

Detection of movement applies only to significant deflections, onset of movements or slowly creeping pipeline movement that takes place over months will remain undetected since the process is leaning heavily on the experience of the spotter. It leaves lots of room for interpretation.

Aircrafts and UAVs are operated only in suitable weather conditions. During heavy rains or storm, when many geotechnical movements occur, they have either limited operability or remain completely grounded.

Other operational limits and challenges include max. time airborne, limits in access of airspace due to government/military regulations and also intervention from the local population.

The cost of these airborne services on a permanent basis often exceeds the budgetary limits of operators, aiming to keep the OPEX as low as reasonably achievable.

2.2.4 LiDAR

Lidar is a surveying method that measures distance to a target by illuminating the target with pulsed laser light and measuring the reflected pulses with a sensor. Differences in laser return times and wavelengths can then be used to make digital 3-D representations of the target. (Source /3/)

Airborne LiDAR is of much higher precision than the aforementioned solutions. It is used to create 3D imagery of the terrain. The resolution depends largely on the aircraft altitude and the laser system used.

FIGURE 7: AIRBORNE LIDAR DATA COLLECTION

Under optimum conditions, the collected data quality and measurement precision is rather impressive: Vertical accuracies of below 50mm can be achieved.

As with most high-end technologies, as soon as the conditions become less than perfect, quality starts to suffer. While data acquired at 150 m altitude is highly accurate, this altitude is very unusual for aircrafts and even dangerous in mountainous areas. In a research project where data was collected at a flying height of 1200m, vertical precision ranges from 17cm to 26cm (Source /4/). Dense vegetation or areas with low surface roughness such as ice, water, sand, or swamp result in a higher margin of error. Similar to the other optical services, limitations apply to Lidar as well. Weather has its impact. Surveying large distance transmission lines of several 100km requires airborne times that often exceed what is reasonably available. In addition, it is not unheard of that aircrafts have been shot at from the ground by third parties, with consequences ranging from aircraft damage to loss of life.

From a cost point of view, it is true that even the smallest jobs start at 20.000 USD plus local taxes and fees, making the monthly or quarterly scan on a complete pipeline length that is needed to ensure a close monitoring and detection of an onset of movement unfeasible.

2.3 Fiber Optics

Fiber optic cable mounted to the pipe can be used for communication purposes, leak detection and real time monitoring system to detect threats to the pipe like deflections (Source /5/). There are two main technical options for optical systems: fiber Bragg grating (FBG) and Distributed Acoustic Sensing (DAS) systems. FBG can be applied for a small range of about 100 m and DAS can be used for large range of about 100 km.

FBG are small mirrors within the fiber each reflecting small bandwidth of light. Because the bandwidth of possible light is limited and each FBG needs an amount of bandwidth the total number is limited for to some thousand. They detect strain and vibrations with extreme high resolution, e.g. the surface shaking caused by caterpillars driving along nearby. However, as the range is limited they can be used only on situations like on risers or beneath water crossings.

Distributed Acoustic Sensing DAS systems detect the acoustic fingerprints as a changing in the scattering of light. It can detected if vehicles move by, mechanical digging or larger machinery work at distances reaching up to 50m aside the cable. The range for this monitoring system is up to 100 km (Source /8/ and /9/).

FIGURE 8: PIPELINE TRENCH WITH FIBER OPTICS SYSTEMS

For offshore platforms and risers optical systems are an effective tool to assess the static and dynamic response of structures (Source /7/). Retrofitting fiber optics to onshore pipelines would require the unearthing of the whole line with significant financial implications. Nevertheless, this technology might be a solution for areas where movement has been detected and where a fiber optics system can be installed during resurrection or construction.

Optical system will allow a permanent strain monitoring of this area and provide a real time warning system (Source /9/):

- Data linkage and communications
- Leak detection (Temperature/Vibration)
- Deformation (Vibration)
- Third party intrusion (Vibration)
- Geotechnical event detection (Strain)

2.4 Inline Inspection technologies

Inline inspection is designed to detect either geometrical or metal loss features, and additionally provides high-resolution pipeline trajectories with measures of an Inertial Measurement Units (IMU).

FIGURE 9: INLINE INSPECTION TOOLS

With a typical tie-point-distance of 2000m, accuracies between 07.m – 1.5m can be achieved, depending on pipeline diameter and gyro model. With shorter tie-point-distance the precision increases up to 0.4m. (Source /10/)

Any pipeline movement can be detected, even before any permanent damage to the pipeline has occurred. It requires serious effort on the logistical and operational side. Similar to the aforementioned solutions, these high costs raise the threshold for regular monthly or quarterly screenings. Common Inline Inspections are typically carried out in 5- to 10-year intervals.

3 The New Service

In the following, we propose a new ILI-based methodology with the high resolution and accuracy on one side, shrinking on the other side significantly the operational and logistical burden by using an inline inspection technique reduced to its essentials for detection of pipe movements based on a regular maintenance-cleaning platform using MEMS (Micro Electro Mechanical System)

3.1 The Tool

The suggested system is a cleaning tool containing an inertial measurement unit to map the pipeline trajectory. It will run during the standard maintenance cleaning operators perform to ensure cleanliness of their asset. No further devices such as pig tracking or similar are required.

FIGURE 10: 20" CLEANING TOOL WITH MEM-GYRO UNIT

3.2 The Process

The service consists of a repetitive 3-step process:
- Screening Inspection
- Mapping Data Comparison
- Pipeline Movement Report

FIGURE 11: PROCESS BASIC STEPS

The main prerequisite for any pipeline drift screening is a baseline inspection that provides an "as-is" or "has-been" statement. With the availability of the "as-is" description of the pipe, the next step is to compare the coordinates of the baseline with the data from the pipeline drift monitoring tool. Any significant deviation between the both is possible pipeline movement. This provides basic information on the length and magnitude of the deflection, to be reported to the pipeline operator.

The process tracks any pipeline position changes through repetitive screening runs and monitoring pipeline trajectory.

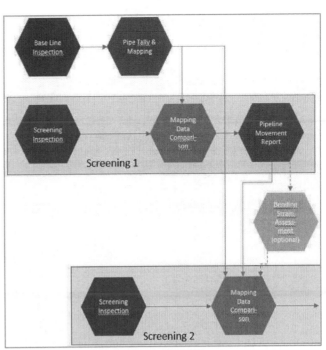

FIGURE 12: REPETITIVE PROCESS

3.3 Pipeline Movement Detection

To extract areas of possible pipeline movement from the recorded data, the following process is used in general:
- Distance Estimation, using tool velocity patterns
- Determination of girthweld positions through signal detection in raw IMU channels
- Alignment of girthweld distances of current inspection to girthweld distances of previous inspections
- Determination of current XYZ trajectory using navigation of IMU data and generated distance system
- Pipeline movement analysis

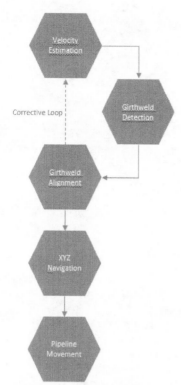

FIGURE 13: ANALYSIS WORKFLOW

3.3.1 Estimation of velocity pattern

In a regular In-Line Inspection tool, generally odometer wheels measure the log-distance along the pipeline For the Pipeline Drift Measurement service the velocity pattern needs to be estimated as accurately as possible, since there are no odometer wheels onboard,. The following process is used:

1. assume a constant velocity profile
2. consider the same velocity profile as the base line inspection and project it onto the current inspection.
3. As add-on information, use the MEMS accelerometer (in the direction of the pipeline) by single or integration, providing an estimation of a velocity profile.

After the next steps, the velocity profile may be updated in an iterative loop.

3.3.2 Girthweld detection

In a regular In-Line Inspection tool, routinely the passage of girthweld is identified by local differences in e.g. magnetic flux, internal diameter changes, or increased tool vibration. Vibration is measured with an IMU. In the Pipeline Drift Measurement evaluation, we use the signals of the girthweld to determine the passage of a girthweld.

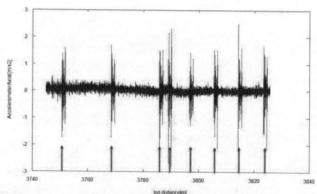

FIGURE 14: INDICATION OF THE DATA OF THE ACCELEROMETER IN AXIAL DIRECTION; BLACK ARROWS: FOUND LOCATIONS OF GIRTHWELD

The girthwelds are detected by using the axial accelerometer data as peak detector. In installation areas or in areas of high vibration, the method may have limited accuracy and a manual crosscheck is recommended.

3.3.3 Distance system alignment using girthweld positions

The methodology to align different pipe distance systems is typically carried out on comparison of the girthwelds and/or other references or features in both data sets. For the pipeline drift service, we propose aligning the datasets on this established process of girthweld alignment.

3.3.4 XYZ navigation

The recorded IMU measurement in is processed with ROSEN latest XYZ techniques recently developed for MEMS in combination with the aligned distance system. Calibration of the navigation is carried out by adopting the same trajectory calibration points (combination of distance with DGPS coordinates) as was used in the base line (i.e. historical XYZ inspection).

3.3.5 Pipeline movement analysis

The two navigated trajectories are compared using traditional pipeline movement analysis techniques. See also Reference [1].

3.4 Predicted Accuracy of Proposed Methodology

As the typical length of pipeline movement areas are typically limited to 40m length standard pipeline movement services exhibit rather good resolution.

The predicted accuracy of the Pipeline Drift Measurement service (under stable run conditions) is similar to the standard Pipeline Movement Service using optical gyros. The inaccuracy in the derived trajectory difference is predicted to be within a few centimeters above the standard pipeline movement service. Accuracy is influenced in two ways:

1) Lateral accuracy by the following two error sources:
    a. Random white noise on the angular rate sensors of the MEMS, which is specified to be higher as in optical IMUs
    b. Increased angular rate sensor bias of the MEMS. This is significantly higher than using a regular fiber optics IMU. Nevertheless, the new processing software removes the most part of this systematic error.
2) Axial accuracy:
    a. The distance calibration is done at the girthwelds, and therefore the inaccuracy in axial direction is deemed rather limited, in the order of 0.2 m maximum. Furthermore, it should be noted that the main focus lies on the lateral direction accuracy.

More specifically, when taking a rather typical example of a 40m area of pipeline movement, the following lateral accuracies are estimated:

Error source	Derivation method	Error level [m]
White noise from raw measurement	Random walk method; level of white noise on angle determinations is derived from actual IMU measurements in a subsea pipeline in smooth run conditions	0.0001m
MEMS gyroscope bias	-Sensor specifications: max 700deg/hr bias -Detailed algorithms can estimate the local bias with approximately 90% accuracy -Geometric analysis of the navigation segment	0.070m
Tool misalignment	-Assumption: a 0.1 degree tool misalignment is obtained halfway the segment	0.015m

FIGURE 15: ACHIEVABLE ERROR LEVELS

According this theoretical approach, in the result approximately 0.1m lateral error is to be expected on a 40m navigation interval. Since the requested service accuracy specification typically is 0.2m, the proposed methodology should be sufficiently accurate.

4   Case Study

The proposed methodology has been tested and implemented on a client pipeline for which
- an base line (XYZ inspection) was present
- an ILI tool with MEMS IMU measurement
- a prototype software was used for evaluation (determine girthwelds in the MEMS measurements, etc.)

Results obtained:
- The evaluation found more than 75% of the girthwelds in the correct position

- The MEMS measurements were processed successfully with the described methodology
- the distance alignment method creates reliably results
- Only in case of high vibration levels (e.g. in installation areas), further manual adaptations were necessary, as shown in below plot of the first 200m.

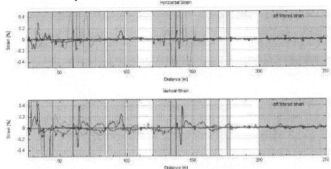

FIGURE 16: SAMPLE ALIGNMENT SHEET FOR FIRST 200M

5   Summary of Services

5.1   Measurement methodology

A last, but immensely important point that needs to be considered is the fact that aerial imagery as well as LiDAR services purely reflect an indirect measurement. They all document the movement of the terrain alone, but not the line itself. Depending on the soil composition, it is possible that the ground is passing around the pipe, which may also damage external coating, enabling external corrosion to be a second risk factor. As an outcome, depending on soil consistency, the line itself may remain in the same position or move less than expected, and the integrity threat is different, presumably even more complex than expected.

In addition, the actual depth of cover of a pipeline in these cases can make a big difference. It is entirely possible that the visually observed ground movement on the surface is higher than at pipeline depth, or even entirely superficial. A direct measurement such as pipeline drift monitoring will avoid unnecessary digs and reduce cost.

In the table below, the new pipeline drift measurement service is compared with other services for detecting geohazard driven pipeline movement.

Survey Method	Pros	Cons
Foot Patrol	Easy to implement Detection of large landslides Low cost	No detection of onset of movement Subjective method Limited accessibility High time requirement
Aerial Imagery	Readily available Detection of large landslides	No detection of onset of movement Limited accessibility High cost Limited precision Weather dependent Indirect measurement
LiDAR	High precision Detection of onset of <u>ground</u> movement	Limited availability in remote regions Limited accessibility High cost Weather dependent Indirect measurement
Inline Inspection	Readily available High precision Direct measurement Detection of onset of <u>pipeline</u> movement Weather independent	Rel. high cost ILI baseline data required
Pipeline Drift Measurement	Readily available Easy to implement High precision Direct measurement Detection of onset of <u>pipeline</u> movement Low cost Weather independent	ILI baseline data required

FIGURE 17: SURVEY METHOD COMPARISON TABLE

6   Conclusion

The proposed, unique service is a valid alternative to detect pipeline movement in geotechnical unstable areas.

Main benefits are:
- Early warning system for pipeline movement
- High-end gyro electronics with proven track record
- Versatile equipment, easily adaptable to a multitude of tool sizes and types from 8" and above
- Cost effective
- Fast mobilization
- Easy handling on site
- Shortened reporting timeline through usage of proprietary software

Further benefits
- Service to provide supplementary information to aid in the decision-making if or when to run a high-resolution geometry tool
- Visualization in a mapping system to aid in the decision-making for an intervention plan (optional)

Optional services based on Pipeline Movement
- Bending strain assessment performed on the measurement data
- Pipeline failure model based on bending strain levels, reviewing the movement and resulting strain dynamics and using FEM simulations to determine when the pipeline will most probably fail.
- Pipeline Geohazards Management, which is a complex, multi-disciplinary process, heavily dependent on data integration and expert judgment. A methodology that allows the identification of critical zones through assessing potential hydrocarbon release mechanisms that could affect waterbodies and adjacent areas, including channel section pipeline failures, approach slope pipeline failures, and spill path effects.

7   References

[1]   IPC paper No. 1839 from 1996; *Measuring Pipeline Movement in Geotechnical Unstable Areas Using an Inertial Geometry Pipeline Inspection Pig*; from *Jaroslaw A. Czyz, Constantino Fraccaroli* and *Alan P. Sergeant.*

8   Sources

/1/   U.S. Geological Survey; www.USGS.gov

/2/   Range Helicopters; www.rangeheli.ca/aerial-pipeline-surveillance/

/3/   Wikipedia; www.en.wikipedia.org/wiki/Lidar

/4/   Reserachgate; www.researchgate.net/publication/279249086_Accuracy_of_Airborne_LIDAR-Derived_Elevation_Empirical_Assessment_and_Error_Budget

/5/   Richard W. Griffiths: Structural monitoring system using fiber optics, https://patentimages.storage.googleapis.com/94/90/7e/e8aef1c98316cf/US4654520.pdf

/6/   Wikipedia: Light, https://en.wikipedia.org/wiki/Light

/7/   D. Inaudi and B. Glisic: Fiber Optic Sensing for Innovative Oil & Gas Production and Transport Systems

/8/   Optasense, https://www.optasense.com/wp-content/uploads/2017/09/Pipeline-Monitoring-Solution_US-Letter17.pdf

/9/   V. Alliot, Dr C. Bridge: Complete pipeline and umbilical monitoring for integrity management, https://www.subseauk.com/documents/presentations/20121207-completepipelineandumbilicalmonitoringforintegritymanagementusingfibreoptics.pdf

/10/   ROSEN XYZ Mapping; High Resolution In-Line Precision Route Mapping Performance Specification, Ver. 17.2.2

This page left blank intentionally.

IPG2019-5332

SIMPLE METHOD FOR DTS/DSS DATA INTERPRETATION: AN APPLICATION TO PIPELINE GEOTECHNICAL MONITORING

Fabien Ravet,[1] Sanghoon Chin, Fabien Briffod, Etienne Rochat
Omnisens, Morges, VD, Switzerland

ABSTRACT

Geotechnical monitoring based on optical fiber sensor technology has been used over more than a decade to detect hazards than can affect the integrity of pipelines. In particular when these sensors are implemented in the form of distributed temperature and strain sensors, respectively known as DTS and DSS, they provide information about hazard location and spatial extension. In addition, these sensors can capture the speed at which the event developing in particular when implemented as a permanent monitoring solution. So far these sensors were implemented as part of an alarming system detecting events such as landslides, erosion and subsidence. The current work aims at presenting simple method to extract additional information about the hazard such as the amplitude of the soil displacement in the case of landslides and subsidence or dirt cover for erosion. Estimation of stress in soil is also discussed based on the cable strain-stress relation obtained from the sensing cable qualification. The approach is validated by academic works conducted in parallel of the technology development. The method use is then illustrated by its application to field data collected from several events occurred over the past 10 years.

Keywords: geotechnical monitoring, optical fiber sensors, distributed strain sensor, distributed temperature sensor.

NOMENCLATURE

Brillouin – A fiber optic scattering & sensing mechanism
BOTDA – Brillouin Optical Time Domain Analyzer
BOTDR – Brillouin Optical Domain Reflectometer
DCS – Distributed Control System
DSS – Distributed Strain Sensing
DTS – Distributed Temperature Sensing
FIMT – Fiber in Metal Tube

FOPIMS – Fiber Optic Pipeline Monitoring System
GIS – Geographical Information System
GRP - Glass-Reinforced Plastic
GTMS – Geotechnical Monitoring System
IEC – International Electrotechnical Commission
ITU – International Telecommunication Union
LDS – Leak Detection System
OO – Owner Operator PA - Polyamide
PE – Polyethylene ROW – Right-of-Way
SCADA – Supervisory Control and Data Acquisition
SMC – Strain Measuring Cable
SSL – Stainless Steel
TMC – Temperature Measuring Cable
TPI – Third Party Intrusion

INTRODUCTION

Geohazards are natural threats that can cause severe damages to transport infrastructures such as pipelines, highways, railways, waterways and power cables. In the case of pipeline, it can eventually result in a rupture with dramatic social and environmental consequences. Depending on the pipeline route, local climate and landscape, different types of geohazards can impact the Right Of Way (ROW) ranging from landslide and rock fall in mountain areas to soil subsidence, erosion and water flooding or other environmental condition changes like permafrost thaw settlement along northern pipeline route or dune migration in arid regions [1, 2, 3, 4, 5, 6, 7, 8].

Pipeline routes often cross remote areas in difficult terrain as the Andes range [4, 9]. Combined with adverse weather conditions, pipeline protection is a difficult operation to conduct. Operators have developed asset integrity programs to secure their pipeline's operation [10, 11, 12, 13]. In difficult environments, remote sensing solutions for pipelines offer significant advantages over conventional inspection techniques.

---

[1] Contact author: fabien.ravet@omnisens.com

Fiber Optic Pipeline Integrity Monitoring Systems are being used to improve pipeline's integrity since 2002 [14].

Pipeline natural threats are detected by one of the components of the pipeline integrity monitoring system: The Geotechnical Monitoring System (GTMS). The GTMS operates as an alarming system which can detect and locate phenomenon such as erosion, landslides and subsidence [15].

The current work aims at presenting that more information can be extracted from the measurements collected. In particular, when strain and temperature profiles are processed in combination with the measurement parameters and the cable mechanical response. A simple model for soil displacement is introduced to compute the amplitude of displacement from the strain sensors. The model accounts for the measurement parameters. Its implementation is presented and applied to theoretical and actual profiles. Its limitation is also discussed experimentally and theoretically. A thermal model is also introduced which accounts for soil characteristics.

SENSING TECHNOLOGY

Geotechnical Monitoring System

In order to benefit of all the advantages of a fiber optic based monitoring system, the GTMS must be composed of the following components:

- Strain and temperature interrogator units;
- SMC and TMC as strain and temperature measurement cable sensors;
- Monitoring software including measuring unit control, GIS (Geographical Information System) visualization and configuration.

Details about the GTMS and example of real-world implementations can be found in reference [15]. In the present section we will only discuss the sensing capabilities of such technology.

Measurement Principle and Performance

The core instrumentation of the GTMS relies on Brillouin Optical Time Domain Analysis (BOTDA). BOTDA uses stimulated Brillouin scattering (SBS) in single-mode fibers. Brillouin scattered light encountered a frequency shift proportional to both temperature and strain variations. This shift can be measured by analyzing the interaction in standard optical fibers between a pump lightwave (pulse) and a counter-propagating probe lightwave (continuous). Such interrogator can use a broad variety of single-mode optical fibers. Typically, the Brillouin frequency shift at ambient temperature of such fiber is comprised between 10.7 and 11.0 GHz at 1.55 μm wavelength and varies with strain and temperature coefficients of 0.05 MHz/με and 1 MHz/°C respectively. This linear relationship makes it an easy method for sensing mechanical and thermal effects, whilst the pulse nature of the pump lightwave allows accurate localization (time of flight measurement) and defines spatial resolution (pulse duration). Further details on the measuring unit configuration, fiber sensitivity to strain and temperature as well as sensing parameter definitions can be found in Niklès works [16, 17, 18]. Performance parameter definitions and verification testing are now formalized in the IEC 61757-3-1 standard for DTS application. The same IEC committee is currently working on a DSS standard. The definitions of the most common parameters are presented in Appendix 1. Recent advances in optical technology extended the measurement range to distances over 100 km per sensing direction without the need of repeaters. Measurement range over 300km can be achieved with periodic optical amplification as demonstrated by Gyger [19]. Such approach is key when the power supply along the monitored infrastructure is scarce or unavailable. Cases of offshore structures with long tie backs and jungle pipelines can benefit of these technology improvements.

There are two important parameters that need to be developed as they play an important role in the application of distributed sensing in the current case: **spatial** and **distance resolution**. All other parameters are defined and discussed in the appendix of this document and in reference [18].

Distributed properties are accessed by time modulating the pump lightwave (pulse), the probe signal remaining a continuous wave. The **spatial resolution** of the sensor is related to the pulse width ($\Delta\tau$) and is mathematically defined as $w = c\Delta\tau / 2n$ where n is the fiber refractive index. More rigorously, the sensor spatial resolution can be defined as the smallest event whose strain can be measured with define or target accuracy [18**Error! Reference source not found.**]. An example of a measurement is shown in Figure 1. In other words, the spatial resolution can also be understood as the sensor gauge length yielding an integrated temperature and/or strain value over the pulse length. With the current state of the art of the technology, the spatial resolution can be as small as 1 m. It must be noted that measurements with finer spatial resolution can be achieved in some conditions as discussed in [18**Error! Reference source not found.**].

In optical time-domain-coding-based systems, the **distance resolution** is de-coupled from the **spatial resolution** in the sense that it depends on the acquisition scheme, i.e. the sampling rate of the detection system. It sets the number of points along the distance (sampling interval). Its only relation with **spatial resolution** lies in *sampling theorem* (Shannon rule) requirement to have a sampling interval half or smaller than the **spatial resolution**. As a consequence the strain or temperature profile obtained with distributed measurements are sampled in constant width slices (w) every $x_{i+1} \leq x_i + w/n$ ($n \geq 2$). Figure 2 schematically represents the operation of sampling the strain profile for $n = 2$.

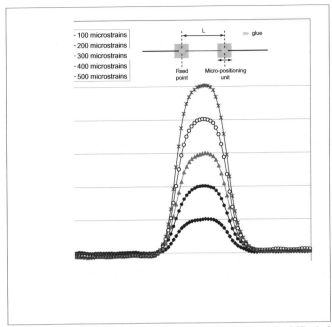

FIGURE 1: STRAIN MEASURED WITH $W=1$M AND A 10 CM SAMPLING RESOLUTION ON A FIBER SECTION $L=2m$ SUBMITTED TO GIVEN STRAIN BY MEANS OF A MICRO-POSITIONING UNIT. NOTE THAT 100 $\mu\varepsilon=$ CORRESPONDS TO 0.001%.

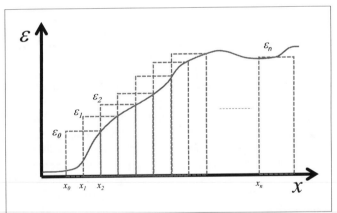

FIGURE 2. SCHEMATIC VIEW OF A STRAIN PROFILE SAMPLED EVERY $\approx x_i - x_{i+1}$ WITH A SPATIAL RESOLUTION OF $\approx w$ Z $x_i - x_{i+2}$

Sensing and Communication Cables

General Considerations

Strain Measurement Cables (SMC) are robust fiber optic cables specifically designed for distributed strain monitoring applications. Unlike telecommunication fiber optic cables, the SMC design allows the cable strain to be transferred to the optical fiber, which in turn can be detected and monitored by the BOTDA interrogators. In order to address a broad variety of conditions, various models of strain measurement cables were developed and qualified [20, 21, 22].

Temperature Measurement Cables (TMC) are high quality grade versions of standard armored telecommunication fiber optics cable usually used for direct burial applications. The cable includes the optical fibers used for temperature monitoring as well as fibers for data communication between the instruments and the control room.

It is key that mechanical and optical characteristics of all sensing and communication cables are in compliance with IEC 794-1 Optical Fiber Cables Specification.

Specific Cable Qualification: the SMC-0

Among the cable types discussed in references [20] and [21], a model is particularly emblematic of the ground movement detection application: the SMC-0 (Figure 3). It is being used in several projects since 2008 (references). It is a robust cable whose design was based on a FIMT structure, where the fiber is embedded in a SSL tube wrapped in galvanized steel wire and protected with an external HDPE layer. The sensor OD is 3.5mm. It was designed to be sensitive to soil displacement but also to support long term axial deformation larger than 1% and accommodate crush load of 1500N/cm. The elastic regime stress-strain relationship as well as Strain Brillouin Frequency are presented in Figure 5 and Figure 6. The slope of the stress-strain curve is the cable Young's modulus (E_{SMC-0}).

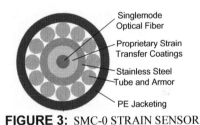

FIGURE 3: SMC-0 STRAIN SENSOR

The relationship between stress and strain is well known in elastic regime. We propose to take advantage of such relationship to estimate load in the ground form the fiber strain measurement. Provided that the cable tensile strength was qualified, such operation can be realized. In all the projects where the SMC-0 is installed, the slope computed from Figure 4 can be used to derive stress component in the soil parallel to the fiber.

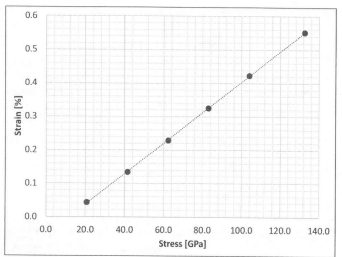

FIGURE 4. STRESS-STRAIN RELATIONSHIP IN ELASTIC REGIME. THE SLOPE WHICH CAN BE INTERPRETED AS THE CABLE YOUNG'S MODULUS IS 0.046GPA^{-1}.

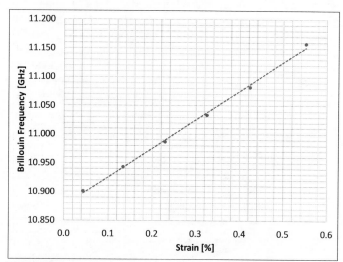

FIGURE 5. STRAIN-BRILLOUIN FREQUENCY RELATIONSHIP IN ELASTIC REGIME. THE SLOPE AND THE OFFSET ARE USED TO CALIBRATE THE STRAIN SENSOR (SLOPE IS 449.8%/MHz).

Cable Installation

GTMS implementation is possible both on new pipeline construction and on existing transport lines. These installations are discussed elsewhere and will not be detailed in the present paper [13, 23, 24].

GEOHAZARDS DETECTION, MONITORING TECHNOLOGY AND DATA INTERPRETATION

The GTMS aims at detecting and locating at an early stage all the natural events that can be a threat to the pipeline. It will emphasize the preliminary signs of these threats. Geohazards and associated sensing parameter which are either strain or temperature are listed in Table 1.

TABLE 1. GEOHAZARDS AND SENSING METHODS

Geohazard	Soil Strain Measurement	Soil Temperature Measurement
Erosion		X
Landslide	X	
Subsidence	X	

The following subsections bring the theoretical background sustaining the use of the GTMS to detect geohazard. In the case of the mechanical model, it also provides a simple description that can be used to characterize the geohazard beyond the usual strain profile.

Erosion Detection

Thermal Model

Among all heat transfer mechanism, the dominant process in soil is conduction [25]. Fourier's work regarding heat propagation in solids and dating back to 1822, lead to the second law of heat conduction which can be expressed in its one-dimensional form as

$$\frac{\partial T(z,t)}{\partial t} = D \frac{\partial^2 T(z,t)}{\partial z^2} \tag{1}$$

where D is the thermal diffusivity coefficient which is defined as the ratio of the thermal conductivity κ to the volumetric heat capacity C_v, or $D = \frac{\kappa}{C_v}$.

The form of these equations assumes that D is independent on depth. That assumption is reasonable as the fiber optic cables are usually buried in a trench presenting uniform soil conditions. Examples of Thermal diffusivity coefficients are listed in Table 2. In the absence of thermal sources or sinks, the temperature change in the ground has diurnal and annual origins. Assuming that these variations at the surface $z=0$ can be approximated by the following linear combination of sinusoids

$$T(0,t) = \bar{T} + A_y(0) \sin(\omega_y t) + A_d(0) \sin(\omega_d t) \tag{2}$$

where $\bar{T}$ is the annual average surface temperature while $A_y(0)$ and $A_d(0)$ are the surface annual and diurnal amplitudes respectively. The temporal behavior is controlled by the annual and diurnal ω_d radial frequencies noted ω_y and ω_d respectively. At $z \rightarrow \infty$, the temperature tend to be constant and reaches the annual average $\bar{T}$. In a uniform medium without heat source and sink, the temperature temporal change should remain periodic and the following general solution is proposed

$$T(z,t) = \bar{T} + A_y(z) \sin\left(\omega_y t + \phi_y(z)\right) + A_d(z) \sin(\omega_d t + \phi_d(z)) \tag{3}$$

Substituting Equation 3 in Equation 1, we obtain the following general temperature relation describing the variation as a function of time and depth

$$T(z,t) = \bar{T} + A_y(0)\sin(\omega_y t - z/d_y)e^{-z/d_y} + A_d(0)\sin(\omega_d t - z/d_d)e^{-z/d_d} \quad (4)$$

Two new parameters are introduced which are the annual and diurnal damping depths, noted d_y and d_d respectively and defined as $d_y = \sqrt{2D/\omega_y}$, and, $d_d = \sqrt{2D/\omega_d}$. Figure 6 and Figure 7 illustrate the influence of diurnal and annual variations as well as depth on soil temperature. There is an obvious delay between surface and underground temperatures. Figure 8 displays the damping rate for diurnal (e^{-z/d_d}) and annual (e^{-z/d_y}) changes. It confirms that the damping effect is significant larger for diurnal variation. Below 20cm, the diurnal temperature change is barely perceptible while the annual change is lightly influenced. A larger depth (over 10m) needs to be considered to see no influence from annual temperature change. The damping depth for annual fluctuations is about 19 times larger than the diurnal ones.

TABLE 2. THERMAL DIFFUSIVITY COEFFICIENTS FOR DISTINCT SOIL TYPES AS PER HILLEL (1982).

Soil	Thermal Diffusivity [m^2/s]
Peat	0.14×10^{-6}
Dry Sand	0.20×10^{-6}
Wet Sand	0.33×10^{-6}
Clay	1.00×10^{-6}

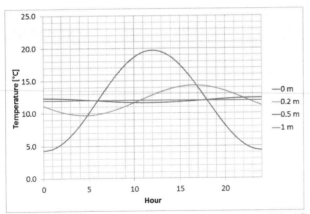

FIGURE 6: DIURNAL TEMPERATURE VARIATION AS A FUNCTION OF BURRIAL DEPTH. CURVES ARE CALCULATED USING METEOROLOGICAL DATA FROM CUZCO, PERU, SITUATED 3400 M THE ABOVE SEA LEVEL AND CONSIDERING THE THERMAL DIFFUSIVITY OF CLAY (TABLE 2).

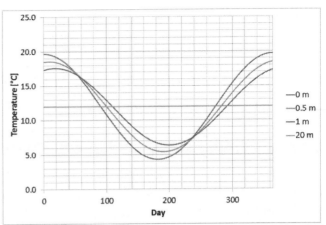

FIGURE 7: ANNUAL TEMPERATURE VARIATIONS AS A FUNCTION OF BURRIAL DEPTH. CURVES ARE CALCULATED USING METEOROLOGICAL DATA FROM CUZCO, PERU, SITUATED 3400 M ABOVE THE SEA LEVEL AND CONSIDERING THE THERMAL DIFFUSIVITY OF CLAY (TABLE 2).

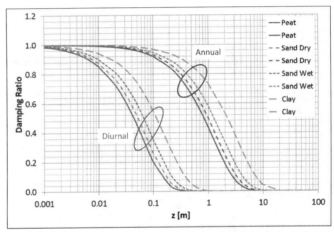

FIGURE 8: ANNUAL AND DIURNAL DAMPING RATE FOR PEAT, DRY AND WET SAND AS WELL AS CLAY (TABLE 2).

Comments about temperature related events

In common pipeline applications, the cable is buried at least one meter from the surface. From previous section discussion, it implies that diurnal temperature changes cannot be captured when the cable depth is over 50cm. The last step of erosion is an exposure to the environment which consequently increases the threat probability against the pipeline integrity. Erosion increases the risk of human interaction with the pipeline or possible hit by dropped objects or materials. These last events are particularly common in the North Sea where an exposed pipeline can be dragged by fishing nets or anchors. Another consequence of erosion when large sections are exposed is a free span inducing excessive strain.

Rainfall infiltration and ground water are known precursors of erosion phenomena. Soil erosion around the pipeline introduces temperature changes as the pipeline is exposed to water or ambient temperature changes. Similarly, water infiltration from flooding and change of soil condition between frozen and thawed states have an impact on the local soil temperature. Soil erosion can leave the pipeline in a hazardous situation leading to a possible mechanical damage and what can be prevented by monitoring the temperature change as the buried cable is not exposed to the same conditions as the exposed cable. Indeed, the monitoring system can detect such temperature changes and an alarm showing their location can be generated. Investigations can then be carried out and risks mitigated in due time.

Similar conclusions can be drawn for erosion originated from wind as it would be observed in deserts and in particular regions covered by sand dunes.

Actual Example

A temperature event with a characteristic validates the model and demonstrates the predictive strength of the DTS. The event is presented in can present other pattern as illustrated in Figure 9 and Figure 10. In this event that was detected along the Peru LNG pipeline, a narrow cold spot was identified which featured a periodic time dependence of 24h, which is a typical behavior when a sensing cable is exposed. The event was confirmed by the inspectors and associated with a manual excavation in the ROW conducted for maintenance purposes. The pattern would have been identical if erosion had exposed the cable. The example behaves as expected by heat transfer theory as presented above: if not completely exposed, the temperature of the cable does not vary periodically and returns slowly to the soil ambient value after completely drying out; when the soil cover of the cable is thin (less than 50cm) or completely removed, the temperature follows a daily change and returns to soil ambient temperature once completely reburied.

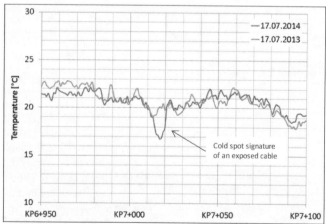

FIGURE 9: TEMPERATURE EVENT DETECTED AT KP7+020 OF PERU LNG PIPELINE: THE TEMPERATURE PROFILES MEASURED IN 2013 AND 2014 SHOW THAT A TEMPERATURE ANOMALY DEVELOPED WHICH APPEARS AS A COLD SPOT AT THE TIME OF THE MEASUREMENT.

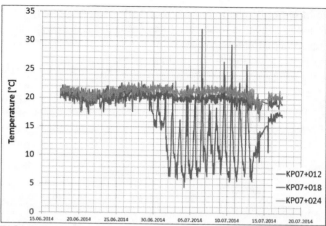

FIGURE 10: TEMPERATURE EVENT DETECTED AT KP7+020 OF PERU LNG PIPELINE: THE TEMPERATURE TEMPORAL EVOLUTION INDICATES THAT THE CABLE WAS EXPOSED TO DAILY CHANGE.

Landslide and Subsidence Detection

Mechanical Model

DSS technology, can be used to monitor soil movement and quantify vertical and horizontal displacement amplitude. In fact the DSS measures transversal and longitudinal strain along a single optical fiber cable buried in the ground.

In previous works [15, 23], it was suggested that information such as the ground movement velocity, its location and its spatial extension was provided by the DSS measurements. DSS could indicate the severity of the event through the measured strain value. The quantification of the actual soil displacement require the integration of the strain profile over the event geometry and strain components in three directions. In some cases, such approach can be completed as in the Crossrail project where vertical displacement is derived from DSS measurements [26].

In the present section, we introduce a simple model of the consolidation phenomenon and how the strain profiles are used to compute the vertical and horizontal displacements amplitude. Such approach can also be applied to landslide detection and monitoring as it is purely geometrical. We first make the assumption that the soil displaces as a compact and uncompressible mass of material. As the end of the section we will discuss the limitation of such approach considering a subsidence experiment where actual data and a specific numerical modelling are presented.

Relation between Measured Strain and Vertical Displacement

Figure 11 illustrates schematically the soil consolidation caused by a vertical load. It induces a vertical displacement δh. The settlement then pulls the underneath cable down and induce a transition zone, whose width is l, at the shear interface due to soil cohesion ensuring a continuous behaviour between the stable and settling grounds. In the present section discussion, we assume that the transition zone suffers a uniform strain over a stationary width (*l*). If an optical fiber sensor is embedded in the ground as shown in the figure (blue line), it will be subjected to a stress when the soil displaces down. As a consequence, it will experience a strain ε. The strain induced along the fiber sensor axis is measured by the DSS interrogator.

(a) *t=0; Soil at rest, no load applied on the soil surface*

(b) *t=t₀; Application of vertical load (σ) on the soil surface*

(c) *t=t₀+Δt; vertical load applied over a period of Δt*

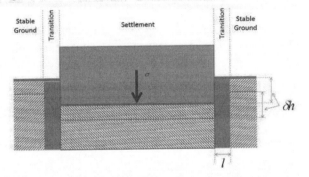

FIGURE 11: SOIL SETTLEMENT (CONSOLIDATION DUE TO A VERTICAL LOAD APPLIED ON ITS SURFACE. AN OPTICAL FIBER STRAIN SENSOR IS LAID UNDERNEATH THE SURFACE (BLUE LINE). THE LOAD INDUCES A VERTICAL DISPLACEMENT δh AND A TRANSITION ZONE (OF LENGTH *l*) AT THE SHEAR INTERFACE.

In a flat area where soil settlement is the only cause of movement and assuming that the stress source is a vertical load σ, we can consider that the shear interface remains stable over time. If the soil is not compressible. there is no physical reason to consider horizontal stress other than induced by the vertical load. A simple relation can then be established between the strain on the fiber ε in the transition zone (*l*) at the shear interface and the vertical displacement δh induced by soil consolidation. Relying on the geometry of the movement illustrated in (Figure 12), the relation can be expressed as

$$\varepsilon = \frac{\delta l}{l} = \sqrt{1 + (\delta h/l)^2} - 1 \qquad (5)$$

The quantity δl is the fiber length increase associated with $\square$ and caused by the settlement. The strain is then a function of the shear interface length l and the amplitude of the vertical displacement δh. Alternatively, the vertical displacement can be calculated from strain ε with the following relation derived from (1)

$$\delta h = l\sqrt{(\varepsilon + 1)^2 - 1} \qquad (6)$$

Figure 13 illustrates the settlement for a 10m long transition zone as a function of strain. The measured strain data can be compared to actual soil displacement as it was reported in reference [23] for landslides in Peru. In the next sections, we propose to develop the approach that allows the quantification of soil displacement using equation (6).

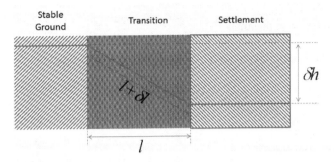

FIGURE 12: OPTICAL FIBER SENSOR ELONGATION IN THE TRANSITION ZONE.

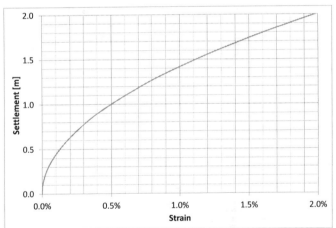

FIGURE 13: DSIPACEMENT COMPUTED FROM STRAIN MEASUREMENT CONSIDERING A TRANSITION ZONE OF 10M.

Vertical Displacement Measurement Sensitivity

The DITEST technique is capable of detecting soil displacement at a very early stage when the soil motion cannot be visually detected as demonstrated by field data [15, 23]. Such performance is possible thanks to the detection sensitivity of the DITEST which can be set to 0.002% or smaller. Figure 14 shows the strain relation with the vertical displacements calculated from equation (6). It is obvious that displacements of a few centimeters over tens of meters can be detected.

Any combination of longitudinal and lateral displacements shall be detected as the DSS measures both strain induced motions with enough sensitivity. Note that vertical settlements push down the sensing cable similarly to the lateral displacement inducing measurable elongation by the DSS.

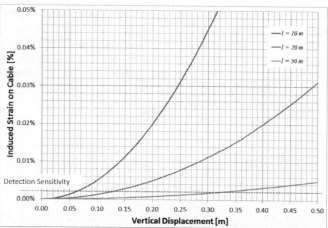

FIGURE 14: DETECTION SENSITIVITY FOR LONGITUDINAL (CONTINUOUS LINES) AND LATERAL (DOTTED LINES) SOIL DISPLACEMENTS. STRAIN DETECTION SENSITIVITY IS SET TO 0.002%.

Longitudinal and Vertical Displacements

Vertical displacement is not the only signature of soil consolidation under uniform load that can be observed with strain measurements. Let us consider the decomposition of the fiber length increase (δl) into its vertical (δl_z) and horizontal (δl_x) components as shown in Figure 15. We can then write three equations that relate these displacements to each other with the objective to express δl_z and δl_x as a function of h and l:

$$(l + \delta l)^2 = l^2 + \delta h^2 \qquad (7),$$
$$\delta l^2 = \delta l_x^2 + \delta l_z^2 \qquad (8), \text{ and,}$$
$$\tan\theta = \frac{\delta h}{l} = \frac{\delta_z}{\delta_x} \qquad (9).$$

Combining these three relations, we obtain the two following expressions:

$$\delta l_z = \frac{1}{\sqrt{(l/\delta h)^2+1}}\left[\delta h\sqrt{(l/\delta h)^2+1}-l\right] \qquad (10), \text{ and,}$$
$$\delta l_x = \frac{l}{\delta h}\frac{1}{\sqrt{(l/\delta h)^2+1}}\left[\delta h\sqrt{(l/\delta h)^2+1}-l\right] \qquad (11).$$

Both displacements can be expressed in function of strain and the transition zone width by combining equations (2), (6) and (7):

$$\delta l_z = l\frac{\varepsilon}{\varepsilon+1}\sqrt{(\varepsilon+1)^2-1} \qquad (12), \text{ and,}$$
$$\delta l_x = l\frac{\varepsilon}{\varepsilon+1} \qquad (13).$$

Displacements Related to Measurement Parameters

So far we have been discussing the displacements quantification regardless of actual measurement parameters. We also assumed that the transition zone width was stationary. Moreover, it is common that the transition zone width cannot be quantified precisely. The difficulty can be overcome thanks to distributed sensing.

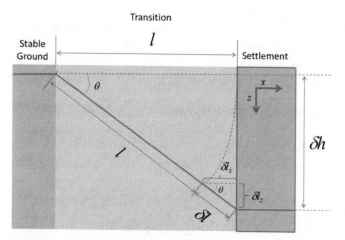

FIGURE 15. FIBER ELONGATION REPRESENTATION IN TERM OF HORIZONTAL (x) AND VERTICAL (y) COORDINATES.

As described in a previous section and illustrated in Figure 2, the measurement of strain as a function of the distance consists in sampling the strain profile in slices of constant width equals to the spatial resolution (w). The vertical displacement and the horizontal displacement component can then be expressed as a function of distance (x), spatial resolution (w) and measured strain profile ($\varepsilon(x)$) which are directly related to the measurement:

$$\delta h(x) = w\sqrt{(\varepsilon(x)+1)^2-1} \qquad (14), \text{ and,}$$
$$\delta l_x(x) = w\frac{\varepsilon(x)}{\varepsilon(x)+1} \qquad (15).$$

Such relations have the advantage to rely on the measurement data and are independent on the uncertainty associated with the transition zone width determination.

As the distance resolution is smaller than the spatial resolution to respect the sampling theorem, the displacements must be expressed as

$$\delta h(x) = \int_x^{x+w}\sqrt{(\varepsilon(x')+1)^2-1}\,dx', \qquad (16), \text{ and,}$$
$$\delta l_x(x) = \int_x^{x+w}\frac{\varepsilon(x')}{\varepsilon(x')+1}\,dx' \qquad (17),$$

where the vertical displacement and the horizontal displacement components are expressed in function of measurement parameters as well as results.

Example

Considering a uniform strain profile and the integration of (16) and (17) yields the expected formulas

$$\delta h = w\sqrt{(\varepsilon+1)^2-1} \qquad (18), \text{ and,}$$
$$\delta l_x = w\frac{\varepsilon}{\varepsilon+1} \qquad (19).$$

If $\varepsilon = 1\%$ and $w = 1\,m$, one obtains $\delta h = 14\,cm$ and $\delta l_x = 1\,cm$.

Assuming a linear strain profile extending over a length L defined by

$$\varepsilon(x) = \varepsilon_0(1-x/L) \qquad (20)$$

For $\varepsilon_0 = 1\%$, $L = 300m$ and $w = 1m$. The result of the integration of (16) and (17) is shown in Figure 16.

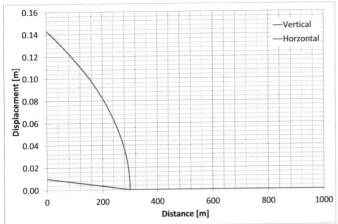

FIGURE 16: VERTICAL DISPLACEMENT AND LONGITUDINAL COMPONENT CALCULATED FROM LINEAR STRAIN PROFILE (ε_0=1%, L=300m AND w=1m).

Strain profiles measured in the Peru LNG project [15, 23] and presented Figure 17 are integrated according to the methodology described in the current document. The integration of the strain profiles gives δh and δl_x values which are presented in Figure 18 and Figure 19. Ratio between longitudinal and horizontal displacements can be as high as 6%.

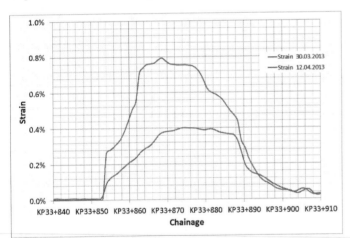

FIGURE 17:=MEASURED STRAIN PROFILES EVOLUTION (MEASUREMENT PERFORMED WITH w=3m); DATA FROM REFERENCES [15] AND [23].

.
Considerations regarding soil behavior and model limitation

The simple model introduced does not account for the mechanism of volume reduction or consolidation when a load is applied. We tested the model in a settlement experiment conducted in the bed of the former Texcoco Lake near Mexico City.

Soil settlement phenomenon was observed during a measurement campaign conducted in summer 2016 with the GTMS. Figure 20 shows the strain profiles measured before and after the load is applied Figure 21 shows how the load was applied. The measured strain profile is not uniform and presents

tensile and compressive effects. The consequent vertical displacement can be computed from the strain profiles as function of time from the positions in elongation using a simple model based on relation (16). A settlement of 3cm is computed from the model. The compressive part of the profile suggests that the model is limited as it does not account for the actual soil compaction.

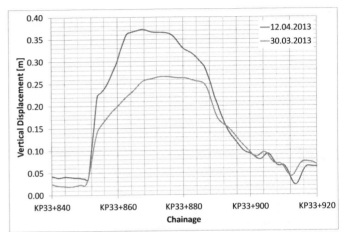

FIGURE 18: VERTICAL DISPLACEMENT PROFILES EVOLUTION (MEASUREMENT PERFORMED WITH w=3m).

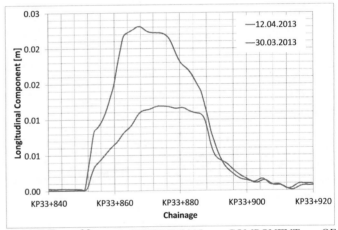

FIGURE 19: LONGITUDINAL COMPONENT OF DISPLACEMENT EVOLUTION (MEASUREMENT PERFORMED WITH w=3m).

In complement to the measurement campaign, a finite element analysis was conducted to understand the strain profile shape which shows tensile and compressive strains. The result of the modelling confirmed qualitatively the measured strain profile shape as presented in Figure 22. A section of the fiber appears to be in compression and is squeezed in between two sections presenting tensile strain. Such behavior can be understood by considering that at the boundary of the loaded area, the cable is pulled and hence in tensile strain. Underneath the load, the soil is compacted. The cable section is then subjected to soil compression and pushed from both ends in tensile strain inducing compression.

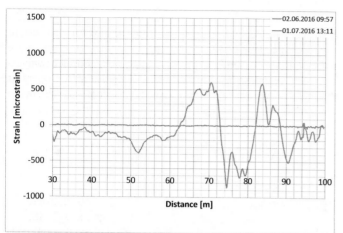

FIGURE 20: THE GRAPH PRESENTS THE STRAIN PROFILE MEASURED BY THE INTERROGATOR AND CAUSED BY THE SUBSIDENCE. ORANGE CURVE IS THE MEASUREMENT BEFORE THE LOAD IS APPLIED. THE GREEN CURVE IS THE STRAIN PROFILE MEASURED ONE MONTH LATER.

FIGURE 21: PRESENTATION ON HOW THE LOAD WAS APPLIED TO THE TERRAIN TO INDUCE THE CONSOLIDATION. THE SESNORS WERE COVERED WITH AN EXCESS OF DIRT.

GUIDELINES FOR DATA AND MODEL USE

DTS/DSS measurements provide information about the geohazard that is useful to take operational decisions. As the DTS/DSS captures strain and temperature profiles, we propose to introduce parameters extracted from these profiles that characterize the event:

- Event peak amplitude, defined of the maximum (minimum) of the strain (ε_{pk}) or temperature (T_{pk}),
- Velocity of development, defined as the derivative against time of the strain ($d\varepsilon_{pk}/dt$) or temperature (dT_{pk}/dt) or temperature event peak amplitude,
- Position, defined as the position of the peak amplitude (z_{pk}),
- Spatial extension, defined as the width of the strain (W_ε) or temperature (W_T) event

An illustration on how these parameters can be extracted to characterize an event is presented in Figure 23, Figure 24 and Figure 25.

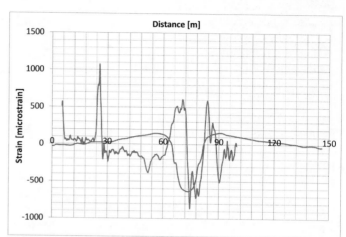

FIGURE 22: COMPARISON OF MEASURED STRAIN PROFILE WITH FINITE ELEMENT MODELLING. THE NUMERICAL ANALYSIS PRESENTS SIMILAR STRUCTURE AS THE ACTUAL MEASUREMENT INDICATING A QUALITATIVE AGREEMENT.

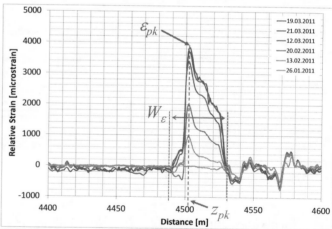

FIGURE 23: ILLUSTRATION OF GEOHAZARD PARAMETERS FOR A LANDSLIDE: EVENT AMPLITUDE (ε_{pk}) AND POSITION (z_{pk}) AS WELL AS SPATIAL EXTENSION (W_ε); DATA FROM REFERENCES [15] AND [23].

FIGURE 24:= LANDSLIDE OF FIGURE 23 USED AS REFEEENCE FOR PARAMETERS INTRODUTION ([15], [23]).

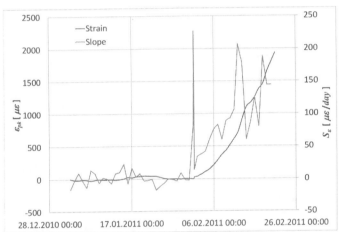

FIGURE 25:=ILLUSTRATION OF GEOHAZARD PARAMETERS FOR A LANDSLIDE: TEMPORAL BEHAVIOR OF (ε_{pk}) AND INSTANTANEOUS VELOCITY (S_ε); COMPUTATION REALISED ON DATA PRESENTED IN FIGURE 23.

Landslide and subsidence can be analyzed further by computing the soil displacement from the strain profile using the simple model previously introduced. The peak displacement values can be obtained from

$$\delta h_{pk}(x) = \int_x^{x+w} \sqrt{\left(\varepsilon_{pk}(x') + 1\right)^2 - 1}\, dx', \quad (21), \text{ and,}$$

$$\delta l_{pk}(x) = \int_x^{x+w} \frac{\varepsilon_{pk}(x')}{\varepsilon_{pk}(x')+1}\, dx' \quad (22).$$

Provided that the strain sensing cable is completely qualified and the stress-strain relationship known, the load in the ground can be profiled and its maximum value in the cable direction can be computed using the relation

$$\varepsilon_{pk} = E_{SMC-0}\sigma_{pk} \quad (23).$$

Beside the benefits listed in the beginning of the current section, the temperature measurements can provide more information about the environment influence. Further analysis and knowledge of the soil characteristics inform the operator about the cable burial depth using the approach introduced in the thermal model section. Such solution is being implemented in buried submarine cables to assess the remaining dirt covering prevent its direct exposure.

CONCLUSIONS

The present work brought some theoretical background on both mechanical and thermal responses of the GTMS. It introduced parameters to allow a systematic characterization of the geohazards. It also presented a simple model for the quantification of soil displacement from the strain measurements. The model takes into account the measurement parameters of the interrogator. The approach can be implemented by the engineers in charge of the pipeline integrity to appreciate the severity of the geohazard. If the GTMS is part of an automated system, the geohazard characteristics can also be transmitted to the operator's SCADA.

ACKNOWLEDGEMENTS

The authors would like to warmly thank Omnisens team for the continuous support in the execution of all projects. Furthermore, the authors are grateful to all partners that helped them develop these projects. In particular, they would like to acknowledge the fruitful cooperation and appreciated feedbacks from Hunt LOC/Peru LNG, COGA/TGP, Techint, Wood Group, Gasoducto de Chihuahua/Ienova, GMCM, Prysmian, Corning, Solifos and ETHZ.

REFERENCES

1. Winter, M.G., Dixon, N., Wasowski, J., Dijkstra, T.A. (2010) "Introduction to land-use and climate change impacts on landslides". Quarterly Journal of Engineering Geology and Hydrogeology, Vol. 43, pp. 367–370
2. Lee, E.M. (2009). "Landslide risk assessment: the challenge of estimating the probability of landsliding", Quarterly Journal of Engineering Geology and Hydrogeology, Vol. 42, pp. 445–458.
3. Bruce, I. (2004). "Estimating the influence of natural hazards on pipeline risk and system reliability.", Proceedings of the 2004 International Pipeline Conference, Calgary, Alberta, Canada, October 4 – 8, paper IPC04-0238.
4. Lee, E.M., Audibert, J.M.E., Hengesh, J.V., Nyman, D.J., (2009). "Landslide-related ruptures of the Camisea pipeline system, Peru" Quarterly Journal of Engineering Geology and Hydrogeology, Vol. 42, pp. 251–259.
5. Hearn, G., Wise, D., Hart, A., Morgan, C., O'Donnell, N. (2012). "Assessing the potential for future first-time slope

failures to impact the oil and gas pipeline corridor through the Makarov Mountains, Sakhalin Island, Russia", Quarterly Journal of Engineering Geology and Hydrogeology, Vol. 45, pp. 79–88.

6. S. Dzyuba, A. Chepkasov, S. Savchenkov, "Experience of Designing Natural Gas Transmission Pipelines in Super Challenging Geological and Environmental Conditions of Eastern Siberia and the Far East." 25th World Gas Conference, Kuala Lumpur, June 2012.

7. Palmer, A. C., and Williams, P. J. (2003) "Frost heave and pipeline upheaval buckling", Can. Geotech. J., Vol. 40, pp. 1033–1038.

8. Det Norske Veritas, (2007). "Global buckling of submarine pipelines – structural design due to high temperature/high pressure", DNV-RP-F110

9. Pipeline International, March 2011. "A long and winding route: overcoming terrain challenges on the Peru LNG pipeline", pp.27-29

10. Gasca, A., Gutierrez, E., "The Challenge of Crossing the Andes: A Data Base Analysis and Peru LNG Project Description", 1st International Pipeline Geotechnical Conference, Bogotá, Colombia, Paper IPG2013-1951 (2013)

11. Malpartida, J., Oliveros, F., Massucco, G., "Integration of monitoring and inspection systems for geohazard assessment on pipelines that cross Amazonian Jungles and the Andes", 9th International Pipeline Conference, Calgary, Alberta, Canada, Paper IPC2012-90501 (2012)

12. Oliveros, F., Leynaud, F., "Integral Management of Risk: From a Corrective to a Preventive Approach", 1st International Pipeline Geotechnical Conference, Bogotá, Colombia, Paper IPG2013-1921 (2013)

13. Malpartida, J., Massucco, G., "Alternative geohazard risk assessment and monitoring for pipelines with limited access: Amazon jungle example" 10th International Pipeline Conference Calgary, Alberta, Canada, paper IPC2014-33628 (2014)

14. Niklès, M., Vogel, B., Briffod, F., Grosswig, S., Sauser, F., Luebbecke, S., Bals A., Pfeiffer, T. (2004) "Leakage detection using fiber optics distributed temperature monitoring." Proc. of the 2004 Symposium on Smart Structure and Material: Smart Sensor Techn. and Meas. Syst., E. Udd, D. Inaudi eds., Proc. SPIE Vol. 5384, pp. 18-25, 2004.

15. Ravet, F., Briffod, F., Chin, S., Rochat, E., Martinez, J.G., "Pipeline Geohazard Risk Monitoring with Optical Fiber Distributed Sensors: Experience with Andean and Arctic Routes", Proceedings of the 12th International Pipeline Conference PC2018, September 24-27, 2018, Calgary, Canada, paper IPC2018-78047

16. Niklès, M., Thévenaz, L., Robert PH. (1996). "Simple distributed fiber sensor based on Brillouin gain spectrum analysis." Optics Letter 21(10), pp.758-760.

17. Niklès, M., Thévenaz, L., Robert PH. (1997). "Brillouin gain spectrum characterization in single-mode optical fibers." Journal of Lightwave Technology, JLT-15, pp. 1842-1851.

18. Niklès, M. (2007). "Fibre optic distributed scattering sensing system: perspectives and challenges for high performance applications." 3rd European Workshop on Optical Fibre Sensors, A. Cutolo, B. Culshaw, J. M. Lopez-Higuera eds., Proc. of SPIE Vol. 6619, 66190D

19. Gyger, F., Chin, S., Rochat, E., Niklès, M., Ravet, F., "Ultra Long Range DTS (>300km) to Support Deep Offshore and Long Tieback Developments" 33rd International Conference on Ocean, Offshore and Arctic Engineering, OMAE 2014, San Francisco, PAPER OMAE2014-24019.

20. Iten, M., Ravet F., Niklès M., Facchini, M., Hertig, TH., Hauswirth, D., Puzrin, A. (2009) "Soil-embedded fiber optic strain sensors for detection of differential soil displacements." Proc. of 4th International Conference on Structural Health Monitoring on Intelligent Infrastructure (SHMII-4), 22-24 July 2009, Zurich, Switzerland, 2009.

21. Du Toit, D., Ryan, K., Rice, J., Bay, J., Ravet, F., (2015). "Analysis of strain sensor cable models and effective deployments for distributed fiber optical geotechnical monitoring system", Proc. of the 2nd International Pipeline Geotechnical Conference, Bogotá, Colombia, Paper IPG2015-8520.

22. Risch, B.G., Lovie, R., Roland, D., Rochat, E., Du Toit, D., "Optical Fiber Cable Design for Distributed Pipeline Sensing and Data Transmission". Proc. of the International Wire and Cable Symposium, IWCS 2015, Paper 0582-000070.

23. Ravet, F., Ortiz, E.G., Peterson, B., Hoglund, G. and Niklès, M. (2011). "Geohazard prevention with online continuous fiber optic monitoring." Proc. of the Rio Pipeline Conference and Exposition, Rio de Janeiro, Brazil, Paper IBP1277_11 (2011).

24. Ravet, F., Borda, C., Rochat, E., Niklès, M., "Geohazard Prevention and Pipeline Deformation Monitoring using Distributed Optical Fiber Sensing", International Pipeline Geotechnical Conference, Bogotá, Colombia, Paper IBP2013-1908 (2013)

25. Hillel, D., Introduction to soil physics. Academic Press, San Diego, CA, 1982

26. Hauswirth, D., Puzrin, A.M., Carrera, A., Standing, J.R. & Wan, M.S.P. Use of fibre-optic sensors for simple assessment of ground surface displacements during tunnelling. Géotechnique, Vol. 64, No. 10, pp. 837-842.

27. Timoshenko, S.P, and Goodier, J.N., (1970), Theory of Elasticity, McGraw Hill, new York, New York.

28. Highland, L.M., and Bobrowsky, Peter, 2008, The landslide handbook – A guide to understanding landslides: Reston, Virginia, U.S. Geological Survey Circular 1325, 129p.

APPENDIX 1: PERFORMANCE PARAMETER DEFINITIONS

Below definitions are given according to the IEC 61757-2-2 standard and SEAFOM MSP-01 specification.

Spatial Resolution

The spatial resolution is the ability to discriminate between two adjacent locations submitted to different temperature/ strain conditions. The spatial resolution is directly related to the optical pulse width or the pulse length W illuminated by the pulse at a given time $w = \tau v_g/2$, where τ is the pulse width and v_g is the group velocity of the pulse. Spatial resolution also depends on receiver bandwidth

Strain and Temperature Resolution – Measurement Repeatability

Strain and temperature resolutions are directly related to the measurement noise. The noise includes spontaneous, short duration deviations in output (reading) about the mean output (reading), which are not caused by temperature changes. The resolution is defined as twice the standard deviation of the noise (+/- twice the standard deviation includes 95.4% of the measurements).

Strain and Temperature Uncertainty

The Strain and temperature uncertainty is the difference between the measurement unit reading and the measurement obtained with a reference device. The measurement uncertainty depends on the calibration precision, i.e. on the quality of the calibration setup and procedure. For instance, the calibration of a piece of fiber as a temperature sensor requires a traceable reference temperature sensor with given uncertainty.

APPENDIX 2: GEOHAZARDS

Subsidence

Ground subsidence is the phenomenon described by a terrain surface moving downward relative to the surrounding soils. Subsidence can be caused by excessive ground water depletion, underground mining, lime stone dissolution, natural gas extraction etc.

Landslide

Reference [28] gave a general definition of a landslide stating: "*A landslide is a downward sloping movement of rock, soil, or both, occurring in the rupture of a surface - rotational sliding or flat collapsing - in which most of the material moves as a coherent or semi-coherent mass, with small internal deformation.*" The authors list and describe several type of landslides such as translational or rotational landslides as well as rock falls.

Erosion

Erosion is the phenomenon that removes soil or rock under the action of waterflow, wind or glaciers and transports the material to another location.

This page left blank intentionally.

IPG2019-5333

GROUND-BASED INTERFEROMETRIC SYNTHETIC APERTURE RADAR COMBINED WITH A CRITICAL SLOPE MONITORING PROGRAM WILL PROVIDE EARLY DETECTION OF SLOPE MOVEMENT ALONG PIPELINE CORRIDORS

Steven E. Borron, C.E.G., P.G.
IDS GeoRadar Inc.
Chula Vista, California, United States

Martin P. Derby, P.G., C.P.G.
Golder Associates
Buffalo, New York, United States

ABSTRACT

The transition of satellite InSAR technology to a ground-based system provides a proven risk reduction technology if combined with a critical slope monitoring (CSM) program. Together the technology with the active engagement of a defined program can detect the onset of slope displacement, acceleration, and provide a method to determine slope collapse. Recently, using the radar software, Guardian, and its ability to document surface velocity in intervals of 24-hours or less has allowed for the development of site-specific levels of rockfall risk.

The ground-based InSAR (interferometric synthetic aperture radar) systems and their near real-time capabilities allow for proactive and early warning monitoring. The technical requirements include the ability to operate 24/7 in all weather conditions, acquire data in near real-time, and visually present data in an interpretable format that requires no end user processing. Since slope failure without acceleration is unlikely, the rapid visual presentation of processed data becomes a crucial component for a CSM technology.

The definition of the CSM program not only requires short intervals for data acquisition, processing, and visual presentation but also requires a monitoring professional that can interpret and communicate changes in slope movement. A specific CSM technology requirement demands, acquiring data at a continuous interval of 2-minutes or less, 24 hours per day for the duration of the monitoring project. Also, the CSM technology must be able to transmit alarm messages at the moment thresholds are met, visually present data with various time series plots, including displacement, and velocity maps while acquired radar data is continuously updated and with no end-user processing. A site-specific document called a trigger action response plan (TARP) needs to be prepared at the start of any CSM project. Currently, only the IBIS-FM and ArcSAR radars developed by IDS (Ingegneria Dei Sistemi) GeoRadar can meet the technical requirements of the defined CSM technology.

During a CSM program, the short interval between each data acquisition provides two specific advantages. First, the short acquisition interval decreases interpolation, which automatically increases data confidence. Second, the short intervals also decrease the effects of atmospheric changes that are a part of all data acquisitions. Although the IBIS-FM and ArcSAR radar systems can operate in nearly all-weather conditions, sudden changes in local atmospheric conditions can still exhibit data effects. Both radar systems include active proprietary algorithms that account for ongoing atmospheric changes during acquisitions. In comparison, some remote sensing data acquired from, LIDAR, and total station technologies can be critically affected by sudden changes in local atmospheric conditions.

Combining the near real-time capabilities of an interferometric synthetic aperture radar system with a dedicated professional will decrease risk to people and property by allowing slope movement trends to be identified and observed in near real-time, 24-hours per/day. The paper will discuss the highlights of several successful CSM programs. We describe deployment versatility, the ability to identify the onset of displacement accurately, and the critical identification of the onset of acceleration.

INTRODUCTION

The phrase, critical slope monitoring and the requirements for a complete CSM program has been introduced by the authors to describe a new method of slope monitoring that is a result of advancements in technology and requires the following:

- The technology must acquire, process, and present displacement, velocity, and inverse velocity data in 2-minutes or less.
- The technology includes the ability to set alarm thresholds and send alarm messages via text messaging and e-mail.

- The technology must be able to monitor continuously, 24-hours per day in all weather conditions.
- Develop a trigger action response plan (TARP), for every CSM monitoring project.
- The project should include a license and experienced monitoring professional from either the disciplines of geology or geotechnical engineering.
- The monitoring professional should be trained to understand that movement trends are more important than the measured amount of actual movement.
- The monitoring professional must understand that slope collapse is not probable in the absence of acceleration.

It is imperative during the monitoring of unstable slopes that the requirements for a CSM program become fully embraced and include the active engagement of a slope monitoring professional to communicate and report on conditions and changes that could present a dangerous risk to people and infrastructure.

The following examples of near real-time CSM programs have direct implications towards improving slope management in pipeline corridors that are either on or near unstable slopes. Although the examples in this paper do not include any pipeline corridor projects, the CSM program and process is generally the same for all slopes. The repercussions from not monitoring are generally expensive, and potentially deadly.

The first IBIS radar system was introduced into the open-pit mining industry over a decade ago. During this period, many open-pit mine operators realized that by combining the near real-time data results with professional interpretation, a reduction of risk to mine operations could be confidently achieved and potentially save lives, protect equipment, boost productivity, improve investor confidence, and decrease potential payouts from insurance claims related to unfavorable outcomes. For these reasons, the CSM radar program has gained the confidence of most large open pit mine companies. Recently, IBIS radars became available to rent allowing many medium and small mining operations to increase safety for their miners and equipment at a reasonable cost.

Ultimately, a CSM program is about safety and risk reduction. Although this paper specifically addresses the use of the IBIS radar in a CSM program, other technologies may qualify if they meet the CSM requirements defined here. More importantly for a long-term proactive approach, a successful CSM program requires a group of engineering geologists or geotechnical professionals committed to safety through active monitoring engagement.

Radar data from an unstable slope in California and an undisclosed mine are presented including an analysis method called under-sampling that is unique to the IBIS radar system. One of the primary benefits of a proactive CSM approach is the additional time it can provide allowing for the early detection of displacement and in some cases the onset of acceleration. Since slope collapse without acceleration is not probable the extra time afforded from early detection is a valuable and potentially life-saving result. The under-sampling routine, which is unique to the IBIS radar system can detect displacement at a smaller scale than regular radar processing. The under-sampling routine often reveals the onset of displacement long before it appears in the regular 2-minute scans. The increased time acquired from detecting onset displacement could allow for the development and completion of an engineered mitigation plan rather than absorbing costly clean-up, repairs to damaged property, possible injuries, and potential litigation expenses from not initiating a proactive CSM program.

DEFERRED MONITORING DATA

The IBIS radar's 2-minute data acquisition interval decreases interpolation and increases data confidence during the analysis of slope movement trends. Alternatively, there is a higher degree of data uncertainty when using deferred data acquisition methods. Deferred data is any monitoring method that presents the results in an interval greater than the CSM requirement. An example of deferred data is satellite InSAR data, which requires acquisition intervals of four to eleven-days and additional time to receive interpreted results. Satellite InSAR is beneficial for specific projects but not as a CSM technology. The extended acquisition interval typically makes trend analysis more subjective, and the gaps between satellite InSAR acquisition can miss rate changes that can occur between the larger acquisition intervals; therefore, satellite InSAR does not qualify as a CSM technology. An additional advantage of the IBIS system is its accuracy, which is partly due to its data acquisition speed.

The accuracy of the IBIS radar data is exhibited during the monitoring of an unstable rock slope in California. During this 5-month monitoring project, the thermal effects occurring on the slope surface were captured by radar scans. At this site, a steel rock netting was attached to the surface of the slope. Shortly after it was installed a portion of the slope failed taking down a portion of the steel netting, Figure 1.

Figure 1. This rockslide in central California encroached on a highway leading to an entrance at Yosemite National Park. Shortly after the installation of steel rock netting a portion of the slope failed. Fortunately, no injuries or damage to equipment occurred.

During the monitoring of the site, two time-series areas were created with the IBIS Guardian software and labeled as Rockfall Drape, and No Drape Figure 2. Both cumulative displacement time series areas exhibited a sinuous pattern that corresponded to the 24-hour changes in temperatures. The blue curve represented the steel drape covered portion of the slope and displayed an impressive response to the thermal changes. Data for the failed portion of the slope also corresponded to the thermal changes, but the pattern was less distinct. The vertical dashed black lines are located at the thermal peaks and valleys of expansion and contraction and extend vertically down to intersect the thermal expansion and contraction of the rock surface (red curve). In addition to the sinuous pattern from apparent thermal effect, a best-fit trend line for the blue curve described a slow, steady displacement trend.

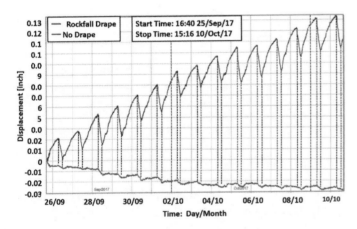

Figure 2. IBIS-FM radar cumulative displacement time series data for both the steel Rockfall Drape and the uncovered (No Drape) portion of the slope. Although it is subtle, the vertical dashed black lines intersect the uncovered portion of the slope (red curve) at the correlating peaks and valleys of the steel drape covered portion of the slope (blue curve). The patterns suggest that the radar has captured the thermal expansion and contraction of both the steel drape and native rocks.

SLOPE MOVEMENT TRENDS

There are three primary slope trends, which represent regressive, steady, and progressive or accelerating displacement. The three trends can easily be identified in the IBIS radar's Guardian software because of the short data acquisition interval, which improves visual acuity of the presented data. Also, when observing cumulative displacement data, the short interval decreases the amount of change from one data point to the next, which is often described as noise in many deferred time series

data. This observation correlates to the advantage of fast data acquisition interval that allows identifying initial movement trends. For example, total station data acquired once a day or once a week will exhibit more noise during slow creep making the identification of a movement trend difficult especially onset acceleration. In general, slow creep enhances the fluctuation between data points since the unstable slope surface is not yet moving together at a consistent rate, but most likely is moving sporadically at different rates and times. During faster rates of movement radar's cumulative displacement data begins to exhibit a smoother displacement curve, most likely a result of an overall consistent surface rate of movement. Also, a selected time series area averages the rate of numerous digital terrain model (DTM) cells located within a user selected area. The averaging provides a more confident data result since a selected area can include thousands of DTM cells as opposed to a few total station survey points that may not necessarily be positioned in the most beneficial locations. A schematic of the three fundamental movement trends is shown in Figure 3.

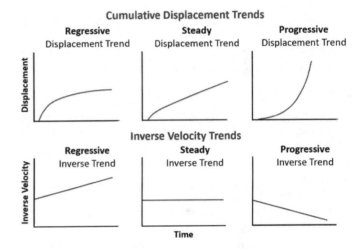

Figure 3. Schematic of the three-movement trends that can be identified using IBIS-FM radar time series data. Regressive, steady, and progressive or acceleration, and includes the corresponding inverse velocity trends.

SURFACE MINE MONITORING

A CSM program using several IBIS radar units were employed at an undisclosed surface mine in North America. The surface mine has very active slopes that are sensitive to shovel vibration, blasting, and pore-water pressure. The crystalline rocks are moderate-to-highly fractured and display numerous faults from tectonic abuse resulting in the porphyry deposit. A daily task at the site was to use analysis tools within the Guardian software that allow the user to insert events, which are then displayed on time series data. The events become a method of record keeping that often reveals compelling correlations that could be a result of induced slope sensitivities or other environmental influences. Documenting site events and sharing the correlations can assist mine planners and the blasting group by allowing adjustments to mine plans, blast designs and the precise use of shovels by reducing removal rates or taking splatter cuts across shot muck in sensitive areas. At the mine site, all three fundamental movement trends occurred during a relatively short time. In comparison, if deferred data acquired from satellite InSAR had been used it would have been difficult to interpret or see the displacement trends depicted in the time series data in Figure 4.

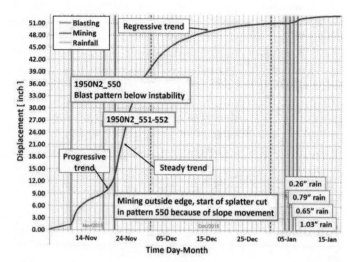

Figure 4. Cumulative displacement data from an undisclosed surface mine. Vertical colored lines represent events occurring at the site. Orange lines represent the time of blasting and correlate well to acceleration trends. The yellow line indicates a recommended mining change to shovel operations to limit vibration on the highwall. The mining change may have initiated deacceleration leading to a steady trend that later begins to regress. Light blue lines indicate precipitation events.

How an area is selected can affect the magnitude of displacement trends shown on time series data especially for cumulative displacement. The DTM cells in the Guardian software are similar and often referred to as pixels. Some users may create a simple polygon shape around an area of displacement that grossly encompasses the instability. With this approach, many DTM cells that may not be showing any displacement are included in the averaging of the time series data. By including DTM cells that are not moving, the magnitude of displacement is decreased and could delay the detection of onset acceleration. The delay could be especially dangerous in rocks sensitive to the slightest amount of stress or strong brittle rocks where the gradual accumulation of stress can change quickly to acceleration. Our experience has shown that in strong crystalline rocks the time to failure when onset acceleration becomes detectable only provides several hours for critical decisions. Alternatively, jointed, fractured, tectonically abused, and chemically or physically weakened rocks generally begin moving at slower rates, gradually increasing in rate for several days or months before accelerating.

Slow displacement rate data typically exhibit fluctuating or differential movement between data points that are most likely a result of rocks or large blocks individually adjusting to stress from pore water pressure, seismic vibration either natural or from blasting, combined with the natural pull of gravity. The cumulative displacement and inverse velocity data appear to verify this observation of differential movement during creep and slow displacement rates. In general, the IBIS radar cumulative displacement data that exhibits fluctuations between data points gives the appearance of noisy or uneven data and typically correlates with creeping or slow, steady displacement. When creep changes and begins to move at a higher displacement rate the data typically begins to smooth, sometimes quickly, and during acceleration, approaches linearity [1].

The importance of identifying the onset of data linearity in both displacement and inverse velocity is the information it provides about the current condition of an unstable area. For example, would it be safe to continue working or living under a high rate of displacement exhibiting a steady trend? At some sites, a high steady rate can result in abundant rockfall without slope collapse. In this instance, possibly large berms of other rockfall protection methods can allow for work to continue. Alternatively, fluctuating displacement rates displaying a slow but steady trend are typically less likely to exhibit rockfall than a high rate steady trend that presents a smoother data curve. Also, inverse velocity data from a slope displaying a steady rate will exhibit a trend parallel to the x-axis, but a high steady inverse velocity rate will also trend parallel to the x-axis but at low inverse velocity values placing the trend much closer to the x-axis. The shorter vertical distance between the x-axis during a high steady rate is important to be aware of since the time to intersect the x-axis will be short if a change to acceleration occurs. For the monitoring professional, a high steady rate could be safe to work under, but a change to acceleration decreases the communication window and response time.

RADAR ANALYSIS AND ROCKFALL RISK

Developing a risk matrix based on steady displacement rate velocities has been a method we have employed based on the site conditions and could be a beneficial outcome during proactive monitoring for other sites. In general, if a slope is creeping at an imperceptible rate or moving at a slow, steady rate it can be considered safe to work under since slope collapse without acceleration is not probable. However, slope conditions should influence this decision since, rock types, and acceptable site risk is unique to each site. Some slopes can move at high-velocity rates and still exhibit a steady trend, although it could be considered safe to work under such conditions the time to slope failure is significantly shorter and needs to be a serious consideration. Some unstable slopes can exhibit high steady rates for months and then begin to accelerate and fail several hours later. The onset of acceleration during a high steady rate of displacement is described in Figure 5 where low inverse velocity values translate to a horizontal trend closer to the x-axis decreasing the amount time to slope failure once acceleration begins. At this site acceleration began August 31 at about 11:00 PM and 17-hours later it failed at about 4:00 PM on September 1. Shortly after failure, the data shows continued displacement at a slower rate.

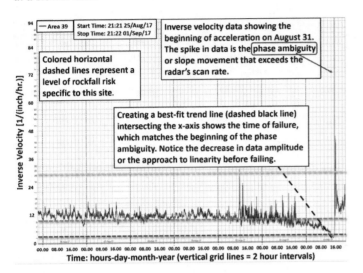

Figure 5. An inverse velocity trend from August 25 through September 1, 2017. Beginning from the left the inverse velocity data shows an approximate average inverse value of 12, which is considered moderate at this site (Figure 6). Late on August 31, the steady trend began to change to acceleration, and the data begins to approach linearity. A best-fit trend line correlated closely to the 2:30 PM failure time and phase ambiguity on September 1.

The colored horizontal dashed lines shown in figure 5 were developed by correlating field documentation of rockfall events to velocity map and time series data in the Guardian software. Although, the IBIS radar system cannot predict rockfall we were able to develop a level of rockfall risk based on the daily observations from spotters correlated to velocity values on the heat map. We then communicated the potential risk to the site as velocity rate changes occurred. The level of rockfall risk table was announced through an email to site engineers and geologists, Figure 6.

Velocity and Inverse Velocity Levels of Rockfall Risk

Risk Levels Based on "Near Real-time Displacement and Velocity" Data

Velocity and Inverse Velocity Based Levels of Risk	Inverse Velocity Value (1/in/hr)	Velocity Average (in/hr)	Total Displacement for 24-Hours (in/hr)(24hrs)	Hazards
Low Risk	100	0.01	0.24	negligible rockfall
	50	0.02	0.48	
	35	0.028	0.67	
Moderate Risk	34	0.029	0.69	sporadic to occasional rockfall
	24	0.04	0.96	
	11	0.09	2.16	
High Risk	10	0.10	2.40	periodic to frequent rockfall,
	8	0.12	2.88	
	6	0.16	3.84	
Extreme Risk	5	0.33	7.92	frequent to near constant rockfall,
	2	0.5	12	
	0.7	1.42	34.08	

Figure 6. Levels of risk were communicated daily on a very active California landslide repair project.

PHASE AMBIGUITY

The near exact time of slope collapse and some rockfall events can be identified by reviewing inverse velocity data and identifying the phase ambiguity. During acceleration, slope velocity can exceed the radar's maximum detectable velocity rate. The ambiguity will occur at a very low inverse velocity value, and when the scan rate is exceeded, the phase ambiguity occurs, which is visually exhibited in the data as a vertical data spike. Back analysis can confirm the phase ambiguity to the time of failure from site observations and creating best-trends of the acceleration event, and where it intersects the x-axis will be the phase ambiguity data spike.

$$\text{Phase ambiguity} = \frac{4.38 \text{ mm}}{\text{scan time}} = \frac{\text{mm}}{\text{hour}}$$

Rockfall can originate from the surface area of a single DTM cell, and a cell often exhibits acceleration before actual rockfall occurs, but individual rocks that are smaller than a DTM cell and fall cannot be detected with the current system. However, if an area of rockfall approximates the surface area of a DTM cell, a phase ambiguity will appear at the time of failure, and the vacated location will appear as negative displacement on time series data. The following describes the dimensions of DTM cells from different scanning distances; at a range 500 meters the cells are 0.75 meters X 2.2 meters, at a range of 1000 meters the cells are 0.75 meters X 4.4 meters, and at a range of 2000 meters, the cell size is 0.75 meters X 8.8 meters [2].

SLOPE FAILURE ANALYSIS AND INVERSE VELOCITY

Large unstable slopes can have hundreds or thousands of DTM cells covering an unstable surface. Typically, data from large deep-seated instabilities will describe a gradual increase in acceleration, and if it continues will eventually exceed the radar's scan rate resulting in a phase ambiguity, which also indicates the time of failure. In contrast, smaller surficial instabilities including single bench failures, in mines, generally fail much sooner once acceleration begins. Identifying the phase ambiguity after an acceleration event allows for comparing the best-fit inverse velocity trend line to the predicted time of failure to the actual time of an observable failure. In Figure 7, we compare cumulative displacement data from two separate areas on the same slope. Initially, both areas showed high displacement rates, but the slightly slower rate blue curve, Area 13. failed. The red curve with a higher displacement rate did not fail but began to display an overall regressive trend that became visually discernable shortly before acceleration started on Area 13. The time series data for the red curve (A_HeadScarp) had a surface area of 16,581 square meters or 54,400 square feet while Area 13 had a surface area of 929 square meters or 3,048 square feet. Comparable to other slope failures we have monitored it appears that the surface area size of an unstable slope correlates to the duration of acceleration on its advance to slope collapse. Our observation suggests the smaller a surface area, the shorter time to collapse and the larger the surface, the longer time to slope collapse. This observation needs more study and analysis since rock type, groundwater and other environmental conditions can influence movement rates but suggests that larger unstable slopes require more time to reach a critical failure threshold, which means during a proactive monitoring program the early detection of acceleration can significantly influence the amount of time available for communicating a possible event.

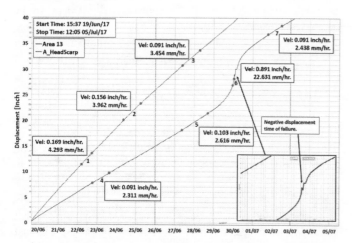

Figure 7. Cumulative displacement time series data from June 19 to July 5, 2017. Line segments show the velocity average for each segment labeled 1 through 7.

The inverse velocity data exhibited in Figure 8 shows the beginning of a slow regressive displacement trend for the A_HeadScarp, the red curve, indicated by an increase of inverse velocity values and data fluctuation (from left to right). The

Area 13, the blue curve, agrees with its slower cumulative displacement rates shown in figure 7 by the larger inverse velocity values and greater data fluctuation until the onset of acceleration began and the data began to approach linearity. The sharp vertical blue data spike in the inverse velocity data is the phase ambiguity indicating the time of failure, which matches the time of the negative displacement data shown in Figure 7. This brief analysis of both data sets illustrates the importance of reviewing and analyzing both cumulative displacement and inverse velocity at different time intervals. Several options are available in Guardian to examine time series data, and they can be accessed quickly with the click of a mouse during active monitoring without interruption to current data processing or updates to the time series data.

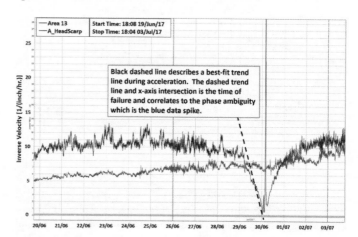

Figure 8. Inverse velocity data for the same areas and interval of the cumulative displacement data displayed in Figure 7.

In November 2012 a successful slope failure prediction was successfully made using an IBIS radar and inverse velocity data from a surface mine. The slope collapse had a volume of about 5-million tons, and all equipment and personnel were evacuated the day before the failure. The predicted failure time was 1:30 AM on November 6, 2012, Figure 9. The actual failure occurred at 2:30 AM when correlated to the phase ambiguity. The data were acquired using an older IBIS-M radar, which had a scan time of seven minutes. The phase ambiguity value of 0.7 is shown as a horizontal dashed black line. The inverse velocity data shows a decrease in data fluctuations or an approach to linearity as acceleration increases. The black dashed line through the inverse velocity data is the best-fit trend line used to predict the approximate time of the five million-ton failure [3].

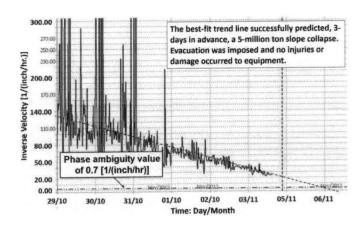

Figure 9. Inverse velocity time series data are showing the approximate location and intersection of the phase ambiguity and the predicted time of failure.

RADAR AND OPTICAL TOTAL STATIONS

Since ground-based radar is relatively new technology, it has initiated interest in how the data compares to other monitoring technologies. In the following, we compare displacement measurements for the IBIS interferometric synthetic aperture radar to the Leica TM-50 optical robotic total station. For clarity, the radar is a line of site instrument and documents only one component of movement, which is either towards or away from the radar. The total station measures all three components of movement. Individual prisms were spread across a large instability and were measured by a total station. Each of the prisms x, y, and z coordinates were imported into the IBIS radar Guardian software, and the corresponding DTM cells were located and selected for a time series comparison. Results showed that total station measurements had a greater magnitude of movement compared to the radar line of site measurements. The greater magnitude of movement was a result of including all three components of movement from the total stations as opposed to the radar's one component of movement from each DTM cell. The more interesting result showed that the movement trends recorded by both instruments were nearly identical. The agreement in movement trend data is a powerful result since the IBIS radar is a near real-time technology and the total station is considered a deferred data technology since it cannot match the overall faster acquisition and presentation of data. The study indicates that the slope movement trends are the same for both instruments, but only the near real-time radar data can describe with confidence the current conditions of a slope at any given moment. The comparison study is described in Figure 10.

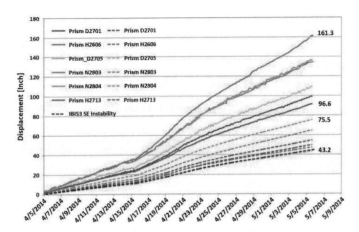

Figure 10. In the comparison chart, the dashed colored lines represent radar cumulative displacement data for individual DTM cells. Matching solid colors represent robotic total station prism data located within the corresponding DTM cell. The prism data shows a higher rate of movement than the corresponding radar DTM cells, but the trends are the same for both data sets. The IBIS3 SE Instability (black dashed line) is the averaged movement trend using over a thousand DTM cells.

When comparing the accuracy of the optical total station's measurements using prism targets, they are consistently lower than that of the ground-based InSAR (cm versus mm) primarily due to the optical sensors' sensitivity to atmospheric variations of temperature, humidity, and air pressure. Also, variation in temperature can degrade optical targets that would affect accuracy. Ground-based radar is a fully remote sensing technology when compared to GNSS, extensometers, and total-stations, which require artificial reflectors or devices to be installed on unstable slope surfaces that can be steep making access dangerous and often not possible. Another important difference is the spatial extent of the information provided. Robotic total stations and other types of sensors provide pointwise data over a network of benchmarks, while the ground-based InSAR system gives a spatially continuous dataset. This characteristic means that it is not necessary to know beforehand the critical portions of a slope prone to collapse since it is always providing the user with full visibility of the movements along the slope surface [4].

RADAR UNDER-SAMPLING

During a normal IBIS scanning routine, any movement that occurs below a set threshold is not considered. The set threshold is partially a result of complex atmospheric algorithms used in the analysis software. However, during an under-sampling routine, data not considered in regular scanning is now considered and often reveals areas of displacement that would not otherwise be detected under the regular scanning routine. The minimum rate of detectable displacement under a regular scanning routine is 10 millimeters per month or greater while an under-sampling routine can detect 10 millimeters or less per month, Figure 11.

	Slow Movements v < 10mm/month	Medium Movements v > 10mm/month v < 260 mm/month	Fast Movements v > 260 mm/month
Regular Processing	✗	✓	✓
Under-Sampled Processing	✓	✓	✗

Figure 11. A table describing the differences between regular processing and under-sampled processing.

During an under-sampling routine one PSV file is pulled from a typical block of PSV files. A standard block size equals four-hours of data or 50 PSV files. For example, a typical subsampled routine could be for 90-days, which equals 27,000 PSV files created during regular scanning but only 90 PSV files would be used for the under-sampling routine, Figure 12. Individual PSV files pulled from each day are compiled to produce displacement maps and time series data in the IBIS Guardian software. The under-sampling routine is analogous to 11-day Satellite InSAR intervals, which also allows for the detection of millimeter-scale displacement.

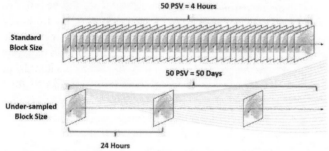

Figure 12. A schematic illustrating how under-sampled data is extracted and then compiled.

The under-sampling analysis provides proactive long-term monitoring projects the ability to detect the onset of displacement or capture pre-existing slow movement not previously recognized. The early detection provides a site with additional time to make crucial decisions regarding mitigation, repairs, and emergency response planning. Surface mines have used the under-sampling routine to improve their mine plans and, in some instances, have helped determine the location of new in-pit structures from the results of under-sampled data. For example, during the planning of a mine expansion, the decision to place a new in-pit rock crusher could years later be affected by slope movement that could require relocation. However, if a proactive effort had been undertaken to check site conditions using the under-sampling routine and detected displacement, it could have potentially saved the site millions of dollars in costly repairs and maintenance. A comparison example of a regular processing routine and an under-sampled routine are shown in Figures 13 and 14. The green DTM color

represents no displacement and blue represent displacement away from the radar.

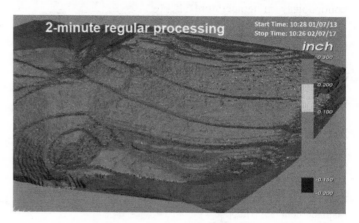

Figure 13. An IBIS radar displacement map of a mine pit surface. This map includes data from a normal scanning routine for a 24-hour interval. The data was acquired on July 1 through July 2, 2013. Even though positive displacement values were set at values of 0.1 to 0.3 inches/24 hours no detectable displacement occurred during the 24-hour interval.

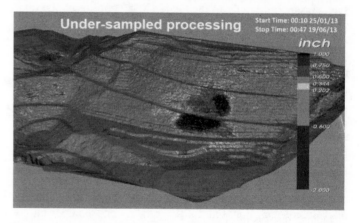

Figure 14. An under-sampling routine was completed on figure 11 slope from January 25 through June 19, 2013. Results show at least 1.0 inches of cumulative displacement occurred during the approximate 6-month interval and before the acquisition of the regular processing radar data in figure 13.

DISCUSSION

Although we have not presented examples of monitoring a slope next to or near natural gas pipelines the data examples presented are valid and show what could be expected. Assuming the acceptable tolerance for any deflection against natural gas pipelines is small, the under-sampling process could be a unique tool to identify onset displacement in suspect or adverse geologic areas and provide additional time for decisions or plans to mitigate an unstable slope.

The IBIS radar system is advantageous for deployment in remote sites and locations with adverse climatic conditions. IDS

GeoRadar has numerous radar deployments in many countries including the northern portions of Canada operating continuously in temperatures below -30 degrees Fahrenheit. Unlike other slope monitoring radar systems, the IBIS-FM radar has one moving part allowing for uptime performance of 97% per year or better. Additional advantages are low profile and small stationary antenna that limit the effects of high winds unlike large aperture dish systems, which typically shut down during high winds.

In addition to the acquisition and data presentation abilities of the IBIS radar, it has an accurate scan range from 10 meters to 3.5 kilometers. The IBIS Guardian software and its analysis tools allow for a single DTM cell or a group of DTM cells to be selected, labeled, and saved to display displacement at various time intervals or display the total amount of accumulated displacement for the entire length of a project. The selected areas can be reviewed as heat maps, figures 13 and 14 and as time series data, which can display cumulative displacement, velocity, inverse velocity, and acceleration, which is an average of the DTM cells within the user selected area. Although data is continuously updated every two minutes in Guardian, the user can make the changes described above and others without any interruption to processing and presentation.

CONCLUSIONS

The information presented in this paper emphasizes the advantages of having additional time by employing a proactive monitoring program on a suspect slope or known unstable slope. Creating additional time is a direct result of the data acquisition and processing speed of the IBIS radar system and the active engagement of the monitoring professional. By implementing the CSM program on a suspect slope, the sub-millimeter accuracy of the IBIS radar system can detect displacement long before deformation can be observed on the slope surface. The user-friendly and dynamic functionality of the Guardian software can present data in various formats including, displacement maps, velocity maps, and time series data every 2-minutes providing an unprecedented capability to review, interpret, and communicate conditions in near real-time.

Within the IBIS software, a unique under-sampling routine allows for the detection of onset displacement long before that same displacement is detectable during regular scanning. The under-sample routine could be described as a method of advanced warning especially for a site that is sensitive to small amounts of displacement such as natural gas pipelines.

A CSM program provides a risk reduction method that has been successfully implemented at many surface mining operations and several civil engineering projects. Beyond the ability to successfully predict slope collapse in hours, days, and sometimes weeks in advance, it is the early detection of slope changes that increase the amount of available time for crucial decisions, which is a fundamental requirement for reducing risk.

Currently, the IBIS radar systems developed by IDS GeoRadar are the only CSM technology that can be used and employed into a CSM program as defined in this paper. The IBIS radar on its own cannot provide actionable information and typically requires a daily commitment from the monitoring professional. From setting alarm thresholds based on current movement rates, making thresholds adjustments as conditions change, to movement trend analysis, and communicating changes in slope conditions, all daily functions that require the skills and experience of the monitoring professional.

Other slope monitoring technologies can provide some of the same accurate data results as the IBIS radar system but lack the acquisition and processing speed to present continuously updated data in an actionable format in nearly all-weather conditions. The speed of the entire IBIS monitoring system combined with professional monitoring will provide the best option to increase the time for critical decisions regarding mitigation efforts, implementing emergency response plans, and communicating slope conditions promptly to the appropriate site authorities.

ACKNOWLEDGMENTS

The opportunity to present this paper would not be possible if not for the influence and knowledge shared by the following professionals from the disciplines of geology, engineering geology, and mine engineering. They include Dr. Patrick Abbott, Garry Anderson, Mike Ness, Steve Schmelter, Matt Sullivan, Keith Taylor, David Travis and special thanks to John Metzger.

REFERENCES

[1] Nick D. Rose and Oldrich Hungr, "Forecasting Potential Rock Slope Failure in Open Pit Mines Using the Inverse Velocity Method," International Journal of Rock Mechanics & Mining Sciences, vol. 44, p. 308-320, 2007.

[2] Ingegneria Dei Sistemi (IDS), "IBIS Guardian Software," v. 01.02 User Manual, 2011.

[3] Fukuzono T, "A New Method for Predicting the Failure Time of a Slope," Proceedings of the Fourth International Conference and Field Workshop on Landslides, Japan Landslide Society, Tokyo, p. 145-150, 1985.

[4] C. Atzeni, M. Barla, M. Pieraccini, F. Antolini, "Early Warning Monitoring of Natural and Engineered Slopes with Ground-Based Synthetic-Aperture Radar," Rock Mechanics and Rock Engineering ISSN 0723-2632, January 2014.

This page left blank intentionally.

Proceedings of the ASME-ARPEL 2019
International Pipeline Geotechnical Conference
IPG2019
June 25-27, 2019, Buenos Aires, Argentina

IPG2019-5344

LEARNINGS ABOUT GEOHAZARDS IN CENIT PIPELINE INTEGRITY MANAGEMENT

Carlos Motta Tierradentro[1], Jaime Aristizabal Ceballos[2], Julian Chaves Agudelo[3], Camilo Eliecer Torres Castro[4]
Cenit Transporte y Logística de Hidrocarburos
Bogotá D.C. Colombia

ABSTRACT

About 20% of Cenit's hydrocarbon transport infrastructure are located on mountainous terrain susceptible to effect of geohazards. There is an integrity management plan based on inspection, monitoring and mitigation activities; however, the occurrence of accidents triggered by geohazards has caused emergencies with effects on environment receiver and on operation of transport systems This paper presents, through management some of these accidents, good practices identified, learning in terms of prevention, preparation and response to emergencies and identification of priorities and gaps, in order to strengthen continuous improvement of the geohazards integrity management strategy.

Keywords: Pipeline Integrity, Geohazard Management.

INTRODUCTION

Pipeline integrity management under geohazards conditions has become a challenge in oil & gas industry. In the present century several invaluable tools have been developed to identify, through inspection and monitoring, the pipeline behavior, which have been complemented by hazard analysis methodologies in order to establishes risk management and assessment plans. An example of this is probabilistic approach for geohazard assessment in Cenit pipelines, which uses a Bayesian Belief Network [1] presented in IPG 2017.

This paper cites some of in-line inspection tools applied to integrity management, their relationship with the most common available standards in oil & gas industry, including fitness for service considerations, and girth weld performance; also presents, through management of some accidents, good practices

identified, learning in terms of prevention, preparation and response to emergencies and identification of priorities and gaps, in order to strengthen continuous improvement of the geohazards integrity management strategy.

1. PIPELINE VULNERABILITY IN CENIT GEOHAZARDS MODEL

Pipeline Vulnerability in Cenit Geohazards Model is defined as the level of potential damage of transport infrastructure due to [1]:

- Physical exposure (disposition, position and relative direction respect to the slope).
- Presence of anomalies (e.g. Bending Strains).
- Advances on mitigation plan.

These variables correspond to a probability distribution in which the results may be report the complete distribution with a probability value for each one of the possible states, the most probable state and the expected value.

The model output, Pipeline Exposure node as shown in Figure 1 ("Infrastructure Hazard" in [1]), represents the probability of a pipeline fail and for decision-making purposes the most probable state and the mean of each variable are compared. When analysis is highly uncertain, these values might differ and allow to identify zones that need reduce uncertainties.

---

[1] Contact author: carlos.motta@cenit-transporte.com
[2] Contact author: jaime.aristizabal@cenit-transporte.com
[3] Contact author: julian.chaves@cenit-transporte.com
[4] Contact author: camilo.torres@cenit-transporte.com

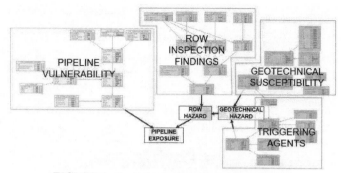

FIGURE 1: Cenit Geohazards Model Structure [2]

2. INTEGRITY MANAGEMENT UNDER GEOHAZARD CONDITIONS

Pipeline integrity assessment, developed from in-line inspection mapping tools and structural analysis, are considered a way to very reliable source in mitigation plans definition on areas at geohazards risk [3] [5] [6]. This approximation allows to identify differences on terrain movements between repeated inspections. However, pipelines design and construction consider industry standards that normally contemplate operation loads but not necessarily analyses mechanical behavior due to geohazards.

2.1 Defects identified on In-Line Inspection

To inspection and diagnosis of transport of hydrocarbons systems, one of the most widely alternatives used is In-line Inspections (ILI). A wide range of technologies are currently offered, which allow identify anomalies generated by pipeline threats described on ASME or API standards.

Techniques most used are those with Magnetic Flux Leakage sensors (MFL) which allow to evaluate anomalies of thickness loss (see Figure 2). In the last years the ultrasonic testing (UT) techniques have been developed and included on ILI programs:

- Straight Ultrasound beam used to measure wall thickness
- Angular Ultrasound beam allows crack detection
- Electro Magnetic Acoustic Transducer (EMAT) capable of identifying zones with adhesion loss of coating or used to crack detection.

Additionally, there are ILI technologies to identify diameter distortion anomalies (Geometric tools) and pipeline layout (Inertial mapping tools) which is possible to carry out a bending strain and pipeline movement analysis [4].

In order to be able to select the best applicable technology when defining pipeline inspection strategy, operator must consider the following conditions:

- Failure history (root cause definition, frequency of occurrence and diagnosis, included recommendations emitted in each investigation) to define the most applicable detection technology option.
- Facilities for tools launching, receipt and navigation.

- Operative Conditions for tools launching, like its propulsion flows control, transport speeds and alignment of stations for launching/receipt operation.
- Enlistment for tool launch (calibration, cleaning and sending drills prior to launch of selected ILI tools).
- Launch, follow-up to the step and receipt of it.
- Raw Data extraction, data processing/debugging and report generation for validation of the run.

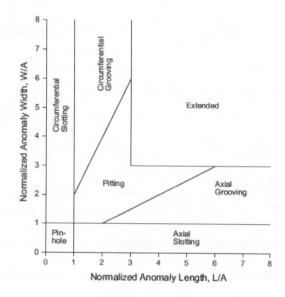

FIGURE 2: ILI Detectable Dimensions of thickness loss [7]

Once final reports are received, is possible generate a maintenance plan based on relevant findings, which are prioritized according to technical criteria of each operator.

2.2 Fitness for Service Analysis and Assessment

With enough information about pipeline conditions, it is necessary to evaluate this fitness for service. Assessment should have a preliminary analysis of data layers alignment, which allows to establish possible causes of the evolution of a diagnosed event. Operator defines in stress/strain terms and risk tolerance criteria for anomalies attention or conditions that may affect pipeline integrity.

These assessments can be carried out considering standards or deterministic aspects, or based on statistical or probabilistic analysis, or with advanced analytical methods like finite element simulations.

2.3 Girth Weld Performance

Most of the pipelines designed and constructed under ASME B31.4 [8] and ASME B31.8 [9] standards are based on API 1104 [10] standard to welding design, welding process qualification and welding staff qualification; this standard has compiled the best welding practices in Oil & Gas industry.

Compliance of API 1104 standard brings acceptance and rejection criteria for phases of welding and quality control using inspections with non-destructive tests (VT, UT, MT, PT and RT) and allows to coexist with anomalies like lack of fusion, lack of penetration, porosities, undercut, among others, with an established limit.

However, external conditions that are not considered on traditional design is not a guarantee for a pipeline to have high resistance to longitudinal stresses or strains, increasing the probability of failure.

2.4 Stress Corrosion Cracking (SCC)

According to the NACE standards, there are three variables that generate Stress Corrosion Cracking (SCC), these are:

- Corrosive environment: this variable corresponds to the effect that the electrolyte exerts on the material of the pipe. The variable includes the barriers against corrosion (coating status and / or the effectiveness of cathodic protection systems).
- Material susceptibility: The variable includes aspects such as low tenacity of the material, age of the pipe and ease to corrode.
- Stress applied: corresponding to applied loads that generate membrane stresses that intensify in interaction with a stress concentrator.

3 EXAMPLES

On a mountain area with complex topographic, geological and climatic conditions (see Figure 3) a pipeline failure arisen due to join occurrence of difficulties on corrosion protection, increase of external load and features or anomalies of pipe.

The corrosion detected by ILI had a deep less than 30% of the wall thickness, which fit for service according with ASME B31G. The stress applied due to the slow landslide, the difficulties identified on barriers to control the corrosion, the soil conditions and the age of the material brewed a cluster of cracks (see figure 4), which propagated and jointed to generate the rupture of the tube (see figure 5).

The conclusion of research was the pipeline failure occurred by simultaneous occurrence of several events: longitudinal stress caused for a slow landslide, coating failure due to cracking and disbound, low potential of the impressed current by the Cathodic Protection, pipeline material with low toughness and highly susceptible to corrosion. The damage mechanism defined in this case was stress corrosion cracking (SCC), see Table 1.

FIGURE 3: Pipeline on complex topographic, geological and climatic conditions [2]

FIGURE 4: Branched cracks, typically SCC.

FIGURE 5: Total transverse pipeline rupture.

TABLE 1. Minimum value of parameters to generate SCC and the evidence.

Variable	Parameter	Evidence
Corrosive environment[5]	-5 to -10	-5
	Soil pH: 5,5 to 7,5	5,65
	Coating type: coal tar (one of the worst coatings in the industry)	Coal tar: age 35 years old disbanded, cracked and easily removable
Material susceptibility	Carbon steel	API 5L X52
	Cracks morphology: Branched network	Cluster and branched cracks (see figure 4)
	Age of pipe material: more than 10 years old	35 years old
Stress applied	Internal pressure: more than 20%SMYS	1300psi (72%SMYS)
	Stress raisers	Metal Loss 24% (external corrosion)
	External load: more than 50% SMYS	49996psi

CONCLUSION

An adequate pipeline integrity management under geohazards conditions requires hazard and vulnerability analysis complemented with inspection and monitoring of the pipeline behavior to establishes risk management and assessment plans.

ACKNOWLEDGEMENTS

To Cenit for allowing us to participate in training events, in which knowledge management and share experiences are the key of continuous improvement.

REFERENCES

[1] Chaves et al (2017). *Probabilistic Approach for Assessing the Weather and External Forces Hazard Using Bayesian Belief Networks IPG2017-2528*. Proceedings of the ASME 2017 International Pipeline Geotechnical Conference. Lima, Perú. July 24-26, 2017

[2] Aristizabal, J et al (2018). *Decision making methodology for geohazards management and its impact on pipeline integrity*. Proceedings of the UN/OECD Workshop Natech Risk Management. Potsdam, Germany. September 5 - 7 2018.

[3] Young, A. and Lockey, A (2013). *The Assessment of Pipeline Integrity in Geohazard Areas Using ILI Data. IPG2013-1971*. Proceedings of the ASME 2013 International Pipeline Geotechnical Conference. Bogota, Colombia.

[4] Galvis, A. (2015). *Procedure for Identifying Deformations in Oil and Gas Pipelines Subject to External Forces, Based on Primary ILI Data - IPG2015 8506*. Proceedings of the ASME 2015 International Pipeline Geotechnical Conference. Bogotá, Colombia

[5] Aristizabal, J. and Rodríguez, P (2015). *Plans of management defined from the verification and validation of the information collected on the right of way patrols. IPG2015-8553*. Proceedings of the ASME 2015 International Pipeline Geotechnical Conference. Bogota, Colombia.

[6] Aristizabal, J. et al (2017). *Structural Integrity Management of Pipelines Based on Monitoring of Slope Movements with Slow Strain Rates. IPG2017-2518*. Proceedings of the ASME 2017 International Pipeline Geotechnical Conference. Lima, Perú. July 24-26, 2017.

[7] API 1163 (2013). *In-line Inspection Systems Qualification*. Second Edition, April 2013

[8] ASME B31.4 (2012). *Liquid Transportation Systems for Hydrocarbons Liquid Petroleum*. 2012.

[9] ASME B31.8 (2016). Gas Transmission and Distribution Piping Systems.

[10] API 1104 (2018). *Welding of Pipelines and Related Facilities*.

---

5 DIN 50929 - Part 3. Corrosion of metal probability of corrosion of metallic materials when subject to corrosion from the outside. Buried and underwater pipelines and structural components.

AUTHOR INDEX

Proceedings of the ASME/ARPEL 2019
International Pipeline Geotechnical Conference

Alvarado Franco, Juan V001T01A002

Amórtegui Gil, José Vicente V001T03A003

Aristizabal Ceballos, Jaime V001T01A002, V001T02A008, V001T03A009

Barlow, Pete V001T02A007, V001T02A009

Blackwell, Chris V001T02A007

Borron, Steven E. V001T03A008

Briffod, Fabien V001T03A007

Campbell, Chris V001T02A007

Carnicero, Martin V001T03A005

Chaves Agudelo, Julian Fernando V001T01A002, V001T02A008, V001T03A009

Chin, Sanghoon V001T03A007

Corrales Cobos, Julian Javier V001T03A004

Costa, Cesar Augusto V001T02A001

Debandi, Carlos V001T02A005

Derby, Martin P. V001T02A006, V001T03A008

Ferris, Gerald V001T02A002

Foessing, Ferdinand V001T03A006

García, Hugo V001T01A001

Hernández, Jon. V001T02A003

Ho, Minh V001T02A002

Huisman, Otto V001T02A004

Karimian, Hamid V001T02A007

Kole, Klaas V001T03A006

Leach, Miguel V001T02A009

Malpartida Moya, John Erick V001T03A002

Marín, Alejandro V001T02A003

Martearena, Fernando V001T02A005

Méndez, Alexis V001T03A001

Montoya Rodríguez, Maria Isabel V001T02A008

Motta Tierradentro, Carlos Eduardo V001T01A002, V001T02A008, V001T03A009

Newton, Sarah. V001T02A002

Oviedo, Karin. V001T03A002

Porter, Michael V001T02A009

Ravet, Fabien V001T03A007

Reyes, Alejandro V001T02A004

Rizkalla, Moness V001T02A004

Rochat, Etienne V001T03A007

Roth, Natalia V001T02A005

Salazar Ferro, Andrés V001T03A001

Santana, Erika V001T02A004

Schorr, Michael V001T03A006

Schultz Neto, Walter V001T02A001

Scordo, Elisa V001T02A009

Theriault, Bailey V001T02A006

Tindall, Matt V001T02A004

Torres Castro, Camilo Eliecer V001T03A009

Vázquez, Maureen V001T03A005

Welkner, Daniela V001T02A009

Zozula, Thiago Wichrestink V001T02A001

This page left blank intentionally.